Asheville-Buncombe Technical Institute
LIBRARY
340 Victoria Road
Asheville, North Carolina 28801

DISCARDED

APR 15 2025

D1712278

PUBLIC FIRE SAFETY ORGANIZATION:

A SYSTEMS APPROACH

by Harry E. Hickey

PUBLIC FIRE SAFETY ORGANIZATION:

A SYSTEMS APPROACH

by Harry E. Hickey

Published by

National Fire Protection Association
470 Atlantic Avenue, Boston, Massachusetts 02210

Printed in U.S.A.

December, 1973

Library of Congress Card Number: 73–90984
NFPA Number: SPP-21
Standard Book Number: 8765–018–7

Copyright © 1973 by

Harry E. Hickey

Foreword

The past decade has been one of controversy and change for the fire departments of America, and the coming decade appears to offer a time of additional rapid change if an effective solution to the fire problem is to be formulated and implemented. Professor Hickey has developed a conceptual model of the application of systems theory and procedures to existing fire department organizations. This publication should be of interest to municipal and public administrators, in addition to Fire Service personnel. The procedures for the organization, management, control, and evaluation of the fire safety organization have been developed in a detailed and effective manner.

Professor Hickey has utilized his unique combination of academic studies in fire protection, government, and systems analysis with his empirical experience obtained in fire departments as a fire fighter, company officer, instructor and fire marshal. He has effectively applied the principles of systems management to the various organizational modes of the Fire Service.

The theory and means to create an efficient, effective, responsive and accountable fire safety system have been developed within this book. Thus, it is earnestly hoped this book will challenge the dedicated, intelligent, and responsible fire department chiefs and administrators to achieve the implementation and verification of the theories and concepts advanced in this book to their existing organizations.

JOHN L. BRYAN

The significance of Professor Harry E. Hickey's work is the wholeness of his perspective of the field of public fire safety. It should be a challenging document for fire department personnel, other public safety officers, and public administrators. The systems concept and approach to real world organization problems in the field of public fire safety and his carefully documented response to identified problems should prove very useful. The content not only covers a broad and original conceptual framework for providing public fire safety services, but equally important, provides a detailed arrangement for implementing each of the selected subsystem components. The book should be studied by all who are actively interested in urban affairs and public safety.

LOWE H. HATTERY
Professor of Management and Public Administration
The American University
Washington, D.C.

Dedicated to
Mom and Dad

Preface

Over the past ten years considerable effort has been expended on identifying the scope and implication of problems associated with both public and private fire safety. Undoubtedly the most important work to date in this field is the Report of the National Commission on Fire Prevention and Control, appointed by President Richard Nixon in 1971. On May 4, 1973 Commission Chairman Richard E. Bland transmitted to President Nixon the final report of the commission. The report is entitled — *America Burning*. This document identifies the national fire problem in relation to several subproblem identification areas, and specifically recommends remedial actions that would logically be expected to have significant impact on reducing the American fire problem.

Concurrent with the work span of the National Commission on Fire Prevention and Control, I began to research the fire problem from one specific perspective. The analysis focused on the organizational fabric of public fire departments and the perceived problems associated with organizational arrangements. There is a considerable body of literature and testimony, reviewed in Chapter 1, to support the contention that the basic quasi-military type of fire department organization, which is hierarchical and hallowed by years of tradition, contains important roots to the overall national fire problem. Selected elements of this problem identification are documented in *America Burning*. Here the similarity ends in both problem identification and alternative measures required to establish a more viable approach to public fire safety. Therefore, I do not consider that this book is a duplication of the work recently completed by the National Commission on Fire Prevention and Control.

I am pleased to report that this book and *America Burning* concur in the necessity for establishing a new set of priorities for public fire safety. There is no argument about the fact that the prevention of fire incidents should be the number one objective and responsibility of the public fire safety organization. I also generally agree with the Commission on other important objectives associated with public fire safety and the master planning concepts required to accomplish objective criteria.

This book attempts to present a theoretical framework for structuring and implementing public fire safety in accordance with an established set of community objectives. The underpinnings for the organization of public fire safety are developed from basic tenets associated with systems theory. I was originally exposed to systems theory as a student in a graduate course required of all doctoral candidates under the School of Government and Public Administration at the American University in Washington, D. C. Over the past several years I have attempted to build on these initial concepts, refine my own thinking relative to systems analysis, and apply this logical theory to problem areas in the fire protection field. This book represents one specific approach to the application of systems concepts to the dynamic function of public fire safety.

The central theme of this writing revolves around the organizational inputs — processing requirements — output service function to achieve defined levels of public fire safety. In the true manner of a system, the established organizational framework includes requisite feedback mechanisms for coordinating, controlling and measuring organizational effectiveness. Systems theory, by its very nature, builds in a monitoring mechanism for constantly assessing the posture of an organization in relation to goal orientation.

A minor theme of this text is best stated from the work of Vincent Ostrom.[1]

Conventional wisdom in public administration indicates for example that efficiency will be enhanced by eliminating overlapping jurisdictions and fragmented authority.

In concert with this observation, I have attempted to make a case for altering the political base of public fire protection *where* the affected citizenry shares the objective criteria of the author. This concept is presented with full knowledge that one could hardly expect the implementation of the reorganization of public fire safety on a new foundation without political consequences. For instance, in contrast to the above assumption, practicing urban administrators feel that political consolidations, mergers, special districts or other legal changes to the service function economic base create a gargantuan system which is ungovernable. If this is a fact instead of a premise, then it would appear that the structural failure mode has been exceeded at some undefined level.

[1]Vincent Ostrom, *The Intellectual Crisis in American Public Administration*. University (Alabama): The University of Alabama Press 1973, p. 4.

Two conditions are inserted into the projected framework of a public fire safety system to avoid this deterrent and to make the proposed system responsive and responsible to grass-roots objectives, in addition to professional objectives. First, optional levels of service are provided to accommodate localized conditions and preferences. Second, the basic core unit consisting of a fire station (i.e., facility) retains its identity at the neighborhood or small community level. Associative functions and services serve as a back-up mechanism, a technical mechanism and administrative mechanisms for assisting in the achievement of localized formulated objectives. The core unit of public fire safety and its political constituency may elect by contract, or tax apportionment, to receive one, several or all of the defined operational facilitating and/or resource functions. Obviously, state legislation will be required in most instances to accomplish or permit the adoption of this system.

The relationships specified in this book are advanced to indicate the connection between theory and practice for a defined area of knowledge. The practice of any profession depends upon the *knowledge* which its members profess. At a time when fire department personnel are seeking to establish professional stature, it appears important to structure a systematic body of knowledge concerning public fire safety organizations. This book is offered with the hope that debate and trial by example will focus on establishment of a "knowledge framework" for public fire safety that will promote and elevate fire administration to a professional plateau.

In addition to concepts and objective cited above, this book has been structured in response to other perceived organizational requirements for public fire safety. These focal points may be summarized as follows:

1. The administration level of public fire safety requires an expertise and temperament that may not be compatible with achievement levels of suppression forces of existing fire departments.
2. The federal perspective on grant-in-aid programs and the broad base considerations of revenue sharing appear to support regional planning activities. A conceptual framework is provided for examining public fire safety on a regional base.
3. A responsive and responsible local government has been characterized as one with open and specific communication channels between facilitating units and the public. Both a general and a specific scheme of interorganization and intraorganization communications has been advanced for public fire safety that should enhance the flow of information between the public fire safety unit of local government, other service units of local government, and the public served by the public fire safety system.
4. Units of local government, as individual entities and as collective organs of the community, appear to be searching constantly for methods of self-evaluation. This book proposes techniques of organizational evaluation that should provide assistance to public fire safety officials who are interested in measuring quantitatively and qualitatively the mission, objectives, efficiency and effectiveness of public fire safety.
5. A significant issue in the professionalism of public fire safety relates to "inbreeding" and an internalized scope of assessment. It is sincerely hoped that this book will stimulate a dialogue between urban administrators and public fire safety personnel.

Finally, this book is offered with the full realization that a great deal of education, study and review would be required for the systems approach to be adapted and implemented to a given city. It is anticipated that this educational process may come about through the extensive network of fire science programs currently being conducted at Junior Colleges and Community Colleges across the United States. In other words, this book is intended as a text for Fire Department Organization, Administration and Management classes. A critical examination of the concepts presented in an educational context should sharpen and refine the conceptual framework of public fire departments.

The following quotations set the stage more eloquently and forcefully than I could as an author:

Some men see things as they are and say "Why?"
I dream of things which never were and ask "Why not?"

ROBERT F. KENNEDY

Certitude is not the test for certainty. We have been cocksure of many things that were not so.

JUSTICE OLIVER WENDELL HOLMES

New times demand new measures and new men;
The world advances, and in time outgrows
The laws that in our fathers' day were best;
And doubtless, after us, some purer scheme
Will be shaped out by wiser men than we,
Made wiser by the steady growth of truth.

JAMES RUSSELL LOWELL

Acknowledgment

Few, if any, authors conduct a solo performance in the writing, the editing and the publishing of a book. My work is no exception to this observation. I am deeply indebted, and at the same time deeply grateful, to a number of individuals for their intellectual stimulation, personal guidance, constructive reflections, and editorial assistance. Without the encouragement from loyal associates, this work would never have reached fruition. However, responsibility for the final narrative rests with the author.

Two individuals have guided this research project since its inception. Dr. John L. Bryan, Professor and Head of the Fire Protection Curriculum, College of Engineering at the University of Maryland has provided incalculable assistance in the process of developing the research proposal, in developing the conceptual framework of ideas for applying systems theory to public fire safety and in sharpening the final manuscript. Dr. Lowell Hattery, Professor of Public Administration, the American University in Washington, D.C., has made an equally important contribution to this work. Dr. Hattery supported the original proposal to write a book in the field of public fire safety as meeting the requirements for a comprehensive field of study in Fire Administration at the doctoral level. He has been responsible for maintaining the high degree of scholarship that the American University demands. Finally, Dr. Hattery served a vital role in shaping the concepts that permitted applying a systems approach to a selected public service area. I am deeply appreciative for the effort of both gentlemen.

The contributions of the following individuals have been so great that they must be noted. Dr. Robert Fristrom, Dr. Walter Berl, Dr. Girard Ordway and Mr. Byron Halpin, research associates with the Fire Problems Program, the Applied Physics Laboratory/The Johns Hopkins University have assisted in various portions of the manuscript development. Dr. Ordway has been especially helpful in reviewing the galley proofs prior to publication. Mrs. Evelyn Smith, Secretary to the Fire Problems Group, must be singled out for special acknowledgment. Mrs. Smith has completed all the manuscript typing and her questioning eye has sharpened the grammar throughout the book. I am indebted to the Fire Problems Program at JHU/APL (supported by the National Science Foundation RANN Program) for assistance in preparing the final manuscript.

I am further indebted to Robert Grant, Anthony O'Neill, George Tryon and Paul Lyons of the National Fire Protection Association for their review of the original manuscript and their endorsement to publish this material. Paul Lyons has been especially helpful and patient during the process of preparing the manuscript for final publication.

Finally, my wife Alice also contributed significantly to this work. She has provided constant assistance in reviewing and editing as the writing progressed and more important she has provided the necessary morale over the three-year span that was required to prepare the manuscript. Under the family umbrella, my children also share in this accomplishment. Sharon, Linda, Kelly and David have sacrificed many pleasures on Saturday and Sunday while this book was in preparation. I firmly believe that it is the encouragement, love, affection, and understanding of one's family that permits the birth of an idea to be written into book form.

Harry E. Hickey

Table of Contents

List of Illustrations

Chapter 7

Chapter 8

Chapter I

Current Problems in the Organization of Public Fire Safety

Introduction

On November 17, 1970, President Richard M. Nixon announced the appointment of a special Presidential Commission to study and report upon the current identified fire problems in the United States.[1]

The National Commission on Fire Prevention and Control represented the most important study group to address itself to the nation's fire problems. Each of the prior study groups discussed below, has attempted to define basic problem areas in fire prevention, fire protection and fire suppression. Published papers from these groups depict broad scale recommendations that chart a path of direction for the future. It is clearly evident that many of the recommendations proposed by the conference groups complement and reinforce each other. Therefore, without further investigation, there appears to be a substantial body of knowledge to identify systematically problems facing the nation's Fire Service. This knowledge can serve as the basis for developing an understanding of the objective performance of the nation's public Fire Service.

Conferences on Public Safety

The Wingspread Conference in February 1966 developed, "statements of National Significance as an aid to clearer understanding of the fire problem and the steps to be taken in achieving the objectives of bringing the national fire problem into focus."[2]

The Wingspread Conference Statements are as follows:[3]

1. Unprecedented demands are being imposed on the Fire Service by rapid social and technological change.

2. The public is complacent toward the rising trend of life and property loss by fire.

3. There is a serious lack of communication between the public and the Fire Service.

4. Behavior patterns of the public have a direct influence on the fire problem.

5. The insurance interest has exerted a strong influence on the organization of the Fire Service. This dominance seems to be waning. The Fire Service must provide the leadership in establishing realistic criteria for determining proper levels of fire protection.

6. Professional status begins with education. The scope, degree and depth of educational requirements for efficient functioning of the Fire Service must be examined.

7. Increased mobility at the executive level of the Fire Service will be important to the achievement of professional status.

8. The career development of the fire executive must be systematic and deliberate.

9. Governing bodies and municipal administrators generally do not recognize the need for executive development of the fire officer.

10. Fire Service labor and management, municipal officers and administrators must join together if professionalism is to become a reality.

11. The traditional concept that fire protection is strictly a responsibility of local government must be reexamined.

---

[1]Robert M. Fristrom, ed., "Foreword," *Fire Research Abstracts and Reviews*, Vol. 13, 1971, No. 1, p. iii.

[2]*Wingspread Conference on Fire Service Administration, Education and Research.* Racine: The Johnson Foundation, 1966, p. 3.

[3]*Ibid.*, p. 3.

The spirit of problem identification was advanced at the Saratoga, New York Symposium on higher education for the Fire Service, held in the early part of 1967. This symposium focused on problems and goals associated with motivation of fire service personnel to higher education, a prospectus of higher fire service education programs and the establishment of curricula guidelines.[4]

One month after the Saratoga meeting, the Editors of *Fire Engineering* conducted a symposium in Chicago to "explore in depth the specifics — present and future — in problem areas defined by the Wingspread Conference."[5] The meeting focused on issues concerning fire department personnel, lateral entry into the Fire Service, labor relations and negotiations, educational development, innovations in fire apparatus and the role of the Federal Government in public fire protection.

A Symposium on the Needs of the Fire Service was held at the National Academy of Sciences in Washington, D.C. in October 1968. Papers were presented and discussions were held on the nature of the Fire Service problems as seen by the fire chiefs;[6] "to report on the progress made to date in the initial attempts by several cities to solve problems by the application of systems analysis and computer technology; to emphasize the critical role of communications in directing fire-fighting operations; and to examine specific items of fire equipment in terms of both their adequacies and their deficiencies." A final summation was made that offered some general observations on what can and should be done by public fire departments in the near future.

Early in 1970, it became apparent that the problems of the Fire Service were of such magnitude that it was desirable for the major national Fire Service organizations to engage in an informal, frank exchange of viewpoints. Under the sponsorship of the National Fire Protection Association, "Williamsburg '70" was convened at Williamsburg, Virginia on August 31, 1970, for the purpose of examining the following objectives.[7]

1. Establishment of goals and priorities based on the needs of the Fire Service.

2. Development of a unified policy on the national goals of the Fire Service.

3. Coordination of the efforts of the national organizations so they will pull together to obtain solutions to national fire problems.

4. Development and implementation of an action program to attain the agreed goals.

A very significant outcome of the Williamsburg Conference was the development of national goals for the United States Fire Service. They are listed as follows:[8]

1. To develop nationally recognized standards for competency and achievement of skills development, technical proficiency and academic knowledge appropriate to every level of the Fire Service career ladder.

2. To make the public aware of the significant contributions made by the Fire Service of this nation in protecting life and property from fire, and the contribution made to the standard of living to which all citizens are entitled.

3. To make public officials at every level of government more aware of their responsibilities in providing increased financial and moral support to aid the Fire Service in carrying out their missions.

4. To reassess public fire protection in light of contemporary demands, assuring appropriate fire protection for all communities at a reasonable cost.

5. To establish realistic standards of educational achievement, and provide to every member of the Fire Service equal educational opportunities commensurate with professional requirements.

6. To identify and establish nationwide information systems that will enable improved analysis of the fire problem with particular emphasis on the life and safety factors for the public and the fire fighter.

7. To encourage and undertake the research and development necessary for the prompt and successful implementation of the goals stated above.

Specific references will be made to each of these conferences in the development of this chapter.

Study Objectives

It is the objective of this first chapter of the study paper to examine critically current problems specifically associated with public fire safety organizations. Identified problems will serve as a base for projecting a public fire safety organizational framework that will be responsive to the problem situations.

The analysis of a problem should start by formulating the proper questions. Therefore, one might ask, what is the mission of public fire safety? A traditional response to this question would be to state that "Public fire safety is concerned with the protection of life and property from the ravages of unwanted

---

[4]Donald F. Favreau, "Crisis in Higher Education," *Fire Engineering*, April 1968, p. 57.

[5]Staff, "The 1970's — The Challenging Years for the Fire Service," *Fire Engineering*, September 1967, p. 106.

[6]James F. Casey, "Science Symposium Explores Needs of the Fire Service," *Fire Engineering*, January 1969, p. 42.

[7]*Williamsburg '70*, Boston: National Fire Protection Association, 1970, p. 7.

[8]*Ibid.*, p. 7.

fire occurrences."[9] To a major extent this objective has been translated to mean the provision of a fire department organization devoted to the suppression of unwanted fires. The basic question and the response form a framework for conceptualizing the role of public fire safety.

The initial question naturally leads to additional questions. Tied to the first question are several logical subquestions. These would appear to include: (a) what is actually meant by public fire safety, (b) what is fire protection, (c) how do the functions of fire protection and fire suppression relate to fire prevention? The notion that the subject area of public fire safety is broader than any singular concept is implicit in each subquestion. Therefore, probably the most relevant question is simply to ask — do mission priorities exist in the area of public fire safety?

The answers to these questions are not simple. However, there is a logical starting point to reflect on the questions. One's point of inquiry must be initiated by assigning operational definitions to terms and concepts associated with the stated questions. A partial list of terms selected for definition in this paper follows. Other special terms will be defined in the context of the paper.

Special Definitions

1. **Public Fire Departments.** Organizations legally composed and responsive to public policy for the purpose of protecting lives and property from fire-imposed casualties and damage.

2. **Public Fire Safety.** The relative condition relating to the degree of protection provided for human life and property from fire effects in a governmental area.

3. **Fire Prevention Functions.** The organizational operations, duties and activities concerned with ignition prevention, the reduction of fire casualties, and the reduction of modular fire loss in buildings.

4. **Fire Protection Functions.** The organizational operations, duties, and activities concerned with the design and engineering of components to extinguish or control fires and fire effects.

5. **Fire Suppression Functions.** The organizational operations, duties and activities concerned with the rescue, fire suppression procedures, and loss reductions activities.

6. **Organization.** A structured system of roles and functional relationships designed to carry out programs inspired by administrative policy.[10]

7. **Organizational Functions.** A concept utilized to indicate activities, duties and/or roles which may be grouped upon the basis of similarity in relation to either purpose or process.[11]

8. **Volunteer Fire Department Organization.** A public fire department in which all of the officer positions are staffed with volunteer personnel.

9. **Combination Fire Department Organization.** A public fire department in which the officer positions are staffed partially with paid personnel and partially with volunteer personnel.

10. **Paid Fire Department Organization.** A public fire department in which all of the officer positions are staffed with paid personnel.

The Mission of Public Fire Safety Evaluated

The preceding definitions include the conceptual components of public fire prevention, protection and suppression in an organizational context. Now it becomes possible to respond to the initial question in a more refined and substantive manner. What is the mission of Public Fire Safety?

An historical review of public fire department organizations in the United States reveals that fire departments are originated to control unwanted fires successfully.[12] The individual citizen in the community appears to express the attitude "that the fire department will take care of it — if I have a fire."[13] The *Wingspread Conference Report on Fire Service Administration, Education and Research*, stated that, "the Fire Service itself seems to be hesitant to go much farther in explaining its function than to indicate — we save life and property."[14]

Firemen sitting in front of a fire station have been characterized as waiting for the next fire. This reflection seems to point up one stereotype of public fire departments. The image implies that the prime purpose of a fire department is to suppress unwanted fires as soon after ignition as possible. Therefore, the public focus on public fire departments is to deal with fires after the occurrence. On this premise, it can be contended that the mission of public fire departments is to fight fires. The author perceives that a large segment of the population, including citizens, elected and appointed governmental administrators, businessmen, industrial executives, plus a significant proportion of volunteer and paid firemen, view fire de-

[9]National Fire Protection Association. *Organization of a Fire Department — 1969* (4A). Boston: National Fire Protection Association, 1969, p. 4.

[10]John M. Pfiffner, and Robert Presthus, *Public Administration*. New York: The Ronald Press, 1967, p. 7.

[11]*Ibid.*, p. 188.

[12]National Fire Protection Association. *Organization of a Fire Department*. (No. 4A), Boston: National Fire Protection Association, 1969, pp. 3–7.

[13]The Johnson Foundation. *Wingspread Conference on Fire Service Administration, Education and Research*. Racine (Wisc.): The Johnson Foundation, 1966, p. 7.

[14]*Ibid.*, p. 7.

partments solely as an organization designed to extinguish fires. Furthermore, it is the author's opinion that both the public and fire service personnel possess a very limited understanding of the complicated and interface relationships existing between fire prevention functions, fire protection functions and fire suppression functions. This book will attempt to project the fire suppression function as a secondary but vital mission of public fire safety.

A necessity exists for examining other possible objectives of public fire safety in order to establish a more viable mission for public fire safety organizations.

The National Fire Protection Association publishes a guide entitled *Organization for Fire Services*.[15] The initial paragraph in this reference states the *Purpose of a Fire Department* as follows:[16]

> Control of the community complex of combustibles should be undertaken by the fire department in furtherance of its fundamental purpose of protecting life and property from fire. The department program should be aimed at keeping the complex of combustibles with which man surrounds himself within reasonable limits.

It may be interpreted from this quote that fire departments have an inherent responsibility to prevent fires from originating as a function of controlling the complex of combustibles. Also, the limitation of combustibles clearly comes under the defined concept of fire protection functions. Through the limitation and arrangement of combustibles it is clearly possible to effect the control of a developing fire.

Establishing Public Fire Safety Objectives

Adding to these mission concepts is the objective list for Fire Departments published in *Municipal Fire Administration*.[17] This text states that the objective function of municipal fire departments is:

1. To prevent fires from starting

2. To prevent loss of life and property when a fire starts

3. To confine a fire to the place of origin

4. To put out the fire with the least amount of damage possible.

It seems important to recognize that the manner of accomplishing these objectives is not fully prescribed. In other words, the accomplishment of these objectives would possibly be effected in one or more ways. For example, objective two from the above list stipulates the prevention of loss of life in case of fire. Some of the significant means of accomplishing this objective would include:

1. Early warning detection equipment and evacuation alarms.

2. Adequate and safe means of egress facilities from a building.

3. Modular building construction to limit the spread of fire.

4. A privately established evacuation and rescue plan.

5. A fire department search and rescue operation.

This list identifies both private and public considerations for preventing loss of life from unwanted fires. A first glance at the list might reveal that the fire department relationship to the overall objectives was reflected in the search and rescue effort. However, a closer look at the alternatives might reveal a broader area of fire department responsibility. This total view of fire department involvement could include such areas as: code development and enforcement, architectural plan review, and early warning technical services.

Finally, there exists still a further purpose for fire department organizations. The National Fire Protection Association's *Organization for Fire Services* pamphlet states under *Scope of Services* that as a purpose "the fire department should be organized to perform fire fighting and emergency services to protect life and property from fire.[18] The area of emergency services has consistently broadened the functional outlook of fire departments. Some fire departments are reporting up to 75 per cent of their response to alarm activity is devoted to non-fire emergencies.[19] "Other services demanded of the fire department, because the fire department force is available and because it has specialized training" needs to be closely examined in terms of mission orientation.[20]

The previous reflections on mission orientation of public fire departments identify a range of organizational objective problems. Probably the most serious concern to the organized effort of public fire safety is the establishment

---

[15]National Fire Protection Association. *Organization for Fire Services*, 1971 (No. 4).

[16]*Ibid.*, 4–3.

[17]International City Managers Association. *Municipal Fire Administration*, 1967, 7th Ed., p. 1;

[18]*Op. Cit.*, NFPA, 4–5.

[19]Obtained from the consolidated six months fire report (Jan. 1970 to June 1970) from Chautauqua County, State of New York.

[20]*Op. Cit.*, NFPA, 4–5.

of a viable mission. The following points are intended to identify the mission problem as it currently exists.

First, there appears to be a significant group of fire department leaders who feel that the real and legal responsibility of fire departments is to suppress fires after they have originated. These individuals demonstrate little or no responsibility toward the fire prevention function and fire protection function as defined in this paper. Other leaders of the Fire Service recognize fire prevention functions and fire protection functions as legitimate and necessary to the objective function of public fire safety but they are powerless to enter into these areas for one or more reasons. The lack of ability to function effectively in the areas of fire prevention and fire protection may stem from the lack of motivation on the part of subordinate men and officers, the lack of technical capability to be competent in these two functional areas and/or the perceived lack of resources to enter these areas.

Second, there appears to be a conflicting notion of just what constitutes a meaningful fire prevention program; what constitutes fire protection functions and, more important, what is the interrelationship of fire prevention, fire protection and fire suppression to the broad mission of Public Fire Safety?

Third, fire departments do not appear to have an organizational structure that will promote an integrated approach to fire prevention functions, fire protection functions and fire suppression functions into a total public fire safety program.

These reflection statements appear quite appropriate and in order. Yet, the mission and objective orientation of current public fire safety represents one of the most significant problems to be faced in the broad spectrum of Public Fire Safety. Why? The reasons can be stated in one word — generalization. The mission is too broad, too general, the mission of public fire safety suffers from lack of specificity of direction. The author is not alone in this observation.

Mr. Robert Grant, Vice President of the National Fire Protection Association, advanced the opinion that the biggest problem faced by the nation's fire service is "a lack of sound objectives."[21] Chief Gratz of the Silver Spring, Maryland Fire Department expresses the opinion that "the Fire Service has attempted to reach out for optimum performance — what-

ever that is."[22] This statement seems to imply that performance is a component of the mission. Emmanuel Fried states that, "Fire departments all over the world have the same purpose: to provide good fire protection."[23] He follows with a key rhetorical question, "But what do we mean by good fire protection . . . the obvious conclusion is that till we define our objective clearly no one can really say what is good or poor fire protection."[24] The Wingspread Conference group noted that the community citizen, the fire chief and the public administrator share "a lack of understanding of what constitutes fire protection."[25] Finally, Gordon Vickery of Seattle describes the American Fire Service as "lacking direction."[26]

An organization must be built on objectives that combine purpose with performance.[27] The concern over problems relating to public fire protection have not stressed this number one priority item. A discussion of public fire safety organization must commence with a critical examination of the interface between the organizational mission and organizational performance. The mission is described by objectives; performance criteria establishes meaning to the objectives. The combination of objectives and performance should be explicit to communicate the organization mission to those involved and affected.

A proper understanding of the organizational objectives in relation to organization performance should tell a uniform story on: the nature of the organization, the purpose of the organization and how well the organizational mission is being achieved. When this understanding is achieved, then the citizen, the fire chief and the public administrator have a common base for communicating about public fire safety. Hopefully they are in a position to say "Ourville" is providing a good level of public fire safety. A common meaning can be advanced for equating the "goodness or badness" of a given public fire safety organization. Furthermore, the degree of goodness or badness of fire safety for a stated com-

[21]Staff, "National Research Council Symposium on Training and Education," *Fire Chief Magazine*, June 1970, p. 38.

[22]David B. Gratz, "The U. S. Fire Service Problems Today and Tomorrow," *Fire Chief Magazine*, January 1970, p. 26.

[23]Emanuel Fried, "The High Cost of Fire Protection," *Fire Chief*, January 1969, p. 36.

[24]*Ibid.*, p. 36.

[25]Staff, "The Wingspread Conference," *Fire Engineering*, January 1967, p. 39.

[26]James F. Casey, "Science Symposium Explores Needs of the Fire Service," *Fire Engineering*, January 1969, p. 42.

[27]Lawrence A. Appley, "Management and the American Future," *General Management Series No. 169*, American Management Association, Inc., 1954, p. 11.

munity can be compared with some authority to another community with similar characteristics.

It is the premise of this book that to achieve the above ends, public fire departments must start with a new beginning. Fire departments must redefine their missions in specific terms of objective performance. It appears necessary to constitute a new organizational structure that responds dynamically to clearly established objectives and the performance of those objectives. The following concepts are advanced to lay a proper foundation for proposing a new organization framework for public fire safety. The goal is to establish the initial step towards what Abraham Kaplan calls "making sense out of our presently disturbing situation with the symbolic construction of a new organizational framework . . . a new theory of organization."[28]

Performance Objectives

Public fire departments have traditionally been organized in response to a problem — the occurrence of destructive fires. There appears to be two main elements to every destructive fire. First there is the occurrence of the event. Without the event, or threat of an event, there would be no problem. The destructive nature or severity of the event, once it occurs, is the second element of the problem. The basic problem can be viewed as a concern over the probability of having an unwanted fire and the consequence of that fire should it occur. Stated another way, we are concerned over the frequency of unwanted fires and the severity of those fires that do initiate.

The problem takes a definite shape when the frequency of unwanted fires and the severity of those fires reach some proportionate level. Two extreme, but real-world events serve to illustrate this concept. In the first instance, let us consider the case of a high-rise complex of buildings in suburbia. One possible event is being considered at this time. The potential of the event will be covered later.

In the first event case, let us consider a high-rise-apartment complex located in Newtown. A check with the Newtown Fire Department shows that they have not responded to a fire alarm at the apartment complex in the three years that it has been occupied. An interview with the apartment complex management reveals that one fire did occur. It was described as a wastepaper basket fire in the manager's

[28]Abraham Kaplan, *The Conduct of Inquiry*. San Francisco: Chandler Publishing Company, 1964, pp. 295–296.

office which was quickly extinguished with tap water. The loss consisted of replacement of the waste container at five dollars. A frequency of one event with a loss severity of five dollars over a three-year time span could be considered a minor fire safety problem from a purely statistical standpoint.

The second instance presents a contrast situation. A similar high-rise-apartment complex in Yourville is experiencing a number of fires each year with fire related injuries and a considerable monetary loss. Last year's fire reports from the Yourville Fire Department file reveal the following facts: The number of reported fires — one hundred and five, or an average of two per week. Ten apartments were severely damaged by fire with a resultant direct loss of one hundred thousand dollars. Twenty-two families were relocated for a total of two thousand occupant days at a total cost of fifty thousand dollars. Two elderly women and four firemen were hospitalized with smoke inhalation as a result of these fires. The hospital expenses alone totaled fifteen thousand dollars. It took the fire department a total of twenty-eight hundred man hours to cope with the fires. The proportional costs to the community for this level of service have not been equated but the taxpayer is paying thirty cents per hundred dollars of property valuation for fire protection.

A frequency of two fires a week in one complex of buildings with the described losses presents a significant problem.

Numerous conditions revolving around both fire examples have not been explained. The purpose is to illustrate a potential range of public fire safety problems. Neither condition supports the extreme range of possible conditions which could be no fires with no loss over a given time span to some infinite number of fires culminating in a total loss during the same reviewed period of time. Furthermore, each fire condition can be described in terms of the established two elements — frequency of events and severity of events.

In the case of Newtown, the citizens, fire chief and public administrator would probably be satisfied with the performance level at the stated high-rise-apartment complex. The citizens, Fire Chief, and Public Administrator of Yourville should be deeply concerned with the events at the stated high-rise complex. A problem has been identified and it can be stated in explicit terms. Since the assumption is made that Public Fire Safety is organized to cope with real and perceived fire problems, one can start to formulate a mission statement and supportive attendant objectives.

The Mission of Public Fire Safety Restated

The perceived mission of Public Fire Safety is to maintain an acceptable destructive fire frequency level and severity level prescribed by the citizens in the area being considered.

There will be fires and there will be direct and indirect losses from these fires. Society must accept this premise. However, a given population also has the right and means to prescribe what level of performance is acceptable. That specific population has the further right and obligation to understand the relative performance position of one political area in relation to other political areas. In other words, a person living in a single family dwelling in a New York community should be able to recognize the degree of public fire safety being afforded to him in relation to a similar dwelling in Oklahoma. The Fire Chief and the Public Administrator in the comparative communities should be able to make similar analysis over a broad range of occupancy-structural classifications. The American fire service is not currently in a position to provide these answers. The American fire service is not organized to provide these answers.

From a Broad Mission to Specific Objectives

The Mission of Public Fire Safety can now be translated into more concrete objectives than currently appear to exist. Each perceived objective is broadly stated to establish a total framework for reference. Each objective statement is then expanded to develop the scope and implications of the concepts presented.

1. The first objective of public fire safety is to provide a fire frequency performance level acceptable to the citizens of the jurisdictional area under consideration.
2. The second objective of public fire safety is to provide a life safety level acceptable to the citizens in the jurisdictional area under consideration.
3. The third objective of public fire safety is to confine initiated fires to the modular level acceptable to the property occupants in the jurisdictional area under consideration.
4. The fourth objective of public fire safety is to suppress initiated fires with the least

amount of property damage and occupancy interruption possible.
5. The fifth objective of public fire safety is to provide selected emergency services relating to life safety and property damage to a defined jurisdictional area.
6. The sixth objective of public fire safety is to meet the intent of the performance levels established under a favorable ratio of cost to performance effectiveness.

The objectives stated by themselves are barely more meaningful than the objectives previously quoted by the International City Managers' Association. Furthermore, the prospect of their reality appears very far removed from present reality. Yet, the objectives form a base for projection, improvement, analysis and a common approach for general understanding. Specific factors relating to each stated objective are constantly developed throughout the entire book. The immediate concern is to explore each objective in terms of the intended scope, the proper definition of selected terms, and to focus on the important questions that the public fire safety organizations must respond to in the future.

An Examination of the New Objectives

Objective One

It has been established that one element of the fire problem is simply to identify properly and catalogue occurrences of destructive fires. The defined frequency and severity levels associated with destructive fires can be analyzed by those affected to determine what are acceptable loss conditions. At some, as yet undefined, point the number or frequency of fires should be unacceptable to defined governmental jurisdictions. The number of events must be reduced to an acceptable level. Therefore, it is a reasonable objective for public fire safety organizations to eliminate unwanted fires. Traditionally this concept has been labeled fire prevention. There is no sound reason to change from the goal of preventing fires. The new objective statement intends to focus on how many fires a public fire safety organization should try to prevent. A pure goal would be simply to prevent all uncontrolled fires. Such a goal appears impossible from both a human and economic point of view. Therefore, a responsibility of public officials should be to determine how many fires are tolerated. It may be assumed that toleration levels are not going to be the same in every community. Some citizens and citizens' groups are going to be more reactive to fire occurrence than others. In some areas the citizens are going to be apathetic about fire safety; this point will be expanded upon later. Where there is a lack of citizen interest concerning fire safety, the frequency and severity of fire incidents becomes the inherent responsibility of the fire chief and the mayor (city administrator) to provide a level of service that the local economy will stand.

It is perceived that a certain degree of intercommunity competition may result when comparative incident figures as outlined in this book become available. The potential competition for improved statistical data results could start a trend that might influence future frequency and severity figures.

When statistical trends over the years for the defined property classifications, occupancy groups, and socioeconomic levels show a decline in frequency and/or probability ratio, individually or in total, then a community can truly say they are preventing fires. The degree of accomplishment can also be stated in quantitative terms. Or, the problem can be more clearly defined on both a quantitative and qualitative basis.

Objective Two

A second objective deals with life safety. It will be pointed out in a subsequent section that a true picture concerning life loss from the fire problem in the United States has not been established. It is important to state that the life loss problem due to fire exceeds 10,000 persons per year. Like the automobile accident death rate, the public seems to be accepting current projections of the problem. The cry for remedial action comes after a catastrophe where a number of people are injured or perish in a single incident. The tendency then seems to be over-reaction with legislation and large capital expenditures for well meaning improvements. Whether the implementation of change by such improvements would actually prevent further occurrences of the same magnitude or whether the interval to the next calamity would be independent of the change is highly speculative.

In any event, it is necessary to provide certain desired levels of human safety within a given community. The feasibility of providing 100 per cent safety, or the probability that no life loss will occur, is unattainable because of technological inadequacies, human factors, and economical limitations. Public fire safety has

not sufficiently addressed itself to the question: What is an acceptable level of life loss in a community? Certain fires like the Harmer House Nursing Home in Marietta, Ohio, and the Jacksonville Hotel Fire as selected illustrations among many similar instances, are known to have provoked cries of inadequacies from the press, the citizens and elected officials. In such instances the threshold of public or society acceptance appears to have been exceeded. Timing, severity conditions, and location appear to change this public acceptance threshold level. What may be acceptable to one community may not be acceptable to another. The sets of conditions necessary to adequately define levels of human safety have yet to be formulated and structured. Such a definitive structure may come after the exact problem becomes more specific. A definition of the life safety problem from fire occurrences may evolve from the responses to the questions raised in this chapter.

Of equal concern is the resultant injury problem from unwanted fires due to both costs and emotional factors. Questions and comments appropriate to both life loss and injuries from fire related events will be dispersed throughout the remaining chapter subsections.

Objective Three

The third objective relates to confining an initiated fire to some prescribed modular level. The term modular level is introduced to depict structural parameters for prescribing objectives and charting severity conditions. A module level is intended to express a functional measurement for fire loss conditions. A module may be thought of as a physical configuration with an imaginary envelope around the configuration. Modules can be quantitatively defined for different structures. For example, in an office building, each desk or work station could be a module, the next module level might be a room, followed by a wing of a building, a floor of a building, X number of floors in the building, and finally the total building. Like modules in like structures would have approximately the same floor areas. Similar modular data sets could be developed for other buildings and occupancy types.

Hypothetically, management in the office building example might be willing to accept the burnout of a single office — a one- or two-room office. A loss beyond this level would be considered unacceptable. An objective level has been established. Public fire safety now has a guideline to measure performance. In Newtown, the effects of the building code, the fire prevention measures and the public fire department acting together may demonstrate a high probability for meeting the one room module criteria. In Yourtown, the same forces may be quite inadequate to meet the objective.

Before justifiable public fire safety can be provided a given area, the homeowners, the merchants, the industrial leaders and public administration must come to grips with defining the severity levels of fires that can be tolerated. The point to be made is that the severity of fires can be defined. Therefore, objectives can be stated in terms of potential severity.

This concept of defining parameters of severity can also be utilized for measuring the effectiveness of public fire safety. When fire incidents are consistently kept small, then it would appear that the interrelated factors of fire safety are working. When the modular losses consistently exceed expectations, one or more factors of fire safety are deficient.

Objective Four

This objective focuses on the suppression effort once a potential fire initiates. Suppression is translated into the confining, controlling and extinguishing action at a fire. Traditionally, fire fighting (suppression or extinguishment) has been the visible reference for equating levels of public fire safety. The association includes perceptions developed by the composite observation of smoke, sirens, red lights, shiny fire apparatus, high velocity water streams, and an unbelievable amount of clamoring and noise. To many citizens this is the principal function of fire safety. This fire safety objective attempts to refine this concept while retaining the essential elements of fire suppression as a vital and visible force.

This objective really has two parts. The parts should go together as stated, but often do not in practice. First, the objective is concerned with the employment of physical and human resources to extinguish an unwanted fire at a defined level as established under objective number three with a minimum amount of associated damage. For example, the fire suppression effort involved with an office building fire might confine the burn damage to the modular office level. However, the techniques utilized to accomplish this objective might result in extensive water damage to adjacent areas. This objective considers that the sup-

pression effort should limit the total damage concept established under objective three.

Objectives three and four are made distinct and separate for the purpose of analysis. Suppression efforts might be suitable for confining the physical fire damage to a given level while permitting associative damage from ventilation, and water (or their extinguishing agent) to extend beyond the prescribed modular level. Therefore, the two objectives should be analyzed separately.

A second part of the objective makes reference to occupancy interruption. Under habitable conditions, a structure is utilized for some ongoing purpose; housing, business, manufacturing, etc. If a fire occurs there is an interruption to this activity. This can range from a minor inconvenience to hours of down time for a process. The significance of this interruptive process is part of the loss problem. The objective is to keep this interruption to a minimum level. The objective may be stated even more specifically for a given set of occupancy conditions.

Objective Five

This objective concerns the provision of selected emergency services relating to life safety and property damage. Optional services might include ambulance service, light and heavy rescue service, on land and/or water, and general public services such as emergency salvaging operations. Such services are taken for granted by many communities as a fire safety responsibility. Such services take manpower, physical resources and indirectly affect the previous fire safety objectives. It is time these services become part of the public fire safety mission package.

Objective Six

The sixth established objective is concerned with meeting all previous objective criteria with the related consideration of cost performance. In other words, it should be recognized that desired performance levels to a significant degree are dependent upon public funding. The objective simply establishes the premise that performance levels must be equated to cost factors. Furthermore, it establishes an obligation on the part of public fire departments to associate the performance services rendered with the cost of providing these services. Chapters IV, V, and VIII will discuss public fire safety in relation to cost benefit analysis techniques.

A Determination of the Effectiveness and Efficiency of Public Fire Department Organizations

Webster states, "Efficiency — operations as measured by a comparison of production with cost in energy, time, money, etc.[29] Synonym: See Effectiveness," while "Effectiveness is producing a decided, decisive or desired effect, such as effective measures. Synonym: Consequence, result, outcome or the like traceable to a cause."

In explanation, Webster states that

. . . effectiveness applies only to those factors in a complex situation that may be definitely attributed to the operation of a cause . . . it suggests the accomplishment of a result or the fulfillment of an intension and looks backward rather than forward; while being efficient is applied especially, but not invariably to, persons, suggests having given proof or power or skill in producing results.

The important point to observe is that concepts revolving around efficiency and effectiveness are intertwined. The efficiency and effectiveness of public fire safety must be thought of as a total concept.

Several objectives relate to the discussion of efficiency and effectiveness under the response to public fire safety problems.

First, public fire safety is not utilizing uniform measures for equating the efficiency and effectiveness of programs and operations. It is pure conjecture to state that a given fire department is efficient and/or effective. When questions of performance are raised, fire department personnel respond with answers that have very little quantitative validity.

Therefore, the performance of established objectives must be subjected to analysis and evaluation. Concepts of efficiency and effectiveness are emphasized because they serve to indicate areas in which objective analysis may be possible and those where it does not appear practical. David Novick states, "the efficiency concept implies that measures taken to achieve economics will not affect the attainment of the objectives of the program when it is carried out at a given level. Consequently, efficiency can be dealt with by analytical methods."[30] The techniques of operations research and cost effectiveness analysis, relatively new techniques, are concerned with efficiency operations.

However, Novick cautions that any distinction between effectiveness and efficiency must be used with extreme care. "Measures that purport to increase efficiency may have pronounced effects, *good or bad*, on effectiveness."[31]

As previously noted the topic of cost-effectiveness only receives an introduction at this point. An operational definition of the terms and specific considerations relating to this concept will be subsequently developed in Chapters II and V.

Second, any problem identification and response to the problem must examine current conditions relating to fire department efficiency and effectiveness. As a matter of orientation it appears advantageous to look at the problem identification first and the response second.

Selected Problems: Identification and Response

A current analysis of public fire safety efficiency and effectiveness is extremely difficult. The following statements, quotations, and responses highlight and reflect the problem.

Problem Statement 1

In the July 1971 issue of the *Fire Journal*, a National Fire Protection Association staff writer made the following observation under "Fire Record of Cities, 1970."[32]

The (fire) data should definitely not be used as a basis for comparing the efficiency of fire departments. The fire departments of different cities face different problems, which depend largely on factors outside the control of the fire department. For instance, a fire department should not be held responsible for fires started by human activities over which it has no control or for fires that spread because of inferior construction. A fire department is responsible for its fire prevention program and for the effectiveness of its fire ground operations — two responsibilities that must be measured by other means than fires per thousand population or average fire loss.

Response to Statement 1

A reflective response is necessary concerning several points made in the preceding paragraph. I positively agree that most of the present fire loss data should not be utilized to measure the effectiveness and efficiency of fire departments. The present array of data collected by public fire departments simply does not lend itself to valid comparison. Evidence of this condition is found in the published figures relating to the

[29]*Webster's New Collegiate Dictionary.* Springfield: G. and C. Merriam Co., Publishers, 1961, p. 262.

[30]David Novick, ed., *Program Budgeting.* Cambridge: Harvard University Press, 1965, p. 49.

[31]*Ibid.,* p. 50.

[32]Staff, "Fire Record of Cities, 1970", *Fire Journal,* National Fire Protection Association, July 1971, p. 79.

number of fires per thousand population, the average fire loss, and total fires reported.[33] Why? Simply because too many variables are ignored. The problem is like looking at a hundred piece puzzle with only twenty of the pieces interlocked. The picture is obviously incomplete. Only a distorted picture can be formed by assuming what goes in the blank spaces. Because many pieces of information are missing, our picture of fire department efficiency and effectiveness is currently distorted and can be considered meaningless in relation to measuring the established objectives.

Selected fire departments may face different problems but they also face similar problems. Fire protection information systems have failed to identify adequately items that could be utilized to compare similar communities. Public fire departments are collecting inadequate information to compare properly the efficiency and effectiveness of one fire department with another fire department.

The following quotation adds a new point and reinforces the above concepts.

Problem Statement 2

In Dick Sylvia's review of a British Fire Research Report the following comparative observation is made:[34]

> In the discussion of fire statistics and their implications, the report sounded as though the survey had been made in the United States. The (British) committee charged that insufficient attention has been paid to the collection and, particularly, to the analysis of statistical data which we consider essential for the identification and successful combating of all fire problems."

Response to Statement 2

Response one focused on the condition that incomplete fire loss data is collected to consider measuring efficiency and effectiveness. It is not enough simply to collect the requisite fire incident data — the prescribed data must be analyzed in a meaningful manner as indicated in the British Report.[34a]

The United States does not appear to be alone in the problem of fire incident data collection and analysis.

Problem Statement 3

Concerning the analysis of data, Warren Kimball makes some interesting observations when he states:[35]

One trouble with statistics is that they deal with averages and fires are not average or normal circumstances. However, the fire service must expect to be measured increasingly by various experts in research and by other consultants who will use such means to attempt to evaluate their effectiveness. One of the arguments advanced by some U. S. fire service leaders for the National Fire Safety and Research Act was an alleged need for more operations research. Without a doubt, one of the areas of most interest to research people is cost effectiveness. Fire service people may be asked to answer the question, "Is your job necessary? We find that you are costing far more than you save in fire loss reduction." For example, it might be shown statistically that the 99.5 per cent of fires can be efficiently handled by three-man fire companies and that in the remaining 0.5 per cent of fires, the five-man crews are not appreciably more effective in preventing major losses. Would those who urged such research to back demands for better company manning be happy with the results?

Response to Statement 3

Averages as implied by Mr. Kimball may not be too meaningful. Averages or mean values established by statistical inference can clearly identify normal and abnormal conditions. The value of statistical measures requires that the proper data be collected, then properly analyzed, and then properly understood.

Mr. Kimball is quite right in assuming that the future will bring more statistical analysis of public fire safety. This paper strongly advocates the application of statistical inference to public fire safety problem analysis. An attempt is made to establish the value of statistical analysis to the mission of public fire safety.

The example cited by Mr. Kimball may be more fact than fiction. The important question to be raised by the implementation of statistical analysis is: how do the resultant statistics relate to the stated objectives? The answer must come from a complete and intimate understanding of the public fire safety organization.

Problem Statement 4

It has been established that concepts of efficiency revolve around cost factors or money. What is the cost of America's fire problem?[36]

In 1967 there were 2,400,000 fires in this country. These fires took 12,200 lives and destroyed $2,070,000,000 in property. Horrible as these figures are they don't begin to tell the full story.

[33]*Ibid.*, p. 80.
[34]Dick Sylvia, "British Look at Fire Service and See Problems Like Ours," *Fire Engineering*, October 1970, p. 40.
[34a]*Ibid.*, p. 40.
[35]Warren Y. Kimball, "The British Look Ahead," *Firemen*, July 1969, p. 30.

[36]Emanuel Fried, "The High Cost of Fire Protection," *Fire Chief*, January 1969, p. 36.

Response to Statement 4

The full story must unfold by fully describing where the fire loss numbers originate. The National Fire Protection Association Fire Record Department collects, tabulates and analyzes fire loss data at the National level.[37] The data sources include fire department reports, and articles from newspaper clipping services. The fire loss data sample size is recognized to be incomplete. As a result, percentage value estimators are added to establish gross totals. Such gross totals, if consistently analyzed, may reflect a trend over the years, thus, the gross nature of the data may reflect a distortion of the true problem.

Public fire safety costs on a national basis appear to have been examined inadequately. The complete cost analysis must include both the direct and indirect cost factors. A specific item analysis of both direct and indirect factors is presented under the sectional title of "Statistical Inference and Objective Four," on page 15 of this book.

Problem Statement 5

For sixty years the insurance industry has measured the strength of the fire defenses in various cities with the Insurance Service Organization's (formerly the National Board of Fire Underwriters) *Standard Schedule for Grading Cities and Towns of the United States with Reference to Their Fire Defenses and Physical Conditions.*[38]

> The Standard Grading Schedule of the I.S.O. is used to measure the relative value of fire defenses. Cities are classified into one of ten grades, from Class 1 to Class 10. The gradings that are established are used by rating bureaus as an aid in determining (insurance) rates in a state.

In addition,[39]

> The fire loss experience for the entire state affects the size of the basis rate in the state. The fire loss experience within a city has little or no direct effect upon the basis rate; hence a good or poor city loss record will not change the level of the insurance rates on buildings and contents except as it affects the total losses of the state.

Also,[40]

> In most states insurance rates on dwellings are not affected by an improvement in the classification of the city when the city is in Class 4 or better. In some states separate dwelling basis rates are provided for each grade of protection, including the better grades such as Classes 1 to 4 inclusive. For mercantile, manufacturing, and public buildings, however, a reduction in basis rates usually results whenever a city moves into a better (or lower) classification.

Furthermore,[41]

> There are three important methods that municipal officials can follow in securing lower insurance costs for citizens: (1) reduce fire losses; (2) aid and encourage individual property owners to make necessary improvements in their property; and (3) obtain a better classification of the city's fire defenses.

Finally,[42]

> City officials have frequently assumed that the "grading schedule" is an administrative yardstick which can be used to measure the efficiency of municipal fire protection services. It must be emphasized that it is not, although it measures some factors which would also be covered in a yardstick of efficient administration of fire, water, and other departments.

Response to Statement 5

The insurance industry has greatly affected public fire safety through the National Board of Fire Underwriters, (now the Insurance Services Office). The "Grading Schedule" concept is evaluated from another aspect later in this chapter. It is important at this time to look at the "Grading Schedule" as an instrument for measuring efficiency and effectiveness.

As stated under the above quotation, the "Grading Schedule" is not a measure of Public Fire Safety efficiency and effectiveness. Actually a city that has a low numerical grading may not be effective in terms of the objectives established for public fire safety. At best a municipal grading value reflects the possible effectiveness of public fire departments to prevent conflagrations.

The "Grading Schedule" currently has a significant impact on the cost of public fire safety. The building of a fire station, the equipment and manpower to service existing stations are often developed in accordance with the stipulations of the *Grading Schedule.* Therefore, any discussion of public fire safety efficiency must take a hard look at the financial impact of the *Grading Schedule* relative to the level of public fire safety being afforded and the relationship of any given level to the community's basis insurance classification. This interrelationship is not fully understood by many public administrators and fire administrators. This equating process should become part of the total data analysis process.

[37]National Fire Protection Association. *Fire Protection Handbook.* Boston: National Fire Protection Association, 1969, pp. 2–7.

[38]I.C.M.A. *Municipal Fire Administration.* Chicago: The International City Managers Association, 1967, p. 16.

[39]*Ibid.*, p. 16.

[40]*Ibid.*, p. 16.

[41]*Ibid.*, p. 17.

[42]*Ibid.*, p. 22.

Issues relating to the Grading Schedule will be frequently evaluated throughout the entire book.

Statistical Inferences

The previous discussion establishes a very important condition relative to public fire safety statistical data. The data gathered and analyzed relative to public fire safety appears incomplete and inappropriate to measure the interface relationship between public fire safety efficiency and effectiveness. Present methods of fire data collection and analysis must be replaced with sound concepts of statistical inference. But what is the implication of this statement?

In common usage the word "statistics" is synonymous with data. The absence of meaningful data is what we have been talking about. Inference relates to the formation of logical conclusions from a set of given data. Professor Huntsberger states:[43]

> In the modern sense, statistics and statisticians are concerned with the development and application of methods and techniques for collecting, analyzing, and interpreting quantitative data in such a way that the reliability of conclusions based on the data may be evaluated objectively in terms of probability statements . . . mathematical theory of probability plays a fundamental role in the theory and applications of statistics.

Statistical methods provide procedures that are valuable aids to a body of knowledge that can be utilized for responding factually to questions that are quantifiable and to making the best possible decisions in the face of uncertainty.

The value of statistical inference applied to public fire safety objectives has not been fully recognized.

Statistical methods can be used by public fire safety administrators and general public administrators for the organization and summarization of numerical data. Statistical inference from selected data can be utilized to illustrate public fire safety performance in relation to stated objectives. Furthermore, the exercise of collecting and organizing the required data sharpens the clarity and responsiveness of the organization structure to the mission.

The Right Questions — The Right Answers

The objectives of public fire safety were formulated in a manner to stimulate questions about performance. Those responsible for public fire safety should be in a position to respond intelligently and factually to objective, related questions.

A further purpose of this paper is to establish concepts for developing a public fire safety organization that will positively respond to objective oriented questions. What are the questions that need answering? The following list represents an initial attempt at identifying some of the possible areas of inquiry. These questions and the detailed substructure of these questions are reviewed in relation to data collection, data analysis, data interpretations, and data dissemination in later chapters.

Statistical Inference and Objective One

Objective one is concerned with providing a fire incident frequency performance level acceptable to citizens of the geographical area under consideration.

A sensitivity to incidents goes beyond a simple analysis for a given area. The problem must be defined in very specific terms. The Public Fire Safety Organization should be able to respond to the following or similar questions:

1. What is the frequency of incidents by occupancy classification?
   a. By building classification for a given occupancy.
   b. By occupancy class and building class in relation to social class areas.

2. What is the frequency of incidents by cause factor?
   a. By cause factor in relation to occupancy factor.
   b. By cause factor in relation to social grouping.
   c. By cause factor in relation to building condition.

3. What is the likelihood or probability of experiencing a fire?
   a. By occupancy grouping.
   b. By occupancy grouping in a prescribed neighborhood.
   c. By occupancy, neighborhood with a given type of construction.

4. When is the most likely time to have a fire?
   a. By hour of the day; day of the week; month of the year.

[43]Huntsberger, David V. *Elements of Statistical Inference.* 2nd Ed., Boston: Allyn and Bacon, 1968, p. 1.

5. How does this year's frequency rate compare with —
   a. Last year?
   b. Five years ago?
   c. Similar communities?
      (1) To be defined in terms of similar risk patterns.

Statistical Inference and Objective Two

The following questions should be raised and answered relative to life safety considerations.

1. What is the frequency of life loss by age, sex, ethnic origin and race for both firemen and citizens according to:
   a. Building classification; occupancy classification; and neighborhood social class?

2. What is the frequency of disabling injuries by age, sex, ethnic origin and race for both firemen and citizens according to:
   a. Building classification; occupancy classification; and neighborhood social class?

3. What is the frequency of nondisabling injuries by age, sex and race for both firemen and citizens according to:
   a. Building classification; occupancy classification; and neighborhood social class?

4. What is the probability of life loss by age, sex and race for both firemen and citizens according to:
   a. Building classification; occupancy classification; and neighborhood social class?

5. What is the probability of disabling injury by age, sex and race for both firemen and citizens according to:
   a. Building classification; occupancy classification; and neighborhood social class?

6. What is the probability of nondisabling injury by age, sex and race for both firemen and citizens according to:
   a. Building classification; occupancy classification; and neighborhood social class?

Statistical Inference and Objective Three

Objective three is concerned with confining a destructive fire to a given modular level. First, the type and level of module must be identified for broad classes of property. The annual and cumulative frequency should be plotted for determined modular property relationships. Next, the probability of confinement of fires to a given modular level should be calculated. With this accomplished the following questions could be answered.

Question Example: What is the probability that an initiated fire will be confined to a given (modular) area level?

Response Example: The probability that a single family dwelling type fire will be confined to the room of origin is 0.81 while the probability of a single family dwelling being totally destroyed is 0.02.

These examples of probability figures of loss effect do not tell the complete story behind the losses but the analysis moves Public Fire Safety in the direction of defining its performance levels. Also, common statistical terms are introduced that Public Administrators can understand and translate to the public at large. The public then has concrete information on which to voice its pleasure or disapproval of performance.

Questions relating to the effect of public fire safety actions versus private fire safety actions also might be answered under this objective section.

Question Example: What is the probability that an initiated fire is extinguished before the public fire department arrives on the scene?

Response Example:

A 0.1 probability for residences

A 0.3 probability for manufacturing

A 0.25 probability for business establishments

Alternate Response Possibility:

A 0.1 probability for single family residences with garden hose extinguishing action

A 0.2 probability for manufacturing places utilizing self-protection force action

A 0.96 probability for manufacturing places equipped with automatic sprinklers

Statistical Inference and Objective Four

This objective is even more concerned with suppression level performance. Again the performance could be a private action, a public action or a combination of both. The elements of the action process needs to be identified.

Questions of the following nature might be asked.

Question Example: What is the mean loss and the range of losses for incidents by modular classification?

Response Example:

Occupancy Class	Modular Level	Low Loss	Mean Loss	High Loss
Single Family Dwelling	Room of Origin	$50	$500	$5,000
Single Family Dwelling	Total House	$5,000	$15,000	$50,000

The objective has two parts. The second part deals with occupancy interruptions. Such interruptions can be divided into two possible categories. Questions similar to this (at right) could be answered from a statistical analysis.

Question Example: What is the minimum, mean, median and maximum amount of man-days lost by occupancy classification for fire incidents?

Response Example:

Occupancy Class	Man-Days Time Loss Temporary Occupancy Interruption		
	Mean	Median	Maximum
Residents	570	620	1,511
Business	640	370	3,700
Industry	1,080	2,111	10,072

Definition of Man-Day: Number of persons temporarily displaced X number of 24-hour periods of displacement.

The man-day value chart not only demonstrates performance levels but the association of figures points to some very definite problems.

Statistical Inference and Objective Five

Objective five relates to the provision of emergency community services. The broad scope of such services will require extensive categories for statistical analysis. As a minimum, the frequency of events by category should be noted, the per cent of these events to the total; the man-hours expended by category, the equipment hours expended by category, and the response mileage, mean and total for each category.

Response Example:

Event	Frequency	% of Total	Man-hours	Equip. Hrs.	Mean Response Mileage	Total Response Mileage
Auto Accident	X	X	X	X	X	X
Truck Accident	X	X	X	X	X	X
Other Transportation Accident	X	X	X	X	X	X
Persons Trapped	X	X	X	X	X	X
Routine Salvage	X	X	X	X	X	X
Water Rescue	X	X	X	X	X	X
Storm Damage	X	X	X	X	X	X

The statistical concepts cited represent the simplest form of inference from the analysis of data. Statistics of this nature may demonstrate that public fire departments are more involved in service areas than in direct fire suppression. This is an image that fire departments might wish to capitalize on in the future.

Statistical Inference and Objective Six

Objective six introduces the term cost-utility. The concept of cost-utility-analysis is relatively new to management science. A few words of introduction are in order. A larger framework of reference to cost-utility concepts is developed in Chapter IV — the *Administrative Process* and Chapter V — the *Management of Resource Allocations*.

David Novick makes the following comments about cost-utility analysis:[44]

> This tool systematically examines costs required to pursue a program and achieve the objectives sought. It also seeks to measure the benefits, gains, or advantages for achieving the objective by each alternative means chosen for examination. It is a concept requiring calculation of all major costs and benefits that make comparisons relevant. It makes comparisons of alternatives from measurements of a common denominator, usually money. It seeks to explore the important long-range implications of alternative decisions.

A few key observations set the stage for considering the application of cost-utility analysis to public fire safety.

1. Techniques of cost analysis almost force an organization to examine its function in depth. The whole system comprising public fire safety should be examined under this concept.

2. In the process of looking at the whole — individual parts are identified. The parts are not viewed as pieces of structure but rather as pieces of performance in relation to the total structure.

3. Performance functions are equated to dollars and cents. Performance functions are also equated to defined levels of service. Therefore, levels of service can be equated to dollar and cents values.

4. If a performance function is changed, it is assumed that one can observe how the dollar obligations change — either increasing or decreasing.

5. Therefore, the utility of a function is compared to a cost. It is important to note that a change in the performance of the function changes the performance of the whole organization. As the cost of one or more functions change, the cost of performance changes.

6. Cost-utility analysis permits a critical examination of change conditions. Change conditions will be referenced as alternatives. Identified alternatives allow organizational administrators to assemble performance packages.

7. Finally, selection of a Public Fire Safety performance package can be utilized to identify a specific level of public service in relation to prior objective criteria for obtaining public response.

It is perceived that many fire departments are not organized to provide public administrators or the public at large with a picture of cost-utility analysis. Some fire departments currently appear to have little interest in moving forward with cost accounting. Other fire departments appear to seek means to respond concretely to performance level questions. For the latter category of fire department, cost-utility analysis holds much promise.

Response Example: The Public Fire Safety System must be conscious of total cost obligations. The following list of fire safety costs is an initial attempt to categorize and identify the total cost package.

1. Structural Incident Loss Data
   a. Summary of direct monetary losses
   b. Variable loss analysis
      (1) By Occupancy — Structural Class — Social Class
         (a) Direct loss covered by insurance
         (b) Direct loss not covered by insurance
         (c) Indirect loss
            1–Displacement Costs
            2–Lost Profits
            3–Lost Tax Revenue

2. Structural Insurance Costs
   a. Estimated Insurance Premiums for the Geographical Area being considered
   b. Insurance loss payments
   c. Net Insurance Cost to Jurisdictional Areas

3. Private Fire Safety Costs
   a. Summation of private fire safety costs
      (1) Prorated costs for fixed fire protection devices
      (2) Prorated costs for portable fire protection devices
      (3) Yearly manpower costs for fire safety efforts

4. Public Fire Safety Costs
   a. Total annual fire department costs

[44]David Novick, ed., *Program Budgeting, Program Analysis and the Federal Budget.* Cambridge: Harvard University Press, 1965, p. 311.

b. Organizational Structures Costs
  (1) Total administrative costs
  (2) Total resource allocation costs
  (3) Total operations costs
    (a) Facilitating System Costs
      1–Communications
      2–Training
      3–Public Relations
      4–Maintenance
    (b) Major Project Systems
      1–Service Systems
      2–Protection Systems
      3–Prevention Systems
c. Prorated Incident Costs
  (1) Prorated High — Low — Mean Costs for Fire Department response to:
      Structural — Occupancy — Social Categories.
  (2) Prorated High — Low — Mean Costs for Defined Modular Levels Relative to:
      Structural — Occupancy — Social Categories.

Types of Public Fire Departments

Generally the classification type of fire department selected to protect a given city or geographical area is dependent upon the size of the area, the nature of the area, and the frequency of fires. To a lesser extent, the type of fire department for any given area may actually be based upon the form of local government and the scope of activities to be administered.

Public fire departments can actually be divided into five types; fully-paid; combination, consisting of paid and volunteer personnel; volunteer, consisting of all or mostly volunteer personnel; public safety departments, consisting of paid personnel employed to perform both fire and police duty; and privately owned and operated fire departments for public protection. Private type fire departments also exist primarily to protect specific industrial and government property. The latter type of private service is excluded from this discussion of public fire safety organization. However, this type of protection is related to the public fire safety organization in a very meaningful way.

Each type of public fire safety organization deserves a brief discussion to identify selected organization problems and to relate each organization type to the structured mission and objectives of public fire safety.

The type of public fire department began to change from all volunteer to part paid and fully paid at the end of the nineteenth century.[45] Several factors were responsible for the evolution from volunteer to paid departments, especially in the larger cities. The causal factors have been stated to include:[46]

> . . . the rising tide of large scale conflagrations; the introduction of horse-drawn apparatus followed by the conversion to motorized apparatus; the influence of the insurance industry on differentiating volunteer and paid services in relation to insurance rates.

One point that has a traditional bearing on the transition of volunteer type public fire protection to paid protection should be identified. This point is very germane to the restructured objectives stated in this chapter.

Volunteers were thought to suffer one major handicap. Bush and McLaughlin state that:[47]

> . . . because of the time that must elapse before men arrive "on site" or at the station, response is necessarily slower than for fully manned, paid departments. This can prove costly, because delay may allow a fire that could have been extinguished easily in its initial stages to gain headway and become a really large fire with heavy losses.

In the above statement, we see the concept of fire loss equated to time intervals. The response time factor for a fire department has been constantly stressed as being a very important variable relating to incident loss. The case for rapid assembly and response of fire suppression forces may have received too much attention in relation to other important variables such as pre-burn time before discovery and sounding of an alarm.

It appears significant to note, the concept of rapid assembly of personnel and response to a fire has often significantly affected a community's selection of a fire department type and to a lesser degree influences the structure of the fire department.

The Paid Fire Service

The paid type fire department is characterized by the organization formation of one or more fire companies. The personnel manning fire apparatus and the personnel performing staff functions are fully paid. The paid fire department is normally directed by a fire chief and such assistants and deputies as appears necessary to establish a desired span of control.

[45]Loren S. Bush and James McLaughlin, *Introduction to Fire Science.* Beverly Hills: Glencoe Press, 1970, p. 28.

[46]*Ibid.*, pp. 28–29.

[47]*Ibid.*, p. 91.

The individual fire company is usually directed by a captain, a relief officer of lower rank and a group of firemen ranging in size from three to ten men. Actual manpower in any given instance is dependent on many factors. Often manpower requirements are equated to the type of fire apparatus assigned to the company (i.e., engine, ladder, snorkel, rescue, etc.), and the area serviced by the company (i.e., residential, mercantile, industrial). Economic constraints often limit manpower assignments to levels below what the fire chief deems necessary for adequate protection.

The National Fire Protection Association reports that approximately fifteen hundred municipalities supported full paid fire departments in the year 1969.[48] Current figures demonstrate that the number of paid fire departments is growing at a very small but undefined rate each year. However, the paid fire service is large enough to currently attract considerable public attention. Labor-management relations, the cost of public services and insurance rates are three focal point issues currently plaguing public administrators and fire administrators. These three issues combine with concerns for professional development, recruitment requirements, college educations, technological development, and executive level mobility combine to present many problem areas for the paid fire service.

The Combination Fire Service

Combination type fire departments utilize fully paid personnel and volunteer personnel. In some, the volunteers maintain dominance and control of the organization. The paid personnel are hired for periods of the day or the week when the volunteer manpower is slack or simply not available. Combination departments have been on the increase since the World War II period. This growth pattern is especially evident in the large metropolitan areas.

The Public Safety Department

The public safety department represents another transition in the development of municipal services. The term connotes the merger of police functions with fire department functions under one administrative head. Personnel are considered to be a part of a unified force with functional responsibilities for both types of services. The public safety type of public fire protection flourished in the mid-1950 period. However, the concept is very much alive today.

Each of the types of fire departments mentioned above will receive a full description under the subtitle "Fire Department Classification Complexity."

Fire Department Classification Complexity

The Volunteer Fire Service

It is estimated that fifteen thousand organized volunteer fire departments were operating in the continental United States in 1969.[49] One might ask, how do volunteer type fire departments affect public fire safety in relation to the established objectives? The answer is obviously complex. Generalities tend to exaggerate or negate important variables associated with volunteer fire departments. Yet some apparent similarities are found in volunteer fire departments that are worthy of noting in relation to the total problem identification.

The volunteer fireman has been on the American scene for 325 years (1647–1972).[50] As an organizational man, the volunteer fireman has developed many images, traditions and attributes over the intervening years. Today's volunteer fireman possesses many parallel characteristics to his predecessor. The early character of the volunteer fire service illuminates some very important considerations in identifying and understanding the volunteer fire organization today.

A celebrated actress, Fanny Kemble penned the following words in New York in 1832.[51]

> The sons of all the gentlemen here are volunteer engineers and firemen and great is the delight they take in tearing up and down the street, accompanied by red light, speaking trumpets, and a rush, roaring escort of running amateur extinguishers, who make night hideous with their howling and bellowing.

Take almost any hometown U.S.A. in the less than twenty thousand population category today and a similar caricature would fit. Technology has forced a few appropriate terminology substitutions. For example, the speaking trumpet has been replaced with hundred watt amplifiers, the roaring escort now has four wheels, a loud horn and maybe a flashing blue light; the red light, a symbol of

[48]National Fire Protection Association, *Fire Protection Handbook*, (13th Ed.), Boston: National Fire Protection Association, 1969, pp. 10–12.

[49]*Op. Cit.*, NFPA Handbook, pp. 10–12.

[50]*Ibid.*

[51]Robert S. Holzman, *Romance of Firefighting.* New York: Bonanza Books, p. 3.

danger and emergency is accompanied by the night shattering wail of a siren.

Dr. Robert S. Holzman, author of the *Romance of Firefighting* in which the Fanny Kemble quotation appears, observes that:[52] "All firemen were not gentlemen's sons. Many a smoke eater would have resented a hint that he was anything but one of the boys." This observation would appear valid today.

One might ask some further relevant questions about the identity of volunteer firemen: Who are they, why are they motivated to be volunteers, what are the strengths and weaknesses of volunteers in meeting the objectives of public fire safety? There does not appear to be any sound body of research to specifically respond to these questions. Rather one has to draw from a limited number of literature sources and personal experiences to place the volunteer fireman in an organizational perspective.

Again, the historical perspective of the volunteer fireman appears to set the stage for understanding the modern-day counterpart. Many traditions have developed over a span of years in the volunteer fire service. A further understanding of identified historical and traditional factors relating to the volunteer type of public fire service should provide some understanding of the roots of modern-day organization problems.

Dr. Holzman indicated that the nineteenth-century volunteer fire department was composed of contrasting individuals. The volunteers were: wealthy merchants, actors, retired soldiers, butchers, shipbuilders, victualers, lowly clerks and street brawlers. In short they were a cross section of America.[53]

Today the names may have changed to: the postman, the pharmacist, the truck driver, the teacher, the dry cleaner, the lawyer, the electrician, the store clerk, and even an occasional Ph.D.

It would be speculative to indicate the present volunteer fire department represents a cross section of U.S.A. Local employment conditions would appear to affect not only the type of individual that joins a volunteer fire department, but equally important, the number of men who are attracted to the fire department as an avocation.

The caricature of the volunteer fireman of a century ago passes on other important images to the present-day counterpart. Dr.

Holzman also gives some clues to the past nature of volunteer involvement.[54]

What did the volunteer firemen get for their pains, loss of time and inconvenience? Usually the firemen received exemption from jury duty and military duty after ten years of service. But public duty was usually the loadstar. There was prestige in belonging to certain companies. There was satisfaction in work well done, and there was the thrill of being a volunteer fireman.

Once he was wearing his red shirt and black helmet, the volunteer fireman knew no peers. Here (as almost nowhere else) was real democracy. The bookkeeper grappled a tow rope next to the banker, and at the fire house socials anyone could introduce his wife to the alderman. There was the leavening influence of common danger. There was a wonderful "esprit de corps."

If the fireman was insignificant when he was alone, he was one of the lords of creation when he was with the boys. Traffic was stopped, municipal life was diverted, the medieval elements of fire and water were subjugated. Local governments trembled before the mighty political force that was the volunteer firemen collectively.

It would appear difficult to default the above quotation in the context of 1972. The volunteer fireman, especially in the small communities and rural areas presents a similar image today. Elements of prestige, esprit de corps and the ability to freeze and divert the community under conditions of emergency stress currently characterize volunteer fire departments. Even more significant to basic organizational considerations is the thrill of action symbol and the political might of the organization when banded together.

A point to be recognized is that an apparently strong motivational factor for a man to join a fire department is the thrill, excitement, and quasi-military ordering associated with fire suppression activities. On the surface these qualities might be admirable for a fireman. However, the same qualities raise a fundamental question. How do volunteer firemen perceive their role towards fire prevention? One volunteer fire chief in a city of about 10,000 population interviewed, stated that the fire department was not organized to prevent fires. "Fire Prevention is somebody else's — maybe the building department's — job. The fire department has all it can do to fight fires."[54a] How widespread this objective feeling carries is undetermined. However, a cursory examination of fire department budgets for fire prevention, and personnel assigned fire prevention duties in volunteer fire departments would support

---

[52]*Ibid.*, p. 3.

[53]*Ibid.*, pp. 3–10.

[54]*Ibid.*, p. 3.

[54a]The fire chief interviewed requested to remain anonymous.

the premise that fire prevention is not the number one mission of volunteer fire departments. This condition appears to be a problem worth remembering in terms of the established organizational objectives.

The above observations do not establish an end-point to organizational problems associated with volunteer fire departments. Actually there are many problems; so many problems that it would appear academic to review the problems in an established order of piority. Therefore the following problem areas should be viewed in relation to the established mission of public fire safety.

Chief Milton Q. Bullock of the Metropolitan Dade County Fire Department, Miami, Florida, has declared:[55] "The Fire Service is in the midst of a scientific, technological and sociological revolution." Chief Bullock's remarks are not restricted to volunteer fire departments. However, his statement carries a special significance to the volunteer type of organization. The implications of science and technology can be viewed from two perspectives. First, science and technology have introduced new fire ground problems. Chemical reactions, radioactive materials, massive storage facilities, high-rise buildings, air rights structures, and plastics are merely representative topics that require a new level of technological assessment in a fire officer's size-up process. The problems are difficult for all fire fighters. They are especially difficult for the volunteer because of the limited knowledge he possesses in these areas; because of the training that is open to him in these areas; and because of the limited resources at his disposal to cope with unusual events. The volunteer fire chief who has never faced anything more serious than a hay barn fully involved, wakes one night to find a train derailment in the center of town. Tank cars begin to explode and before that night is over more than half the town is destroyed.[56] (Crescent City, Illinois). Few volunteer fire departments have the training, manpower and equipment complements requisite to an efficient and effective operation on large scale incidents. This comment should not discredit the marvelous job done by the volunteers under adverse conditions. Rather, the point is intended to raise this question: would the unusual operation have been carried out more effectively under the support of a different organizational ar-

rangement? The author's response is "yes." The response support will be advanced at the conclusion of this subsection.

Chief David B. Gratz, Silver Spring, Maryland Volunteer Fire Department, made the following observations under the title,[57] "Volunteers: The Competition for a Man's Time." Chief Gratz recalls that when he became a volunteer some twenty years ago, he did not have money or a car to go anywhere, so he was at the fire station when he was not working or going to school. He states, "this is no longer true of volunteers. They have an entirely different set of values — and more money."

This problem recognition is continued by Chief Gratz with the following observations:[58]

As the job becomes more dangerous, with greater problems, the mothers and fathers of the youngsters now look at this thing a little differently. It is no longer a question of jumping off the back step and running like hell down the street to a brush fire. Now that boy comes in, and he is on the 20th floor of a building with the hallway charged so thick he can't see, and it is hotter than the devil. Or he is running to a nuclear laboratory we have or biological laboratories — and all of these things which are so much more hazardous. They say, "No, this isn't for me. I am not getting paid. What am I doing here?"

Furthermore, when a department does get another volunteer, it gets him until he goes to college, until he gets married, until he gets drafted, or until something else. So I feel that we are going to see in many urban areas a substantial reduction in volunteer manpower . . . the competition for a man's time today is much greater than it used to be.

Don O'Brien, General Manager of the International Association of Fire Chiefs, advances some corollary remarks and adds a few points concerning the problems growing out of technological and sociological conditions.[59]

Mr. O'Brien states:

In some areas where daytime lack of manpower is a problem, the situation has resulted in women being trained as active fire fighters. In other cases, it has been solved by hiring a few paid men. In one case in recent weeks, an entire county fire service petitioned the county governing body to set up a paid department and relieve the volunteers of their self-imposed responsibilities. The reason: . . . these men have realized they are not able to obtain replacements and cannot foresee a reversal of the trend. The young men of today are just not interested. In addition, the manpower they do have available are nearly 100% commuters and can be counted on only during short periods of the evening hours. Finally, those who are available are mature persons and can look forward to very few more years of active service.

[55]Staff, "The 1970's — The Challenging Years for the Fire Service," *Fire Engineering*, September 1967, p. 106.

[56]Staff, "Anticipating the Unexpected!", *Firemen*, July 1969, p. 25.

[57]*Op. Cit.*, Staff, *Fire Engineering*, p. 91.

[58]*Ibid.*, p. 91.

[59]Donald M. O'Brien, "Current Problems of the Fire Service," *Firemen*, August 1967, pp. 14–15.

The quotations lead to a current fundamental concern of volunteer fire department manpower. Manpower is seen as a double factor element. First, manpower availability can be related to effective operations. Second, manpower is equally tied to efficiency. Both factors, intertwined as they are, reflect on the organization of public fire safety. Therefore, some supplemental words about manpower are in order.

Initially, let us pick up the thread of manpower availability. The words of Don O'Brien, again, are quite to the point.[60]

> (Volunteer) manpower is perhaps the most difficult problem in many areas of this country. Many observers of the volunteer scene have become quite alarmed at the trend. It is becoming evident all across the country that many long-established volunteer departments are suddenly growing old from a membership point of view. Instead of having a steady flow of new young men into the departments, they are gaining only a trickle of replacements and are beginning to depend on older men for fire response. Unless this trend can be reversed, and soon, the future is bleak.

Manpower availability in volunteer fire departments is a significant problem to public fire safety. Where volunteer manpower is on the decline or where it is considered inadequate to the need, effectiveness suffers or the local economy is changing to accommodate paid personnel. The combination type fire department and the fully paid type fire department will be treated separately under appropriate subsection titles. The concern at this stage of review is to appraise the economic savings of the volunteer.

Warren Kimball, formerly Chief Fire Service representative for the National Fire Protection Association considered in 1967 that the average volunteer fireman was "rendering a service to his community which would cost $4,580 with a paid department."[61] Considering the number of volunteer firemen in the United States (estimated at well over 1,000,000 active members), it would appear the volunteers are rendering a public service conservatively estimated at at least five billion dollars annually. In terms of pricing public fire safety on an efficiency basis, figures of this magnitude cannot be neglected.

Gross summary figures make it obvious that total volunteer fire departments are providing a varying degree of economical savings for many communities. The volunteer service makes it possible to achieve substantial savings to the residence of communities so protected.

But what is the level of the service provided by volunteer fire departments; how effective are these departments?

The question posed is difficult to answer. The published literature reflecting on the question appears to be so general as to give no substantive answers beyond speculation. However, Robert G. Kahrmann, Jr., Director of Fire Science Technology at Jersey City State College does identify two important considerations:

Mr. Kahrmann states:[62]

> In examining the adequacy of protection a volunteer fire department provides when compared to other types of departments, it is necessary to establish some measures of performance. Bennett, Wang and Wasserman carried out a study of the performance of the fire protection system in Montgomery County, Maryland, in 1966 and established certain measures of performance to determine the adequacy and efficiency of a fire department. They felt the final measure was the fire loss of a given area. Three measures of performance applied by this concept are:

1. Fire loss per thousand dollars of assessed valuation.

2. Loss per building fire.

3. Number of building fires per $1000 assessed valuation.

In conducting their study, Bennett, Wang and Wasserman found the following (lower values correspond to better performance):[63]

Mean Performance by Type Department

Performance Measure Type of Performance	Loss Per $1000 Valuation	Loss Per Building Fire	Number of Building Fires Per $1000 Valuation
Volunteer	2.85	1.92	1.71
Mixed (Part Paid)	0.78	0.73	1.08
Paid	1.05	1.25	0.85

Kahrmann concludes that by looking at the mean performance values, one would judge that volunteers do not perform as well as either mixed (combination) or fully paid departments.

Mr. Kahrmann considers that another key factor in evaluating the volunteer fire department is its relationship to the fire insurance rating of the community covered by this service. This rating is discussed in terms of municipal

---

[60]*Ibid.*, p. 15.

[61]Warren Y. Kimball, "Fire Departments in a Receding Economy," *Firemen*, p. 36.

[62]Robert Kahrmann, "Can the Volunteers Survive the '70s," *Fire Command!*, July 1970, p. 29.

[63]*Ibid.*, p. 29.

gradings established for fire protection facilities in the state of New Jersey. The conclusion is drawn that

> while the volunteers greatly outnumber the paid and part-paid departments, they clearly are below the insurance rates of those departments. If the fire departments in New Jersey may be considered typical of fire departments in the United States, volunteer fire departments simply do not compare to part-paid and paid departments in terms of the insurance structure.

The validity of insurance evaluation measures of fire departments is the subject of another subsection.

Obviously volunteer fire departments are faced with severe problems. In light of these problems, one can question the role and capability of the volunteer organization to the public fire safety objective set outlined in this paper. It is perceived that volunteer type organizations can play a vital part in providing desired levels of fire safety. However, to fulfill their proper role in the total scheme of fire safety, volunteer fire departments are going to be required to exhibit some significant changes in their operations and mode of organization. This view is considered consistent with Warren Kimball's concluding remarks about the "Volunteers." He states:[64]

> The volunteer firemen are providing a very economical service in many communities. Where the volunteers are backed up by professional fire prevention bureaus, training officers, administrative personnel, and communications centers, the level of service rendered may be exceptionally good. Certainly, the interest and enthusiasm of the typical volunteer is something money cannot buy.

Mr. Kimball's point is well taken and this view will be both endorsed and supplemented in later subsections. For now it appears sufficient to state that the volunteer system of organization has the potential for being both efficient and effective when considered within the framework of a total systems organization.

Combination Fire Departments

Probably the greatest problem revolving around combination type fire departments is a precise and unified concept of what constitutes a combination fire department. For purposes of this paper, a combination fire department is defined as one in which the officer positions are staffed partially with paid personnel and partially with volunteer personnel. Some fine distinction needs to be made. A fire department that employs paid drivers, or a few paid men to augment the volunteer response would

be classed as a volunteer fire department providing the paid personnel do not hold officer rank. If one or more paid personnel holds officer rank then the department is considered to be a combination unit. The concept relates to the condition that administrative and management functions are implemented by a shared body of paid and volunteer personnel.

In some cases, a fully paid fire department might be augmented by a volunteer company to perform special services such as salvage or rescue. In such instances the fire department in total perspective is a paid force. The volunteer unit can be considered somewhat a separate entity to the overall and should be so identified.

Combination type fire departments currently face many problems. Unfortunately, they bear the burden of most of the volunteer problems plus the problems of the fully paid service. To avoid redundancy, this subsection will concentrate on those conditions that are peculiar to the combination type service. It should be emphasized that the problems discussed under the respective subsections Volunteer Fire Departments (page 18) and Paid Fire Departments (page 23) may very well overlap into this category.

Some fire officials look upon the combination fire department as an organization in transition. The volunteer organization, by and of itself may no longer be considered able to cope with the local fire problems. Example: In a few short years Huntington Township on Long Island, New York blossomed from 37,000 people to a population of 170,000.[65] This type of growth pattern is being experienced along many urban corridors. The accompanying demand for public services skyrockets.

Under the demand for expanded services, faced with rising fire frequencies, and limited by the number of men available to respond to emergencies, volunteer fire departments engage in the practice of hiring a few paid men to augment the volunteer service. Especially in the suburban growth corridors, the few paid men may soon grow to a sizable work force. The paid work element in combination with the volunteer unit has produced some problems.

The range of problems may be wide in scope and/or specific in nature. From the organization point of view these problems revolve around: the personnel relationship between paid and volunteer forces; the management of paid personnel by volunteer officers; the budget process associated with full-time personnel and

[64]Warren Y. Kimball, "Fire Departments — Volunteer and Part Paid," *Firemen*, January 1968, p. 23.

[65]Bruce G. Blower: "Volunteers Face Population Explosion," *Fire Engineering*, April 1967, pp. 50–51.

volunteers; a more rapid response from the fire station with paid personnel may mean that a certain group of volunteers no longer get to ride the apparatus; the unique officer command conditions where a volunteer officer gives orders to a paid officer; where a paid officer on one shift may be a higher ranking volunteer officer on another shift and where the paid private on one fire department is the volunteer chief on a neighboring fire department. These problem conditions are not insignificant. They tend to breed friction, they affect performance levels and the budget considerations for combination fire departments can run into seven figures.

In some cases, the gains achieved by employing combination type fire departments may outweigh the current range of problems. Some of the strengths of this type of organizational arrangement appear to be as follows. Men are more readily available for more immediate response to emergency situations. Because of time availability, paid personnel are capable of being more highly trained than the volunteer firemen. Paid personnel are more readily available for special service duties such as building inspections that often go unattended in a volunteer organization. In light of the objectives stated in this paper a more significant promise for instituting combination type fire departments appears to be in the area of fire prevention. Men are available and can be assigned to inservice inspections; maintenance programs can be enhanced and communications systems can be fully attended.

The combination type public fire department, despite a growing list of problem areas, has demonstrated that the concept is most worthy of consideration in the scheme of organized public fire safety. It seems that this type of fire department suffers from the lack of an organizational concept that would most advantageously utilize the merits of the combination approach to meet the established objectives. The combination type department would seem to possess the unique quality of maintaining a volunteer service for economy measures with a nucleus of paid personnel to fulfill the requirements of reliability and adequacy.

The precise technique for obtaining maximum objective utility from the combination type organization will be reviewed in the concluding parts of Chapter II.

Paid Fire Departments

There are an estimated twenty-three thousand fire departments in the United States.[65a]

Roughly five thousand of these fire departments belong to the fully paid class. With a few exceptions, the International City Managers Association reports that cities over one hundred thousand population are served by fully paid type fire departments. A large fraction of the cities in the fifty thousand to one hundred thousand population grouping are served by this type of department and possibly one-half of the cities under fifty thousand claim full paid service. Therefore, it is recognized that large urban areas are generally serviced by fully paid fire safety services.

The paid fire service has no shortage of problems and issues to be resolved. While still not as visible to the public as the police department, public fire departments in many sections of the country are capturing their fair share of attention. Problems reflect on images — and the image of the paid fire service has changed drastically in the past few years. This point is adequately reflected upon by Don O'Brien of the International Association of Fire Chiefs in the following statement:[66]

Any discussion of current administrative problems of the fire service must take into account the feelings and the headlines which the fire service is presently receiving in the nation's press. Since last summer, when one fire department was struck by an independent union and other departments were beset by slowdowns, sick demonstrations, etc., the fire service has been in the news constantly. Threats of strike action and of slowdowns have made headlines for the paid fire service.

Since this has occurred, the image of the paid service has suddenly diminished from the traditional friend of all in time of need to that of a militant labor group which is determined to make its voice heard at City Hall. The old City Hall answer of "Wait till next year" is no longer accepted in the paid ranks. Believe it or not, the tactics have been fairly successful, and I anticipate more of the same in the immediate future.

A new set of dictionary definitions is in order to understand the paid fire service. These phrases should include definitions concerning: Fire Service professionalism, pay parity, transfer mobility, educational requirements, recruitment prerequisites, technological assessment, labor contracts, and integrated services. These terms are only representative of some problem areas of the paid Fire Service. It is perceived that many of the identified problems fall under the broad concept of organizational problems.

The paid fire fighter is searching for a professional self. He wishes to reflect a par relationship with his municipal counterpart, the policeman. However, the identification does not fit and this lack of identity is part of the

[65a]*Municipal Fire Administration*, p. 40.

[66]Donald M. O'Brien, "Current Problems of the Fire Service," *Firemen*, August 1967, p. 14.

paid Fire Service problem. In a sense all of the areas mentioned relating to the scope, condition, and position of the paid personnel in public fire safety reflect on the formation of a proper profile of the paid fire fighter. A response to the problem must come from the development of a concrete answer to the following question: How does the paid fire fighter fit into the structural-functional relationship of providing public fire safety within the boundaries of the objectives established? It is intended that the final answer will unfold throughout the remaining chapters.

A partial answer to the above question can be injected at this point. First, the mass of problems must be segmented into specific items for examination. The following subtopics and response are structured to focus on what are considered to be major concerns. Again, an integrated response to the problems comes later.

Item Six of the Wingspread Conference report states:[67]

"Professional Status Begins with Education."

The above heading actually focuses on two or more of the perceived problems associated with the paid Fire Service. It would seem that title not only reflects on professionalism and education but inherently reflects on recruitment. The full problem definition and any associative response must consider the intertwining effect of the three terms: professionalism — education — recruitment.

The Wingspread report references the Gordon-Howell Report to suggest criteria for defining professionalism. A main point stands out as being fundamental to the premises of this book. The point is quoted as follows:[68]

> A profession should rest on a systematic body of knowledge of substantial intellectual content and on the development of personal skill in the application of this knowledge to specific cases.

An associate subpoint: "Levels need to be established within the profession."[69] The following reflections serve as an interpretation of both quotes. Professionalism is based upon intellectual content. Intellectual content conveys an inherent requirement for education. Since it is perceived that levels should exist within a profession, it follows that different education levels are also required. A further deduction might conclude that since there is a

leveling process in the professional-educational search, there must be an organizational framework by levels to accommodate the degrees of professionalism or levels of professionalism. In a way this is all quite academic, but it does serve a purpose. Professionalism relates directly to the scope of activity framed by a man's work environment. The work pattern relating to public fire safety involves groups of people and therefore must be organized for the accomplishment of a defined purpose. Therefore, professionalism is inherently related to the public fire safety organization. The need, or lack of a need, for professionalism should be evidenced in the organization framework. The third point — recruitment — is tied to projected roles in the organization: which is related to professionalism; which is related to educational requirements.

A response to the search for professionalism, education and recruitment has its roots in the structural-functional complex of public fire safety organization. The need for a professional educational level in the public fire safety organization hinges on the initial and subsequential placement of individuals in the organizational structure. For example: If a man is hired for the purpose of catching a fire hydrant at the time of a fire response, one can hardly stake a claim for professionalism. Also, the educational requirement for filling this position can be considered quite minimal. The recruitment process does not need to be too choosey. However, if this fire hydrant catching position is but a stepping stone in an experience sequence that may culminate in a management-level position, the rules should change. The essence of ability and the mastery of skills widen, as the educational prerequisites for the management role begin to shape the professional stature. The dependent factor focuses on the organization and where a person fits into the organization structure during the entire career sequence. The opportunities, the options and the functional fitting process represents threads that weave throughout the several chapters.

The remaining concerns of paid fire department personnel really evolve from the previous discussion. Pay parity can be tied to both education and professionalism. Where educational background cannot be functionally supported and where professionalism of position cannot be demonstrated, the leverages for pay equality become weak. Pay considerations often become the focal point of labor negotiations. But the labor bargaining table

[67]*Wingspread Conference on Fire Service Administration, Education and Research.* Racine: The Johnson Foundation, 1966, p. 10.

[68]*Ibid.*, p. 10.   [69]*Ibid.*, p. 10.

can also include a variety of other issues. Those other issues relating to service risk conditions, work arrangements, increased manpower and fringe benefits inherently relate to organizational functions which in turn relate to organizational objectives. The bargaining condition is weak because the current objectives are weak and the organizational structure is not matched to the objectives.

A further potential problem associated with paid fire departments needs to be identified. The problem is related to a lack of professionalism viewed from another perspective. The Fire Service is gathering a clan of critics. These critics are beginning to hammer at the appraisal process of public fire departments. Warren Kimball has some harsh words for Fire Service critics but the rebuttal is really quite weak in content.[70] A response letter to Mr. Kimball's article provides a better focus on the condition. The letter states:[71]

> Underlying the entire problem of having outsiders point critical fingers at the Fire Service is a simple fact: The Fire Service is not truly a profession. It does not criticize or analyze itself. This leaves it open for outsiders to be critics of the Fire Service.

If the paid Fire Service does attempt to appraise itself, it appears to be in terms of experience. Experience can be good or it can be bad. An analysis is required to make the differentiation. This analysis is lacking. Part of the reason for this condition rests with absence of analytical techniques for equating activities to objectives. This point completes a full circle to the opening remarks. The structured public fire safety objectives do not complement the present mode of fire department organization. A part of this dilemma should be the realization that the Fire Service talks to itself but not to other professional groups. The cross-fertilization of an interdisciplinary approach to public fire safety is conspicuous by its absence. The point is worth remembering in relation to organizational prerequisites, the educational process and the development of a professional image.

The parochial nature of the public fire service leads to another area of concern slanted towards the paid type of fire service. That concern can be expressed in one word — mobility. Chief Volkamer of Chicago discusses the frequency with which "lateral transfers, or the mobility of changing from one fire department to another is the subject of fire service meetings.[72] The chief states unequivocally:"

> I am opposed to this practice for many reasons, one of which is that without a well-regulated system of checks and balances, a Chief of Department might suddenly find his fire-fighting force depleted in one cross-country movement.

If the condition perceived is an actual threat, then the organizational system must be faulty. If the recruitment and retainment of public fire safety personnel is to be confined to a narrowly circumscribed geographical region, public fire safety can abandon any goal of professionalism, any goal of incentivism, any goal of education and any goal for achieving objective excellence. This observation is supported and reinforced by Chief William E. Clark when he states:[73]

> One appealing factor of the county type service, particularly in Britain, but to some extent here, is the opportunity for a man of ability to move from one fire department to another. This allows the capable volunteer to become a professional; and it opens up greater promotional opportunities for all. Further, it enables a department to get the best talent available and reduces the inbreeding which is one of the problems of America's fire service.

The concept of personnel mobility is expanded upon under *Levels of Service* in Chapter II. One concluding remark with special emphasis on paid type fire departments. Most of the perceived and real ills of public fire departments can be traced to the lack of a viable organization. Current organizational structures with associated functional characteristics simply do not provide a base to efficiently and effectively carry forth an objectives program of that nature outlined in this book. It is sincerely felt that the systems type of organization advanced in Chapter II will go a long way towards solving many of the identified problems.

Public Safety Departments

The literature relevant to the classification types of public fire departments is generally lean. This observation does not apply to the above subtopic area. One can develop a bountiful reference list concerning the subject headings: Public Safety Departments, Fire-Police Integration, Combined Police-Fire Services, and Consolidated Public Services. The

[70]Warren Y. Kimball, "Fire Service Critics," *Firemen*, May 1970, p. 26.

[71]Staff, "Voice of the Fire Service," *Fire Command!*, August 1970, p. 6.

[72]Chief Fire Marshal Curtis W. Volkamer, "What Lies Ahead for the Fire Service?", *Fire Command!*, July 1970, p. 81.

[73]William E. Clark, "Advantages of a County Fire Service," *Fire Engineering*, p. 39.

general subject area of a single municipal department embracing the functions of public fire safety and police safety has received considerable attention since the middle 1950's. While the focus on the subject area is somewhat subdued at the present moment, the general concept of unified public safety departments is very much alive today.

During the early 1960's considerable discussion, debate, and controversy took place among city managers, fire chiefs, police chiefs, fire insurance rating bureaus and other public spirited groups concerned with integrations, consolidations and combinations. The terms utilized to express a unified function of fire and police protection identifies an initial problem. The terminology associated with the unification was not well defined nor understood from a conceptual point of view. The concept meant different things to different people. The definition problem will be treated shortly.

Charles S. James' book titled *Frontier of Municipal Safety* appears to be the basic reference source that excited the imagination of many mayors, city managers and public administrators.[74] It seems safe to state that this text did not turn too many fire chiefs "on." James' aim at an integration concept was to provide a more efficient public service by essentially moving firemen out of the firehouse to perform police duties when a fire was not in progress. The focus was on the utility of man's time. The watchful waiting nature of the Fire Service, already identified, can be considered as the thrust point that stimulated the unification concept. Indirectly, the point can be assessed from the lack of organizational vitality.

A pause for establishing some definition boundaries is in order. The terminology revolving around the concept integrated-unified services has never been well understood. Conceptual interpretations have ranged all the way from a complete and definitive merger of police and fire functions into one city department to conscious efforts to extend formal cooperative efforts between fire and police departments particularly at the scene of fires. The term "integration" poses overtones of other considerations and should be avoided in the merger context. The most appropriate definitions appear to be structured by Harry W. More, Jr. in his 1970 text: *The New Era of Public Safety.*[75]

[74]Charles S. James, *Police and Fire Integration in the Small City*, Chicago: Public Administration Service, 1955, p. xiii.

[75]Harry W. More, Jr., *The New Era of Public Safety*. Springfield: Charles C. Thomas, 1970, p. vii.

The following definitions are directly quoted.

Consolidated Services: The term consolidated services describes a single unified force in which the police and fire services have been combined into a department of public safety. Officers perform both functions and have usually been identified as public-safety officers.

Partial Consolidation: A situation in which the positive identity of the fire and police services has been retained and a special patrol created to perform combined police-fire duties is defined as "partial consolidation." Officers assigned to the special patrol are usually designated as "public safety officers."

Functional Consideration: "Functional consideration" is interpreted as a degree of consolidation in which separate police and fire services are retained, but one or more duties normally performed by one department have been assigned to members of the other department.

Nominal Consolidation: A term that describes a public-safety department in which the police and fire services have been placed under the direction of a safety director is "nominal consolidation." Each service reserves its individual and distinct identity, both operationally and administratively.

The four definitions are necessary to establish boundary lines for the several types of consolidation. While the subject of this paper is generally removed from the consolidation movement, reference to potentials for partial, functional and nominal consolidations will be advanced in later chapters.

For twenty years the debate has continued over the pros and cons of some form of consolidation. A restructuring of the debate would serve no useful purpose. The bibliography lists selected references for the reader who wishes to gain further insight to the specific problem areas revolving around the consolidation movement. Attention is called to Harry W. More, Jr.'s book. This text seems to present the most total and objective primer on the public safety concept.

The spectrum issues of consolidation are found in more fundamental issues. These issues have a direct bearing on the objectives and scope of this paper. Therefore, a few words on issue identity are in order.

Events of the past twenty years have demonstrated a constantly increasing demand for improved public-safety services. Consequently, public officials have been compelled to question the traditional means of coping with the public safety responsibility. They have searched for more suitable ways of protecting the lives and property of citizens. The consolidation schemes in one of the four forms defined have been advocated as means of providing improved and expanded public-safety services. More identifies one hundred twenty-nine unified departments in the United States in 1965.[76]

The questioning of traditional means of coping with public fire safety responsibilities is the subject matter of this book. Traditional concepts are the underlying thread to the present problems. The shorter work week and associated financial considerations prompted the initial examination of traditional modes of operation. In the examination process public administrators and officials focused on what might be termed administrative and management weaknesses in the Fire Service.

Nonproductive time can be factored out as the contributing condition to many problem areas in public fire safety. Certainly this point had a significant impact on the consolidation movement. Mr. More sharpens this point when he states:[77]

> The unproductive time spent by firemen when on duty has primarily been significant. Many people have visualized the average fireman as being constantly engaged in fire suppression activities, a training program or in insuring the maintenance of equipment, but this has not necessarily been the case. In fact, assembling and holding firemen in stations has resulted in varying degrees of ineffective use of manpower.
>
> In a study conducted by the city manager of San Diego, it was found that over 67 percent of each fireman's duty time was completely unproductive. The study also reflected that only 1.3 percent of the firefighter's duty time was utilized in actually responding to alarms. Additional studies in other cities revealed a similar percentage pattern: Evanston, Illinois, less than 1 percent; Glencoe, Illinois, .7 of 1 percent; Greensboro, North Carolina, less than .9 of 1 percent; and Los Angeles, California, less than 1 percent.

The two related quotations begin to clarify a problem. In the studies conducted by More, or investigated by More, very little of a fire fighter's on-duty time was productively utilized. The studies make note that this condition in no way reflects on the employee, but it does seem to be a justifiable criticism of fire administration and personnel administration specifically and public administration in general.

A key concept to the potential utilization of Fire Service personnel is the prescription that a given number of men must be on standby to answer an alarm of fire. While it is generally perceived that response time must be minimal, it does not necessarily follow that *all* firemen are to be held in reserve at the fire station. The technology of communications can release fire fighters from the confines of the fire station. This point was stressed by Robert Earle, who stated:[78]

With protection of life and property as the basic purpose of both services (police and fire) and with the primary emphasis on prevention, it is no longer desirable, nor is it necessary for men to sit and wait for emergencies to happen. Modern radio communications have made it possible for them to go about the performance of other duties while waiting for an emergency call.

Consolidated services to a large degree have been prompted by the failure of fire departments to maximize the utilization of their manpower resource. From the Fire Service point of view, a new response to the question of providing consolidated services is needed. A new form of the structural functional organization could be the answer to the problem. Under the proposed public fire safety organization outlined in this book, the volunteer fireman might still be on standby but the paid personnel would have no time for police patrol duty since they would be *totally* engaged in the mission of public fire safety.

The Structure of Fire Department Organizations

Public fire protection organization in most cities, towns and communities is patterned after what might be described as a semimilitary framework. From the loosely organized volunteer groups of the nineteenth century sprang a more rigid organization developed in New York City.[79] When the New York City Department converted from a volunteer status to a paid force, the organizational framework took shape under the titles of Division, Battalions and Companies. The terminology associated with the army chain of command is quite evident today.

Bush and McLaughlin make an interesting point about the above fact.[80]

> Since the Army was the model for early firefighting organizations in most American cities, the use of Army terms to describe various parts of our fire departments became the practice. While this vocabulary has largely persisted, there are often great differences in the meaning of the words in the military organizations and in the Fire Service. For example, a fire company rarely exceeds seven men on duty, including an officer; a standard infantry company (US Army) rarely numbers less than 125 men and six officers.

Public fire safety is again faced with a terminology and understanding problem.

The semimilitary arrangement of public fire departments has persisted partly out of tradition and partly out of the perceived need for

[76]*Ibid.*, p. 32.   [77]*Ibid.*, p. 50.

[78]Robert A. Earle, "Personnel Implications of Police-Fire Integration." *Public Personnel Review*, July 1958, p. 192.

[79]Loren S. Bush and James McLaughlin, *Introduction to Fire Science*, Beverley Hills: Glencoe Press, 1970, p. 29.

[80]*Ibid.*, p. 30.

FIRE COMPANY (Population less than 1,500)
(Fire department)

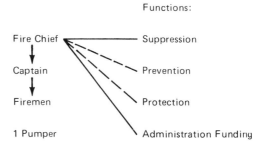

Functions:

Fire Chief — Suppression

Captain

Firemen — Prevention

— Protection

1 Pumper — Administration Funding

Department Type: Volunteer

ILLUSTRATION I-1 BASIC VOLUNTEER TYPE FIRE DEPARTMENT ORGANIZATION FRAMEWORK

a military type command and discipline structure at the time of a fire. The authoritative chain of command relationship between a fire chief, a division commander, a battalion commander and a company officer is deemed necessary to the execution of effective fire ground operations.

The fire department is based upon a traditional form of organization that nicely complements the theory relating to the "classical" hierarchical pyramid. The strengths and weaknesses of several traditional types of organization structures is presented in Chapter II. The concern under the problem identification and response is to identify the basic structural-functional framework of public fire departments. The identification process is intended to illuminate perceived problems that bear on the structured objectives which are intended to emphasize efficiency and effectiveness.

The basic unit at the bottom of the organization pyramid is the fire company. A fire company is labeled by its intended function concerning fire suppression. The most common type of company unit is the engine or pumper company. This company classification utilizes a mobile piece of apparatus equipped with a rated fire pump, water tank, hose complement and usually short-reach ladders. Such an engine pumper unit represents the principal attack on the fire ground. In communities or built up areas where several buildings exceed thirty-five feet in height, ladder capabilities are required. Thus one type of support unit

to the engine company is a ladder company or truck company as it is often termed. As service requirements increase and/or as special hazards are identified, other special service companies are organized to further support the fundamental engine and ladder companies. Special Service companies might include: rescue units, salvage units, tower units, fireboats, tanker units, brush units, etc.

In the most basic type of public fire safety organization, a single engine company constitutes a fire department organization. Even at this level the officer organization can begin to resemble a pyramid of authority. Illustration I-1 depicts the simplest of organization types. Note that the organization is headed by a fire chief. There is a company officer and the complement of manpower. The fire chief is the leader of the department. In this role he usually wears two hats. One is the administrative hat required to run the organization. When the alarm of fire rings, he dons a white helmet and leads the company in the fire suppression effort. At this level of complexity the problem of wearing two different hats does not become too cumbersome nor does it appear to have too much effect on efficiency and effectiveness. This last statement is pure conjecture since there is no known evidence to support or refute the statement.

The layering process begins as more companies are added to the organizational framework. Each company may support a captain and a lieutenant. At the organization level one

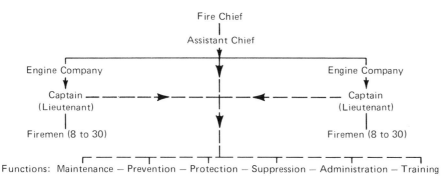

Fire Chief

Assistant Chief

Engine Company   Engine Company

Captain   Captain
(Lieutenant)   (Lieutenant)

Firemen (8 to 30)   Firemen (8 to 30)

Functions: Maintenance — Prevention — Protection — Suppression — Administration — Training

Department Type: Paid

ILLUSTRATION I-2 BASIC PAID TYPE FIRE DEPARTMENT ORGANIZATION FRAMEWORK

or more assistant chiefs may enter the organization picture. The organization now begins to look like Illustration I-2.

At this point let us consider the differentiation between the pattern of development for paid type fire departments, combination fire departments and volunteer fire departments. First, the paid department resembles the structure established in Illustration I-2. The chief officer still wears both the administrative hat and the white hat. In the combination type of fire department case, a simple version of the stated organization would convert one of the companies to a paid unit under the command of a paid captain. This arrangement is shown in Illustration I-3. The volunteer chief still commands the department. Unfortunately, in some instances, the paid captain becomes a glorified bookkeeper. Where this situation occurs, a problem and a weakness also occur. Another example relates to a projected volunteer organization. The volunteer organization may be subjected to a further layering process or a tacked on organizational entity. Several arrangements could occur; two will be explored.

The volunteer organization may be developed around two companion roles. The first role is

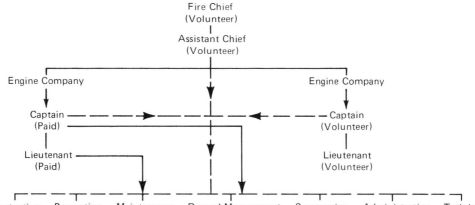

Fire Chief
(Volunteer)

Assistant Chief
(Volunteer)

Engine Company   Engine Company

Captain   Captain
(Paid)   (Volunteer)

Lieutenant   Lieutenant
(Paid)   (Volunteer)

Functions: Protection — Prevention — Maintenance — Record Management — Suppression — Administration — Training

ILLUSTRATION I-3 BASIC COMBINATION TYPE FIRE DEPARTMENT ORGANIZATION FRAMEWORK

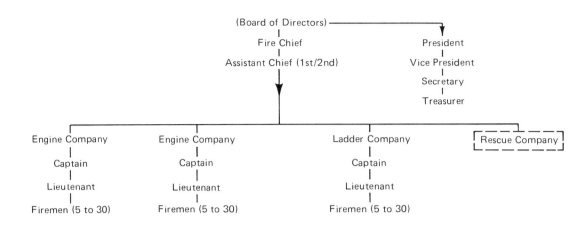

FIRE DEPARTMENT (Population 7,000 to 15,000)

ILLUSTRATION I-4 INTERMEDIATE SIZE VOLUNTEER TYPE FIRE DEPARTMENT ORGANIZATIC
STRUCTURE

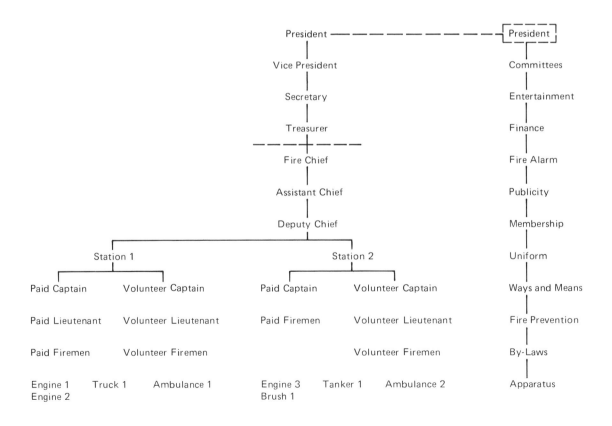

FIRE DEPARTMENT (Population 20,000)

ILLUSTRATION I-5 INTERMEDIATE SIZE COMBINATION TYPE FIRE DEPARTMENT ORGANIZATION
STRUCTURE

that of an emergency service organization. The second role is that of a social organization to attract and maintain manpower for the emergency service role. In other words, the social organization keeps the fire department active; provides a base for raising money, and exercises the political muscle necessary to equip the fire department. The results of this dual structure is a fragmented entity that attaches to the base organization in a number of ways. The more prevalent observed techniques include a structure over the fire chief and a parallel structure tied to the fire chief. The first case is shown in Illustration I-4. The second case is shown in Illustration I-5.

Several interesting possibilities exist concerning organizational authority. In the vertical sense under Illustration I-4, one may find the president actually running the total organization with a tight control over the budget and the organizational functions. A working relationship between the president and the fire chief is essential to the objective accomplishment of the organization. The horizontal organizational framework provides another possibility. Since the fire chief and the department (or company) president are viewed on the same plane, the authoritative relationship sometimes gets quite confusing.

There are some inherent difficulties experienced in any of the prototype organizational arrangements. Constitutions, by-laws, rules and regulations are promulgated to establish working relationships, authority and responsibilities. The point to be made relative to the depicted volunteer type organizations is that there appears to be more opportunities for the informal organization to operate, more opportunity for split authority relationships, more fragmentation of loyalties and more opportunities for social objectives to outweigh fire safety objectives. These problems are real and they must be given due consideration in developing proposed structural-functional relationships of public fire safety organizations.

Now it is possible to return to the description of the growth pattern for typical fire department organizations. The evolutionary process continues, primarily based upon size of the city, until eight or more companies are organized. At this level of growth the concept of span of control is introduced and the pyra-

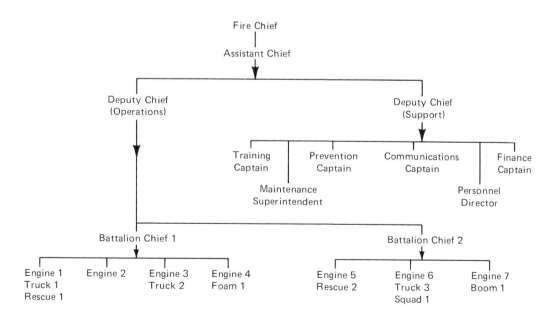

FIRE DEPARTMENT (Population 50,000)

ILLUSTRATION I-6 INTERMEDIATE SIZE PAID TYPE FIRE DEPARTMENT ORGANIZATION
STRUCTURE

mid gains a new level. Primarily influenced by the National Board of Fire Underwriters' *Standard Schedule for Grading Cities and Towns of the United States with Reference to Their Fire Defenses and Physical Conditions* (now the Insurance Services Office), battalions are formed for each eight companies or fraction thereof.[81] Also a deputy chief is now recommended so that a senior chief officer is on duty at all times. This organization extension is depicted in Illustration I-6.

[81]NBFU, *Standard Schedule for Grading Cities and Towns of the United States with Reference to Their Fire Defenses and Physical Conditions*. New York: National Board of Fire Underwriters, 1956, p. 44.

On or before a department reaches the size of eight individual companies, another organizational development takes place. The administrative load is becoming sufficient to require staff support. Therefore, one finds an organizational division taking place that separates the total structure into what are normally called line functions and staff functions. This divisional process begins to identify some additional organizational problems.

The normal organizational intention of staff functions is to spread the administrative and management staff load. In the typical fire department organization the following staff functions are generated: One of the first areas to be

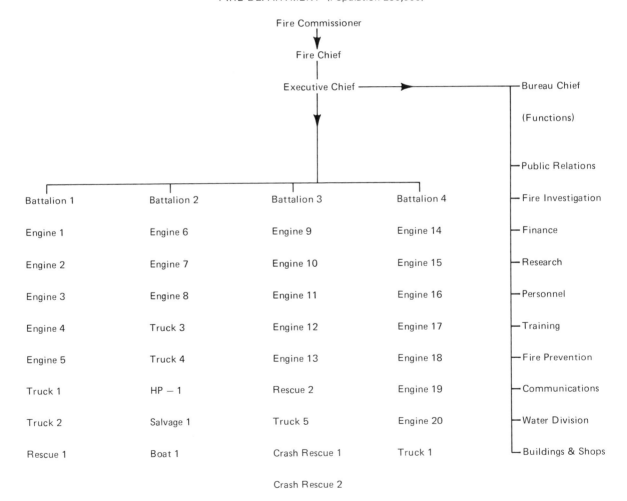

ILLUSTRATION I-7 LARGE SIZE PAID TYPE FIRE DEPARTMENT ORGANIZATION STRUCTURE

created as the organization expands is the training staff, then a maintenance staff, followed by a fire prevention staff and based upon work load, a communications staff, personnel staff, finance staff, public relations staff and other special designations. This evolutionary process is demonstrated in Illustration I-7. The basic function of a staff group in any organization is to support the administrative effort and the line functions. In the specific case of fire department organizations, the staff functions should complement and reinforce the suppression function. In practice, the basic separatism that is found on the organizational chart prevails in actual operation of some departments. The staff groups get involved with their own segment of activities and the fire companies go about their duties without following the practice of coordination and communication between the organization blocks. Typically the communication process is downward from the chief to the individual segments of the organization. A dynamic communications and coordinations intra-flow is lacking.

One major problem with existing public fire department organizations is compartmentalization. Each unit on the organizational chart seems to develop its own internal objectives. The unit objectives predominate to the detriment of the total organization. This makes organizational coordination extremely difficult for the top administrator.

The subject of administration focuses on another current problem. The administrative hat and the fireground white hat are worn by the same man — the fire chief. It should be recognized that as the organization becomes more complex so does the administrative task. An unfortunate corollary is that the fire chief still remains as commander of fire suppression functions. He feels this sense of responsibility for fire control to be a legal condition, a moral condition, a condition of desire and/or a combination of all three. This divided sense of duty requires that the fire chief be a specialist in two areas. Few fire chiefs serve both masters well.

The organization and administration of public fire safety must be significantly altered *if* public fire safety is to become truly responsive to the objective criteria outlined in this book. The specific nature of this reorganization is the subject matter for the subsequent chapters in this book.

The Interest Group Effect on Public Fire Department Organizations

Public fire department organizations have been strongly influenced by groups external to the community level. It actually appears that organizations outside a given city, town or community influence the scope and activity of public fire safety more than the internal residence. Private and governmental groups can be singled out for exhibiting an effect on local fire protection. This subsection will endeavor to examine some of these influences in terms of further problem identification. A response to this level of special problems will culminate the section.

The fire insurance industry can be easily singled out as demonstrating an impact on the organization of public fire safety. In agreement with this contention is the fifth statement of significance drafted by the "Wingspread Conference." That statement reads:[82]

> The Insurance Interest Has Exerted A Strong Influence On The Organization Of The Fire Service. This Dominance Seems To Be Waning. The Fire Service Must Provide The Leadership In Establishing Realistic Criteria For Determining Proper Levels Of Fire Protection.

Three points are made in this statement. The first point concerning insurance influence will be reviewed at this time.

The justification for many a fire chief's budget request has read, "This is what the Rating Bureau or the National Board of Fire Underwriters requires."

The term "requires" is most likely utilized to reference the content statements contained in the *Standard Schedule for Grading Cities and Towns of the United States With Reference to Their Fire Defenses and Physical Conditions*.[83] Essentially this document presents criteria developed by the National Board of Fire Underwriters (now the Insurance Services Organization) to measure the relative conflagration potential of municipalities and the relative ability of the fire defenses of municipalities to protect against the conflagration potential.

The municipal grading process was initiated in 1917 and still continues today. The Grading Schedule, utilized in the grading process, establishes standards for various features of the fire defenses. Existing conditions are compared to the standards and deficiency points assessed for conditions which fall short of the standards. The stated maximum number of

---

[82]*Op. Cit.*, Wingspread Conference, p. 8.

[83]*Op. Cit.*, NBFU.

deficiency points is five thousand. There are ten classes of protection so that each increment of five hundred points determines a class.

The Grading Schedule was originally developed to be used by fire insurance companies as a guide in their underwriting practices.[84] Various fire insurance rating bureaus soon recognized that the document was a useful tool for classifying the fire protection facilities of various municipalities. Today, the Grading Schedule is used by rating organizations in almost all states as one of the tools in establishing basis fire insurance rates. Normally the Insurance Services Organization Municipal Engineering Department applies the schedule in the larger cities in the United States and the rating organization applies the schedule to smaller cities and state communities.

In addition to the Grading Schedule, most rating organizations have separate schedules to evaluate the effectiveness of small towns and fire protection districts in protecting against the conflagration scale fire. These separate schedules are generally minimum standards which must be met in order to achieve recognition as an organized fire department. These schedules are used to evaluate fire protection districts which provide fire department service essentially to rural areas without recognized water supply systems. If the fire protection districts provide service to areas which are essentially urban in character and have water supply systems, normally the Grading Schedule is used for evaluation purposes.

Particularly in recent years, the Grading Schedule has been criticized. From the insurance industry standpoint it must be pointed out that many of the criticisms are the result of municipal officials attempting to use the schedule for purposes for which it was not intended. It is a schedule for measuring property loss considerations; it is not a device for measuring the economic efficiency of municipal fire defenses.

Related to the establishment of fire protection organization problem areas, it should be noted that without the Grading Schedule, however, no one can say what the condition of our municipal fire defense would be since no other organization or group has attempted to establish similar grading. There is no doubt that the Grading Schedule has contributed in a very large degree to the present general condition of municipal fire defenses.

Fire insurance companies have another aspect to the business that indirectly may affect public fire safety organization. Insurance companies, directly or through jurisdictional rating organizations, establish fire insurance rates. Rating, as differentiated from grading, is the process of determining the cost of fire insurance for an individual building or group of buildings.[85] The fire insurance rates in any state are largely dependent upon the experience in that state. Thus, the rates for very similar buildings can vary quite considerably from state to state even though they are located in cities graded in the same class.

The starting point in the rate determination is the basis rate, the cents amount which for a particular building may vary from state to state and from city to city, but normally it will not vary within a city and will be the same for all municipalities having the same Grading Class within the state.[86] Therefore, the municipal grading level (one to ten) affects the basis rate. Added to the basis rate are charges that reflect on the assumed insurance risk for a particular building. This might be called evaluating the chance of loss. The end point is a premium rate which is usually quoted as an annual rate per one hundred dollars of insurance.

There are essentially two rating methods utilized to develop the rate on a given building, namely class rates and schedule rates. Class rates are used for occupancies that are very similar in character and for which the expense of actually inspecting the individual risks to differentiate among them is not warranted. Schedule rates are the product of actual physical inspection of individual risks and the application of appropriate insurance rate schedules.[87] Under one of the schedule rating techniques utilized, the Analytic System, the rating process is divided into four parts:[88]

> . . . the first dealing with rules for each of three classes of construction, the second classifying the occupancy and establishing charges for combustibility of the contents and for causes which originate combustion, the third dealing with fire exposures between separate buildings, and the fourth part establishing "after charges" for easily corrected hazards and for certain hazardous or objectionable conditions.

The brevity of the above description covering the establishment of fire insurance rates should be underscored. The process is really quite

[84]National League of Cities, *The Grading of Municipal Fire Protection Facilities.* Washington: National League of Cities, 1967, p. 13.

[85]Robert Riegel and Jerome S. Miller, Insurance Principles and Practices, (4th Ed.), Englewood Cliffs, N.J.: Prentice-Hall, Inc., pp. 59–89.

[86]*Ibid.*, p. 61.   [87]*Ibid.*, p. 549.

[88]*Op. Cit.*, Municipal Fire Administration, p. 20.

complicated. The highlights have been established to form a foundation on which to advance some problem conditions and some reflective observations.

One of the prime concerns of this book is to set public fire safety in the context of performance levels and to then examine levels of service in relation to effectiveness and efficiency. At this point it should become clearly evident that the insurance industry has exhibited a significant impact on the performance, efficiency and effectiveness of public fire department organizations. The grading schedule with a published list of criteria covering fire departments, water supply, fire alarm systems, fire prevention and structural conditions within a city has set the stage for one measure of public fire safety. This measure in terms of a grading from one to ten has been misused as a yardstick of efficiency and effectiveness.

Quite often, extensive and costly improvements in the fire defenses are requested by fire officials with the main justification given that the improvements will result in a better insurance classification. If requested improvements can be justified by the improved levels of service offered to the public on a quantitative and qualitative basis (which is the way they should be justified) then the possible reduction in insurance rates should be presented as *one* tangible benefit: the question of insurance rates would not predominate although the subject area is still of interest. The question also arises when a grading survey indicates that the grading has retrogressed to a poorer class and a list of recommendations are presented to the jurisdictional government to regain the previous class. There is always a question if all the recommendations are needed and, if not, which ones cost the least.

The cost of the suggested municipal improvements or of complying with the recommendations can be determined generally quite accurately and without great difficulty. Unfortunately, the same is not true for determining the possible savings in the cost of purchasing fire insurance or the actual grading benefit. The cost of insurance cannot be calculated with any great degree of accuracy nor can a reasonable estimate be made without great difficulty because insurance companies do not keep statistics segregated for an individual city; they are generally kept on a statewide basis.

From the Grading Schedule point of view three problems can be clearly identified.

1. The grading of municipal fire defenses does not affect all insurance rates; in some cities the amount of insurance not affected by the grading can be quite considerable.

2. Trying to estimate the actual effect that a change in class will have on insurance rates, in dollars, is difficult and can only be an approximation.

3. Compliance with recommendations received from the grading of a city does not necessarily mean that a desired performance level will be achieved nor does it mean that cost-effectiveness will increase.

Also, problems can be clearly identified in relation to the fire insurance rate established for a given building in a given city.

1. Local building codes and fire prevention codes properly enforced appear to have a direct bearing on the risk potential of a structure. Therefore, such laws which are designed for community safety affect the property insurance rate.

2. Some insurance rates are established on the basis of a physical inspection covering the building and contents. Hazards that have been properly removed or corrected through fire department inspections can affect the insurance rate.

3. Rate penalties can be invoked upon a property owner where municipal requirements conflict with conditions in the rating schedule. Examples of this condition may be found in relation to water supply requirements, fixed and mobile fire extinguishing equipment.

4. There is a considerable duplication of effort in the inspection of schedule rated type property in a city. The insurance company and/or rating bureau may inspect the property, a local building official may inspect the property, the fire prevention bureau may inspect the property and a fire company doing inservice inspections may inspect the property. Experience has demonstrated that conflicting recommendations are supplied to the property owner as a result of these inspections. It should also be noted that very little coordination is evidenced between the special interest groups conducting the inspections.

A portion of the summary and response to these problem conditions can once again be found in the words of the Wingspread Report.[89]

> There has been considerable evidence in recent years of a gradual withdrawal of ancillary services by the fire insurance industry; so much so, that the operational fire service would do well to prepare now for complete cessation of these activities.
>
> The insurance companies are businesses. Their primary obligation is to conduct their business in a manner that is satisfactory to their policyholders and profitable to their stockholders. They are not obligated to improve municipal fire protection. This is a public responsibility, through government. Public officials must recognize that adequate protection of lives and property is their obligation.
>
> The operational fire service must have the maturity, professional approach and capability to establish its own standards and to keep them current. Public officials must become willing to accept criteria that are realistic and based on life and property protection without depending upon insurance rates as the primary guide.
>
> This whole area of evaluating today's fire protection requirements needs to be studied in light of the many changes that are taking place in our whole way of life in the United States.

This author completely endorses the above view.

The search for new guidelines on which to build a foundation of public fire safety has not yet found a supporting organization. There has been some discussion that such a role should fall to the International Association of Fire Chiefs; some discussion that the National Fire Protection Association should enter this area; and concern that the Federal Government will enter this area. Therefore a few words are in order concerning both the role of the National Fire Protection Association and the Federal Government as they affect public fire safety.

Probably the most widely known fire protection organization is the National Fire Protection Association (NFPA). The NFPA states three aims: (1) promotion of the science and improvement of fire protection methods; (2) preparation and circulation of information; and (3) cooperation of members and the public in establishing proper safeguards against loss of life and property by fire.[90] Probably the most significant NFPA function is the development of fire safety standards. These standards are *advisory rules* covering the many different areas and elements of fire hazard. Although the NFPA's standards are widely adopted and incorporated into the laws of the states and the ordinances of counties and municipalities, the Association itself considers its standards as simply advisory.

It is important to realize that many cities and municipalities utilize the NFPA fire safety standards extensively as municipal ordinances. From this view, NFPA has a striking effect on public fire safety. Specific standards such as NFPA No. 4 — *Organization for Fire Services* and No. 4A *Organization of a Fire Department* present detailed procedures for the organization, administration and management of public fire departments.[91,92] This material provides a good foundation for the traditional type of public fire department organization; the material does not cover the new public administration approach to organizations. Furthermore, it appears that the referenced NFPA publications are fragmented into relative specific areas.

The role of the Federal Government was drawn to the reader's attention in the opening of this chapter. A group of fire chiefs see the role of the Federal Government in the Fire Service as being an important development in the 1970's.[93] Any development that comes from the Federal Government in the subject area of fire safety organization will probably be carried forth as a result of the Fire Research and Safety Act of 1968. This act authorized the establishment of a Fire Research Center at the National Bureau of Standards, Department of Commerce, for the development of broad programs of research, training, education and data gathering.[94]

Under Title I of this act, the Secretary of Commerce is authorized to carry out the provisions of the act through the National Bureau of Standards, which is under the Department of Commerce. The Secretary of Commerce also is empowered to establish a Fire Research and Safety Center and to cooperate with and assist public and private agencies. The act also calls for "demonstrations of new approaches and improvements in fire prevention and control, and reduction of death, personal injury, and property damage."[95] Education programs

[89]*Op. Cit.*, Wingspread Conference, p. 9.

[90]National Fire Protection Association, Fire Protection Handbook, 13th Edition, Boston: National Fire Protection Association, 1969, section 2, p. 2.

[91]*Op. Cit.*, NFPA, Organization for Fire Services.

[92]*Op. Cit.*, NFPA, Organization of a Fire Department, 1969.

[93]Staff, "The 1970's — The Challenging Years for the Fire Service," *Fire Engineering*, September 1967, pp. 106–120.

[94]Staff, "Fire Inquiry Bill Signed by Johnson," *Fire Engineering*, April 1968, pp. 60–61.

[95]Senate, "Fire Research and Safety Act of 1967," *Congressional Record*, Vol. 113, No. 31, February 28, 1967.

are authorized to inform the public about fire hazards and fire safety techniques and to encourage the use of such techniques and the avoidance of hazards. Also, educational and training programs may be developed to improve "the efficiency, operation and organization of fire services," and "the capability of controlling unusual fire related hazards and fire disasters."[96] Projects can be conducted to demonstrate improved or experimental fire control and prevention programs, as well as ways of raising the efficiency and improving the operation and organization of fire services.

Title II of the act established a National Commission on Fire Prevention and Control. The President made the Commission appointments and the Commission conducted hearings and collected data during 1971–73. The Commission was charged with examination of the "ways in which fires can be more effectively prevented through technological advances, construction techniques, and improved inspection procedures."[97] Administrative problems of the Fire Service were investigated by the Commission to determine their effect on the efficiency of local fire departments. The Commission was also empowered to consider standardization of fire apparatus and equipment and the adequacy of present fire department communication techniques. The Commission made its report to the President and Congress in June, 1973.

The Fire Research and Safety Act could have considerable impact on the organization of public fire safety.

The research efforts of the Fire Research Center at the Bureau of Standards are just beginning to be established. It would appear to be too early in that program to make value judgments as to the results of the Center. One can only hope that the research effort will be comprehensive and will not be fragmented studies and reports that require further unification to establish an effective program.

A number of fire chiefs appear to be enthusiastic about the new federal programs. Chief O'Hagan of New York City reports that a sampling of twenty chief officers from the International Association of Fire Chiefs' Metropolitan Committee revealed that only one Chief was not in favor of accepting federal aid to bolster the nation's Fire Service. Most of the Chiefs felt the cities should get involved with the Federal Government.[98]

Warren Kimball of the NFPA Staff does not share this view.[99] He states:

Where standards are prepared and enforced nationally, the weight of statistics and cost effectiveness tends to be far more dominant than the wishes of local citizens and the recommendations of local fire officials. It is better to have one more pumper than you need than to be short one in a critical fire situation.

Mr. Kimball's quotation reminds one that the objectives and the evaluation of objectives concerning public fire safety must be clearly understood by the public before they are implemented. This reminder brings to focus another interest group that should rightly affect the scope and nature of public fire safety — the citizens of the community serviced by the particular jurisdictional fire safety organization.

The Wingspread Conference report is once more utilized for a significant comment. As previously quoted, the second significant statement reads:[100] "The Public is Complacent Towards the Rising Trend of Life and Property Loss by Fire."

In support of this statement, the following observations are made by the Wingspread Conference Committee.[101]

Society in general in the United States seems to establish tolerable limits which we are willing to accept. Many fire officials felt that a one-billion-dollar loss was the maximum. Now we are approaching two billion dollars with apparent apathy. The United States leads the world in number of fires, fire deaths and property loss.

Insulating factors from a fire appears to have an effect on the public attitude. The Wingspread report utilizes the following quotation to make this point.[102]

In the next two days, (after the fire) numb shock and relief, protected by the fast sympathy and affection of friends and neighbors, we did not think too much about the loss. A friend's sweater fits almost as well as my own, and my younger daughter's bicycle and menagerie of stuffed animals were magically replaced. The fact of insurance coverage insulated us still further.

The American system of fire protection, despite the deficiencies noted in this paper, and the American system of insurance loss coverage appear to contribute to the complacent attitude. This attitude is depicted by such comments as "Why worry, I'm insured" or "The fire department will take care of it."

---

[96]*Ibid.*, p. 160.   [97]*Ibid.*, p. 160.

[98]*Op. Cit.*, Staff, "The 1970's — The Challenging Years for the Fire Service," p. 117.

[99]Kimball, Warren Y. "The British Look Ahead," *Firemen*, July 1969, p. 29.

[100]*Op. Cit.*, Wingspread Conference, p. 6.

[101]*Ibid.*, p. 6.   [102]*Ibid.*, p. 7.

A staff writer for the NFPA summarizes the complacent attitude problem this way.[103]

> We honestly believe that our citizens are constantly interested in what we are doing. Yet, a surprising — perhaps 99 percent — couldn't care less about the day-to-day operation of the fire department. It is assumed that it is manned and equipped, and will function effectively . . . as does the water department, sewer department, sanitation department, or police department.

From experience, it seems as though the new-car syndrome might be applied to the public's evaluation of public fire protection. This is simply to mean that public fire protection appears to be measured by the luster of paint and the brightness of chrome on the local fire engine.

What is the solution to this public apathy, if in truth it does exist? It would seem that part of the answer consists of the presentation of a proper perspective of fire protection to the citizen. From the analysis techniques utilized today, the public does not know whether the fire department is good, bad or indifferent. This response therefore brings one back to the previously formulated objectives. When these objectives are implemented in a specific situation it will be possible to institute a program for measuring the objectives. When the public understands the objective results of this measure, the complacency *may* hopefully wain in favor of a more affirmative action.

The Effect of Science and Technology on Public Fire Department Organizations

Technological changes and scientific developments are "confronting fire departments with problems far greater than they can handle."[104] Once again the Wingspread Conference Report has identified a problem. Chief Milton Q. Bullock of the Metropolitan Dade County Fire Department, Miami, Florida, echoes this opinion by noting that the Fire Service is in the midst of a scientific and technological revolution.[105] Emmett Cox of the International Association of Fire Fighters feels that the modern-day fire fighter must prepare himself to deal with scientific and technological factors he will deal with in the prevention and protection of lives and property.[106]

Few could argue that science and technology are exhibiting a tremendous impact on every segment of society. But, what are the special concerns of public fire safety in relation to science and technology?

A proper response to the above question could be voluminous. Therefore, the following reflection on this topic area must necessarily be severely limited in depth and to some extent in scope. Specific areas have been selected for review and analysis. These areas were chosen on the basis of their special implications for the organization of public fire safety with a special emphasis on the understanding of the expertise needed to adequately cope with science and technological change.

This book is constructed on the thesis that public fire safety must be organized both structurally and functionally to cope with the identified fire safety problems. If there are real problems that exist, and these problems are not fully comprehended or understood, public fire safety may organize to cope with false or unreal problems. Therefore, the first point should examine those aspects of science and technology that lead to a definition of the urban fire problem.

Science and technological application have introduced a near infinite amount of hazardous elements into the urban environment. To make the limits of concern manageable, reflections are advanced concerning those special problems that have been identified since World War II. For succinctness and objectivity single line items are horizontally line listed and these problems are identified as to the magnitude of the identification rather than any attempt of classification as to the ramification of the problem.

Spot Hazards: Radioactive materials, electronic gear, high piled storage, chemical concentrates, automated processes, nuclear reactors, flammable fabrics.

Building Hazards: High-rise buildings with unprecedented evacuation problems, access problems, and extinguishment problems; synthetic materials producing rapid flamespread and high smoke densities; congested structures that are severely depreciated; solid wall structures; open plan structures, air rights structures, and air-supported structures.

Human Hazards: Arson, fire bombing, civil disruption, mobility of society with less fire consciousness.

Transportation Hazards: Unmarked hazardous commodities in shipment causing widespread damage when involved in an accident.

[103]Staff, "The Seventy-third NFPA Annual Meeting," *Fire Journal*, September 1969, p. 29.

[104]*Op. Cit.*, Wingspread Conference, p. 6.

[105]Staff, "Seminars at IAFC Conference Cover Many Fire Problems," *Fire Engineering*, April 1967, p. 58.

[106]*Ibid.*, p. 58.

As a counter force or deterrent, public fire safety has employed a number of science and technological means to combat the problems. However, one can hardly say there has been a technological revolution in public fire safety. The breakthrough appears spotty and there is a deep gulf between the basic research effort in such areas as combustion theory and the actual suppression of fires. Some of the more significant areas to be noted in relation to science and technology would appear to include: self-contained breathing equipment, extinguishing agents, larger diameter water supply lines; faster and larger pumping capacity fire apparatus; improved protective clothing; improved capability and range of communication equipment.

There exists a gray line between the division of some identified fire protection features as to whether they are of a public or private nature. While the purpose of this paper is to concentrate on the public aspect of urban fire safety, the interface between public and private aspects of fire safety cannot legitimately be excluded. A number of significant private fire protection devices have been developed over the past few years. Notably these include: smoke and/or ionization fire detection devices, heat responsive sprinkler valves, high expansion foam generators, dry chemical systems, dual agent extinguishing systems, and explosion suppression devices.

The general area of organization, administration and management has been strongly affected by science and technological breakthroughs in the last dozen years. Probably the greatest single impact area has been the introduction of the computer into the system of operation in government, business and industry. Unfortunately, computer application to the business of public fire protection is still in the think stage. There are noted exceptions. These exceptions will be discussed in Chapter III.

The reference to Chapter III in relation to computers needs a further word of explanation. The impact of computers on public fire safety organization and operations is perceived to be so significant as to require a separate chapter to present the specific details. The implication and application of computers to organized fire protection was originally conceived as the culminating chapter to this book. However, it has become clearly evident that computers are tied so intricately to a systems theory of organization that the subject area is considered a foundation stone instead of a caping stone.

Therefore, Chapter III introduces the computer as a requisite utility for the organization and operation of public fire safety.

It is important to point up the realization that the computer, a product of science and technology, will play an indispensable role in the organizational complex of public fire safety. In the area of administration, computers are seen to complement an overall management information system which in turn will support the decision-making process of administration. Computers, because of their tremendous capability to store, manipulate and retrieve data should contribute to the streamlining of fire department record keeping. The time devoted to record management in many fire departments is considered to be a serious problem. Data management systems utilizing computer support appears to be a very good answer to the problem. Computers are also viewed as being important to the fire administrator in relation to the budget process, in developing a management by exception program, in organizational performance evaluations and in educational development. These title areas represent concepts that will be expanded upon in Chapter III.

The computer is also perceived to possess capabilities that make it a potentially attractive tool in the operational phase of the organization relating to prevention, protection and suppression activities. Fire chiefs with vision are already noting some of the possible applications.

Chief O'Hagan of New York City states that:[107]

> Some day we will have to have a computer with the building department so that when a chief responds to the scene of a fire — and he gives the address — within a minute he will have the information back on the date of construction, type of construction, location of shafts, floor loading, occupancy, and what have you.

Referring to the two men who died in the Twenty-third Street fire in New York, O'Hagan said,[108]

> If they had known of the structural alterations that had taken place in the cellar, of the increased dead load that had been placed on the floor, of the highly flammable contents and occupancy of the cellar, it is quite possible that the loss of life could have been averted. Conditions on the fire scene did not make it apparent.

Chief David Gratz perceives some additional operational utilization for computers. Gratz thinks the time will come when a chief will feed into a computer the wind velocity and di-

---

[107]Op. Cit., Staff, "The 1970's — The Challenging Years for the Fire Service," Fire Engineering, April 1967, p. 115.

[108]Ibid., p. 115.

rection, humidity, temperature, structural conditions, occupancy information and such "to get a reasonable prediction of what might be expected" at that fire.[109] Chief Gratz declares,

> From all of this the chief officer will be able to get additional information. That is going to be the tricky part, but if we could just at this moment get all of the information available in the trunk of the chief's car or in a company officer's file — get that back — what a tremendous advantage that would be at that fire.

Keith Royer of Iowa State University indicates that one of the problems right now is how the information the fire service needs is to be fed into computers. Associated with Royer's remark is a quote by Keith Klinger, former Chief, Los Angeles County Fire Department. Chief Klinger presents a key point when he states:[110]

> California counties are setting up a computer system which will operate out of Sacramento and will contain information needed throughout the state by various government agencies. I have a man who sits on the committee and they want to know from the fire service what we need . . . and this gets to be a real problem. We don't know . . . what do you want to know from all the fire agencies in the State of California?[111]

One of the advantages of computer utilization is to assess rapidly large banks of data according to some prearranged plan — a program — to print out requested findings. The Fire Service has not thought of this area in terms of solid objectives and the analytical measurement of these objectives. This book proposes to illustrate how the organization relates to specific objectives so that public fire safety administrators will have an indication of what information is needed to analyze operations, efficiency and effectiveness. The information requirement will in turn dictate certain data requirements. The data elements can then be programmed to give a desired output in the form of a logic report. The computer is the processor of this report. This notation is overly simplified but it is inserted at this point to establish one area for perceived implementation of the computer to public fire safety operations. The range of potential computer applications along with a detailed evaluation of how the computer can be utilized to complement a modern fire safety organization will be advanced in Chapter III.

Once again it should be recognized that science and technology present an almost limitless list of possibilities for public fire safety. It seems that the traditional line and staff organization does not present a viable base of interacting functions to take full advantage of technological developments in the administrative areas as well as the operational area of fire departments. This book attempts to respond to this perceived condition with the advancement of an organizational framework that is both sensitive and accommodative to science and technology.

An Examination of the Organization Base For Public Fire Safety

The American fire service has traditionally been organized on a local autonomy basis. Don O'Brien indicates that almost everyone accepts the notion that:[112] "it is a constitutional requirement that fire protection be provided by local government." He counters "There is nothing in the law that I can perceive, however, which states how the locality shall provide this protection." The door seems open to explore the whole concept of providing public fire safety on a strictly self-contained basis. The question simply phrased asks: Can the objectives and interests of public fire safety be served better through the introduction of a broader organizational base?

The Fire Service literature gives many examples concerning shortcomings of the attempts to retain public fire safety as an entity unto itself within the confines of an incorporated city, town or municipality. The following statements have been selected to identify the perceived problems.

1. Don O'Brien:

> Fire protection as a strictly local function is being questioned in the light of cost and practicality.[113]

2. Fire Chief Emanuel Fried:

> There is no question that in hundreds of localities fire stations can be disbanded and companies consolidated with no loss of efficiency. Small communities can band together into centralized departments, eliminating expensive duplication of personnel and equipment with increased services to the public.[114]

3. Fire Chief William Clark:

> Fire has traditionally been regarded as strictly a local problem, . . . this has impeded progress in many ways. I think it is safe to predict that in the very near future we shall see a rapidly growing trend to consolidate many small fire departments into broader-based organizations such as county fire departments or fire districts embracing several towns.[115]

[109]*Ibid.*, p. 115.   [110]*Ibid.*, p. 115.   [111]*Ibid.*, p. 115.

[112]Donald M. O'Brien, "Current Problems of the Fire Service," *Firemen*, August 1967, pp. 14–15.

[113]*Ibid.*, p. 15.

[114]Emanuel Fried, "The High Cost of Fire Protection," *Fire Chief*, January 1970, p. 36.

[115]*Op. Cit.*, Staff, "The 1970's — The Challenging Years for the Fire Service," p. 117.

4. The development of individual fire departments to cover entire counties, metropolitan areas, or possibly regional areas, was discussed by Anthony Granito, Supervisor of Fire Training, New York State Division of Fire Safety. Granito notes:[116, 117.]

> The magna unit, encompassing groups of municipalities, would eliminate many overlapping conditions. Fire prevention codes and fire prevention practices would be unified for extensive areas, management could be more efficient and economical on this larger scale, manpower could be better utilized, and financial problems could be solved more easily through a broader tax base.
>
> The effectiveness of mutual aid is sometimes handicapped by a lack of equipment and training standardization, when fire department jurisdictions are limited. Also, recruitment and leadership may suffer because of a department's limited geographical area and residence requirement. A broader geographic base can provide greater manpower to fill the ranks of an expanding fire service.

5. Comments on this subject area by the Wingspread Conference Committee:[118]

> a. "It is economically unfeasible for any single governmental jurisdiction to equip and man itself with sufficient forces to cope with the maximum situation with which it may be faced."
>
> b. Many local governmental jurisdictions find themselves, in too many cases, too small to be large and too large to be small. As a result, individual communities cannot do some of the things which can be done if the economic base for the service involved is enlarged.
>
> c. Many individual fire department jurisdictions find themselves unable to cope with the financial burden of providing fire protection as a service. The economic stresses and strains become very pronounced as increased demands for other governmental services occur.
>
> d. A thorough cost-analysis study needs to be made to determine if fire protection, as a responsibility of local government, is economically feasible.

An interview with members of the Wingspread Conference Committee by James Casey of *Fire Engineering* produced a very reflective summary point.[119]

> The Fire Service as a whole lacks uniform standards of performance, educational achievement or skill. And because local governments cling to their prerogatives, it is extremely difficult to bring into being any organized method for general improvement in any large segment of the fire service.

The cited references exhibit considerable concern over what might be termed the operational base of public fire safety. There appears to be some specific identifiable problems associated with continuing to operate public fire protection at strictly the lowest level of local government. The restrictive nature of local autonomy can be summarized under the following points:

1. The financial resources for public fire safety simply may not be sufficient to achieve desired levels of public fire safety.

2. Manpower and equipment resources may be totally inadequate for a serious fire situation.

3. The manpower talent may not be available to provide the associative technical services needed to carry out the established fire service objectives.

4. Tied indirectly to the financial problem is the possible inability to provide a viable fire prevention program, a maintenance program, a command-control-communications system, research facilities, organized public relations, and data processing needs.

5. The talent required for the efficient and effective administration, management and operations of public fire safety may simply not be available.

The concept of providing public fire safety on an alternate organizational base needs to be carefully examined. There exists the dual points of providing desired levels of public fire safety through the adequate provision of resources along with the necessity to achieve levels of fire safety in a responsive manner to local interests. The development of an organization to provide the proper mix of resources and responsiveness will require careful consideration. One approach to this problem is to enlarge the local geographical base to a county administrative and service level.

Chief William E. Clark talks about the advantages of a county fire service.[120] The focus of Chief Clark's remarks relate to the concept that one of the most obvious answers to broadening the base of public fire safety is to make the step from the strictly local municipality to the county form of government. It is noted that the concept of county-wide fire departments is not widespread as yet in this country, but has been well established in England where almost all fire departments are county operated. There already exists some county fire departments in the United States. Chief Clark indicates:

[116]*Ibid.*, p. 116. *Ibid.*, p. 117.
[118]*Op Cit.*, Wingspread Conference, p. 15.
[119]*Ibid.*, p. 38.

[120]William E. Clark, "Advantages of a County Fire Service," *Fire Engineering*, p. 38.

The largest and best known is that of Los Angeles County which is the fourth largest fire department in the United States. Other large county fire departments are in Baltimore, Ann Arundel and Prince Goerge's counties in Maryland; Dade and Jacksonville-Duval counties in Florida; and Fairfax and Arlington Counties in Virginia.

He summarizes the advantages of a county fire service according to the following points:[121]

1. The county concept provides a broader tax base allowing larger expenditures with less pain to the taxpayer.

2. The county system eliminates or reduces overlap and duplication.

3. Centralized purchase and maintenance result in considerable savings.

4. One of the biggest benefits of county-wide service is central communications.

5. Fire prevention can be well handled on a county-wide basis.

6. Training is another function that can be well provided by the county.

Warren Kimball of NFPA does not appear to view the county concept with Chief Clark's enthusiasm. He states:[122]

These proposals for reorganization of the fire protection service in the country cannot be taken lightly as long as such legislation and appropriations are before Congress. If they are adopted (reference to the Fire Research and Safety Act — 1968) the million volunteer firemen of the country can expect gradually to be phased out by state or regional fire departments. The 22,000 fire chiefs throughout the country, particularly those in smaller cities and towns, can expect to be subordinate officers in the master plan.

Some response comments appear in order. It would seem that the failure to show more evidence of a broader base for providing fire protection in the United States has at least on the surface been identified by Warren Kimball.

---

[121]*Ibid.*, p. 38.

[122]Warren Y. Kimball, "Which Way — For the Fire Service," *Firemen*, May 1967, pp. 13–14.

Local fire departments fear an organizational layering effect that will abort the opportunity for local command and control in their community. The local fire department as an entity unto itself is an historical and strong tradition in many areas of the United States. The success of any attempt to enlarge the geographical and political base of public fire safety must consider this local *esprit de corps* of the fire service.

This book does not perceive that the strict concept of local fire safety can continue to exist *IF* the objectives advanced are to be realized. The resources needed to perform adequate levels of fire safety simply cannot be supported on a strictly local tax base. The term *strict* sense of local provisions is the key to this whole matter and deserves to be emphasized. The distinction must be made between specific cases and broad generalizations. The concept of insufficient resources would appear to hold for the large majority of the nation's twenty-two thousand odd fire departments. However, the large cities may be able to provide the requisite structural-functional relationships necessary to carry out the perceived objectives of fire safety. A precise population category to demonstrate sufficiency versus non-sufficiency would be speculative, however, this speculation is attempted in Chapter II.

It would seem the important point to be established is the notion that the identity of a structural base for public fire safety must consider the preservation of locality autonomy under the following sets of conditions: The preservation of incentives in the organizational ranks; the preservation of a partial local command structure; the preservation of local responsiveness to desired levels of public fire safety — the provision for risk assumption rather than a strict protection plan. Only by adhering to the above conditions will it be possible to implement an alternate means of providing public fire safety.

Chapter 1

Bibliographical Entries

Books

Bush, Loren S., and J. McLaughlin. *Introduction to Fire Science.* Beverly Hills: Glencoe Press, 1970.

Holzman, R. *Romance of Firefighting.* New York: Bonanza Books, 1960.

Huntsberger, David. *Elements of Statistical Inference* (2nd Ed.). Boston: Allyn and Bacon, 1968.

International City Managers Association. *Municipal Fire Administration.* Chicago: International City Managers Association, 1969.

James, Charles S. *Police and Fire Integration in the Small City.* Chicago: Public Administration Service, 1955.

More, Harry. *The New Era of Public Safety.* Springfield: Charles C. Thomas, 1970.

National Board of Fire Underwriters. *Standard Schedule for Grading Cities and Towns of the United States with Reference to Their Fire Defenses and Physical Conditions.* New York: National Board of Fire Underwriters, 1955.

National Fire Protection Association. *Fire Protection Handbook* (13th Ed.). Boston: National Fire Protection Association, 1969.

National Fire Protection Association. *Management of a Fire Department* (No. 4B–1968). Boston: National Fire Protection Association, 1968.

National Fire Protection Association. *Organization of a Fire Department* (No. 4A–1969). Boston: National Fire Protection Association, 1969.

Novick, David, ed. *Program Budgeting, Program Analysis and the Federal Budget.* Cambridge: Harvard University Press, 1965.

Kaplan, Abraham. *The Conduct of Inquiry.* San Francisco: Chandler Publishing Company, 1964.

Pfiffner, John R., and Robert Presthus. *Public Administration.* New York: The Ronald Press, 1967.

Webster's New Collegiate Dictionary. Springfield: G. and C. Merriam Co., 1961.

Publications of the Government, Learned Societies, and Other Organizations

Appley, Lawrence. *Management and the American Future,* General Management Series 169. Washington: American Management Association, Inc. 1954.

National League of Cities. *The Grading of Municipal Fire Department Facilities.* Washington: National League of Cities, 1967.

Senate. "Fire Research and Safety Act of 1967." *Congressional Record,* Vol. 113, No. 31, February 28, 1967. Washington: Government Printing Office.

Williamsburg 70, Boston: National Fire Protection Association, 1970.

Wingspread Conference on Fire Service Administration, Education and Research — Statements of National Significance to the Fire Problem in the United States. Racine: The Johnson Foundation, 1966.

Periodicals

Ahern, John. "The National Fire Profile," *Fire Journal,* March 1972, p. 7.

Bland, Richard E. "The Evaluation Program of the National Commission on Fire Prevention and Control." *Fire Journal,* July 1972, p. 18.

Casey, James F. "Science Symposium Explores Needs of the Fire Service," *Fire Engineering,* January 1969, p. 42.

Clark, William E. "Advantages of a County Fire Service," *Fire Engineering,* December 1969, p. 38.

Earle, Robert A. "Personnel Implications of Police Fire Integration," *Public Personnel Review,* July 1958, p. 192.

Favreau, Donald F. "Crisis in Higher Education," *Fire Engineering,* April 1968, p. 57.

Fried, Emanuel. "The High Cost of Fire Protection," *Fire Chief,* January 1969, p. 36.

Fristrom, Robert M., ed. "Foreword," *Fire Research Abstracts and Reviews,* Vol. 13, 1971, No. 1, p. iii.

Gratz, David B. "The United States Fire Service Problems — Today and Tomorrow," *Fire Chief Magazine,* January 1970, p. 26.

Kahrmann, Robert. "Can the Volunteers Survive the '70s," *Fire Command!,* July 1970, p. 28.

Kimball, Warren Y. "Fire Departments in a Receding Economy," *Firemen,* March 1967, p. 36.

Kimball, Warren Y. "Changing Fire Fighting Problems," *Fire Command!,* October 1971, p. 16.

Kimball, Warren Y. "Fire Departments — Volunteer and Part Paid," *Firemen,* January 1968, p. 23.

Kimball, Warren Y. "Fire Service Critics," *Firemen,* May 1970, p. 26.

Kimball, Warren Y. "The British Look Ahead," *Firemen,* July 1969, p. 29.

Kimball, Warren Y. "Which Way For the Fire Service," *Firemen,* May 1967, p. 13.

O'Brien, Donald M. "Current Problems of the Fire Service," *Firemen,* August 1967, p. 14.

Staff. "Anticipating the Unexpected," *Firemen,* July 1969, p. 25.

Staff. "Fire Inquiry Bill Signed by Johnson," *Fire Engineering,* April 1968, p. 60.

Staff. "Fire Record of Cities, 1970," *Fire Journal,* July 1971, p. 79.

Staff. "National Research Council Symposium on Training and Education," *Fire Chief Magazine,* June 1970, p. 38.

Staff. "Seminars at I.A.F.C. Conference Cover Many Fire Problems," *Fire Engineering,* April 1967, p. 58.

Staff. "The 1970's, The Challenging Years for the Fire Service," *Fire Engineering,* September 1967, p. 106.

Staff. "The Seventy-Third NFPA Annual Meeting," *Fire Journal,* September 1969, p. 29.

Staff. "The Wingspread Conference," *Fire Engineering,* January 1967, p. 38.

Staff. "Voice of the Fire Service," *Fire Command!,* August 1970, p. 6.

Sylvia, Dick. "British Look at Fire Service and See Problems Like Ours," *Fire Engineering,* October 1970, p. 39.

Volkamer, C. W. "What Lies Ahead For the Fire Service," *Fire Command!,* July 1970, p. 81.

Unpublished Materials

Six Months Fire Report, Chautauqua County, New York State, January–June, 1970.

Chapter II

A Systems Theory of Organization for Public Fire Safety

Introduction

Little direct reference was made in Chapter I to the public fire safety systems organization in a specific manner. It is believed a basic understanding of the systems concept is a necessary prelude to the application of that concept to a specific situation. Prior to delving into specific applications, attention is focused on the significant characteristics of the systems approach to organization. The principal characteristics of an organization as a system consists of the following variables: a division of units; the interaction of these units between themselves and with their environment; the maintenance of a structure of information flow and communications; the assurance of growth and viability; a requirement for integrated and effective decision-making process.

Based on this realization of system organization, it is the purpose of this chapter to concentrate on the central theme — the development of an operational structure for placing public fire safety under a systems organization concept. Therefore, the following subsections propose to develop a workable framework within which public administrators and fire administrators can function according to the prescribed objectives of public fire safety in a more effective and efficient manner. Furthermore, administrative personnel can understand and administer specified subsystems of public fire safety with new clarity and responsiveness. Finally, the public fire safety systems organization can be more comprehensively understood in relation to the total urban system.

Historical Concepts Relating to Systems Organization

James W. Culliton states that we are in an age of synthesis. Coupled with this observation is a very interesting thesis of Mr. Culliton.[1]

> . . . My thesis is that quietly, necessarily, and inevitably we are entering a period that forces man to find more accurate answers to questions involving the "wholeness" of an operation and that demands entirely new approaches to these questions.

The reconstituted objectives of public fire safety established in Chapter I conform to this thesis. The impact of these objectives in terms of the public fire safety organizational structure is greater than would appear from a segmented examination. The objectives and the structured questions associated with the objectives imply a wholeness to the organizational operation of public fire safety. As developed in Mr. Culliton's thesis, emphasis on wholeness requires an entirely new approach mechanism to respond to the objectives and the inherent questions that arise in relation to the objectives.

The term "wholeness" implies the whole structure, and further implies that a framework must be built to demonstrate how the individual parts fit into the whole structure. This concept leads to the conclusion that an organized pattern must exist for relating the parts to the whole. Therefore, the wholeness of Mr. Culliton's operation must be related to an organization complex. In fact this is what

---

[1]James W. Culliton, "Age of Synthesis," *Harvard Business Review*, September-October, 1962, pp. 36–38.

Webster states to be the meaning of organization under the following definition.[2]

> to arrange or form into a coherent unity or functioning whole.

The objective of this chapter is to present a new and different approach to the subject of organized public fire safety. Inherent in this objective is the formulation of an organizational structure that involves all the component operations in the process of being responsive to the established mission of public fire safety. This approach involves building an organizational framework that is conceptually different from the traditional line and staff hierarchical arrangement found in public fire departments. The new framework will be referred to as a Systems Concept of Organization.

Since the words organization and system appear to have similar connotations, it is important to understand what is meant by the term organization. Pfiffner and Sherwood state that:[3]

> . . . an organization is the pattern of ways in which large numbers of people, too many to have intimate face-to-face contact with all others, and engaged in a complexity of tasks, relate themselves to each other in the conscious, systematic establishment and accomplishment of mutually agreed purposes.

A complement definition has been composed by Talcott Parsons which adds an important sociological flavor to the organization complex. Parsons states:[4]

> It seems appropriate to define an organization as a social system which is organized for the attainment of a particular type of goal; the attainment of that goal is at the same time a performance of a type of function on behalf of a more inclusive system, the society.

Key to both definitions is the attainment of goals or mutually agreed purposes through a systematic association of patterned relationships. The systematic relationship implies a wholeness of context. Therefore, a definition of organization stresses the systematic interrelationship between people in group arrangements and in societal arrangements to accomplish designated purposes. The interconnecting ways and means of people relationships is the essence of explaining the systems approach.

Prior to a detailed examination of the systems concept of organization it appears advantageous to examine selected traditional organizational theories in order to establish their shortcomings relative to the prescribed objectives of public fire safety.

In Chapter I it was suggested that traditional fire department organization theory has emphasized structural parts and structural segments of the organization. The present organization framework is concerned with the separation of activities into tasks or operational units. This means that staff functions and operational or line functions are widely separated on the organizational chart and that this separation does not give sufficient emphasis to the interrelationships or the integration of line and staff activities. This viewpoint is consistent with the traditional theory of all organization structures.

Closely related to the traditional structure of organization is the concept of hierarchical relationships. Under the hierarchy of organization the whole structure is divided into units, which are subdivided into smaller units, which are in turn subdivided further into smaller units.[5] The typical arrangement of hierachy for fire departments is depicted in the Chart II-1 — *An Example of the Traditional Fire Department Organization*. The example utilized of traditional fire department organizational framework has promoted the concept that the working force revolves within the defined units instead of relating themselves to each other in systematic ways. The organizational process has been to carry out unit objectives instead of total organizational objectives.

The traditional hierarchical organization is defended by fire officers who feel the structural arrangement is necessary for the purpose of clear-cut chain-of-command and authoritative relationships between officers and men. Peter Blau and Richard Scott respond to this point by noting that traditional concepts of organization tend to promote compliance with directives and foster discipline while not providing the working group with an understanding of individual roles in the organizational mission.[6] Therefore, these authors note, the traditional type of organization "does not encourage employees to exert effort, to accept responsibilities, or to exercise initiative."[7]

Closely associated with the traditional concept of organization theory is the classical theory of organizations. This latter theory promotes

[2]*Webster's Seventh New Collegiate Dictionary.* Springfield: G. and C. Merriam Company, 1963, p. 595.

[3]John M. Pfiffner and Frank P. Sherwood, *Administrative Organization*, Englewood Cliffs: Prentice-Hall, Inc., 1960, p. 30.

[4]Talcott Parsons, "Suggestions for a Sociological Approach to the Theory of Organizations," *Administrative Science Quarterly*, September 1956, p. 238.

[5]Herbert Simon, *The New Science of Management Decision.* New York: Harper and Row, Inc., 1960, p. 41.

[6]Peter M. Blau and W. Richard Scott, *Formal Organizations.* San Francisco: Chandler Publishing Company, 1962, p. 140.

[7]*Ibid.*, p. 141.

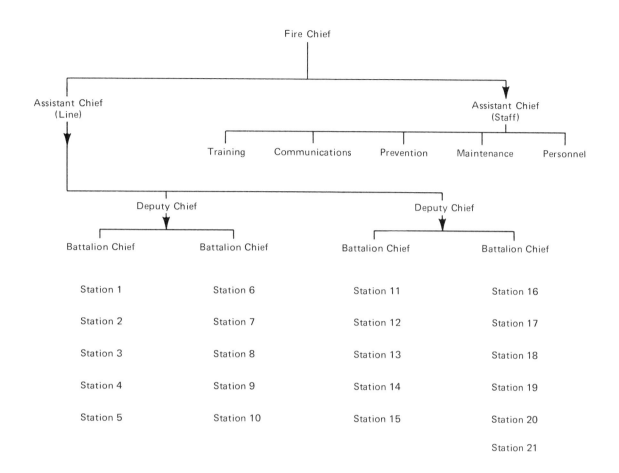

CHART II-1 AN EXAMPLE OF THE TRADITIONAL FIRE DEPARTMENT ORGANIZATION STRUCTURE

some significant points that reflect on structural arrangements of fire department organizations as depicted in Chart II-1. In the classical theory of organizations, the line organization is vested with the primary source of authority and the staff functions support and advise the line. Through the use of special staffs reporting directly to the Executive, it appears possible to increase the authoritative span of control without sacrificing the ability to coordinate activities.

As the classical organization model evolved, staffs have come to play a much more important role, providing services information and even control over the line organizational units.[8] As a result, the clear delineation between line and staff relationships is no longer possible. This becomes particularly true in what has been described as "functional staff operations."[9] The outgrowth of this movement has been the formation of functional authority which refers to the authority that resides within a specialized staff and is exercised within other operational units.[10]

The concept of functional authority represents a substantial variation from the traditional hierarchical organization, where the relationships are based upon the unity-of-command concept, with authority directed from only one superior and with each subordinate responsible to only one superior for his total ac-

[8]Richard A. Johnson, Fremont E. Kast, and James E. Rosenzweig. *The Theory and Management of Systems.* New York: McGraw-Hill Book Company, 1967, p. 57.

[9]*Ibid.*, p. 57.
[10]*Ibid.*, p. 57

tivities. The organization enterprise with functional staffs does severe damage to the unity-of-command concept. With functional staffs, "a number of specialists in each of the functional areas exercise an authoritarian relationship which results in multiple rather than unified supervision."[11] It should be noted that the clear-cut organizational relationship that also existed under the traditional organization is fused together in the classical organization model.

A discussion of organizational theory would be incomplete without reference to Max Weber's *Bureaucratic Model*. A public fire department is certainly a part of the local bureaucracy, however, the fire department is also a part of a larger system, the urban system. Therefore, the organizational points made by Weber should be viewed not only in terms of the fire department construct but in terms of the larger community organization.

The literature on Weberian bureaucracy suggests the following dimensions or key elements of the "ideal" bureaucratic organization.[12]

1. A division of labor based upon functional specialization.

2. A well-defined hierarchy of authority.

3. A system of rules covering the rights and duties of positional incumbents.

4. A system of procedures for dealing with work situations.

5. Impersonality of interpersonal relations.

6. Promotion and selection for employment based upon technical competence.

Basically it was Weber's contention that man was unpredictable, often emotional, not necessarily rational, and would often interfere with any organizational performance.[13] Based upon this concept, Weber set forth an ideal model that depersonalized the organization to minimize the impact of unpredictable change. As a result, the bureaucratic mechanism is anchored in institutionalized authority. The bureaucratic model is basically concerned with a highly systematic organization composed of functional specialization and hierarchy of authority.

The neoclassical, or human relations, model of organization structure and organization behavior evolved as a reaction against the more mechanistic and impersonal biases developed in the traditional, classical, and bureaucratic models.[14] It appears that the Hawthorne-Western Electric studies transformed the focus from the rational model of prior theories to a behavioristic model which accepted man as a human individual. Basically, the behavioral school accepted the structural aspects of organization as discussed previously but modified the concepts regarding human resources and informal group relationships within the organization.

Shepard has identified five key differences between traditional and human relations organizational theory:[15]

1. Wide participation in decision-making rather than centralized decision-making.

2. The face-to-face group rather than the individuals as the basic unit of organization.

3. Mutual confidence rather than authority as the integrative force in organization.

4. The supervisor as the agent for maintaining intra-group and inter-group communications rather than the agent of higher authority.

5. Growth of members of the organization to greater responsibility rather than external control of the members' performance of their tasks.

The above models of organizational theory are presented as a foundation for understanding the systems concept of organization. Several of the elements associated with the systems concept have their roots in earlier organizational models. It would appear advantageous at this point to consider a parallelism between the human relations model and the systems model. Renis Likert and associates draw a likeness between the two concepts.

Likert suggests that organizational processes and patterns of managerial leadership are related closely to motivation and must be consistent and compatible if the organization is to perform efficiently. Specifically Likert states that:[16]

[11]*Ibid.*, p. 57.

[12]H. H. Gerth and C. Wright Mills. *From Max Weber: Essays in Sociology*, New York: Oxford University Press, New York, 1946, p. 214.

[13]Richard H. Hall, "The Concept of Bureaucracy: An Empirical Assessment," *American Journal of Sociology*, July 1963, p. 33.

[14]*Op. Cit.*, Johnson, Kast and Rosenzweig, p. 59.

[15]H. Shepard, "Superiors and Subordinates in Research," *Journal of Business*, October 1956, p. 261.

[16]Renis Likert, *New Patterns of Management*. New York: McGraw-Hill Book Company, New York, 1961, p. 179.

These independent motivations and processes constitute an overall system which coordinates, integrates, and guides the activities of the organization and all its members. Its quality determines the organization's capacity to achieve effective communication, to make decisions, and to motivate, influence, and coordinate the activities of its members.

Likert labels this concept "the interaction-influence systems" and suggests that it should become the central focus for the administration of organizations.[17] Many of Likert's ideas are important in understanding the human aspects of systems concepts.

The model organizations or organizational theories discussed to this point fail to describe adequately the problems associated with one certain type of organization — namely the professional organization. The public fire department hardly falls into the class of a professional organization as defined by Amitai Etzioni. However, there is hope that in the future public fire safety will become more professionalized. Therefore, it seems important to look at the professional model and its influence on organization.

The professional organizational model is described as one in which knowledge is produced, applied, preserved, or communicated in systems especially established for these purposes.[18] Etzioni adds that,[19]

... professional organizations are characterized not only by the goals they pursue but also by the high proportion of professions on their staff (at least 50 per cent) and by the authority relations between professionals and non-professionals which are so structured that professionals have superior authority over the major goal activities of the organization.

The professional organization model differs in many ways from the traditional organization model. The traditional organization assumes that there is one major source of authority (the line organization) which is the basis of final decisions and control. In the professional organization, control is exerted through professional norms and colleague interactions. In the professional organization there may be major conflicts between administrative authority and professional knowledge and individual autonomy.[20]

Herbert Simon has drawn the attention of organizational theorists with his focus on the decision-making process within the organization.

To a major extent, Simon rejects most of the traditional concepts of organization and in place of structure focuses on the human problem-solving processes and decision mechanisms as primary forces in organizational behavior. According to the Simon thesis, organizational participants should not be viewed as mere mechanical instrumentalities. They should be perceived as individuals with wants, motives, aspirations levels, and drives who have limited rationality and capacity for problem solving.[21]

Simon uses the term decision-making as though it were synonymous with managing. He states that decision-making has three principal states: "intelligence — searching the environment for conditions calling for decision; design — inventing, developing, and analyzing possible courses of action; and choice — selecting a particular course of action from available alternatives."[22]

Herbert Simon in collaboration with James March utilized the decision-making process as a frame of reference to set forth a more general theory of organization. A key concept of this theory is illustrated by the following.[23]

The basic features of organization structure and function derive from the characteristics of human problem-solving processes and rational human choice. Because of the limits of human intellective capacities in comparison with the complexities of the problems that individuals and organizations face, rational behavior calls for simplified models that capture the main features of a problem without capturing all its complexities.

The Simon concepts augment the traditional, classical, bureaucratic and neoclassical concepts of organization theory with current knowledge from social sciences about the motivational aspects, conflicts of interest, perception, and restrictions on rationality, all of which influence organizational behavior significantly.

Moving Towards a Modern Organization Theory

The view traditional organization theory presents has generally emphasized parts and segments of the organization. The concern of organizations has been the separation of activities into tasks or operational units that are almost autonomous from the remainder of the organization. It appears that the traditional

---

[17]*Ibid.*, p. 179.

[18]*Op. Cit.*, Johnson, Kast and Rosenzweig, p. 61.

[19]Amitai Etzioni, *Modern Organizations*. Prentice-Hall, Inc., Englewood Cliffs, N. J. 1964, p. 77.

[20]*Op. Cit.*, Johnson, Kast and Rosenzweig, p. 61.

[21]Herbert A. Simon, *The New Science of Management Decision*. New York: Harper and Row, Inc. 1960, p. 41.

[22]*Ibid.*, pp. 1–4.

[23]James G. March and Herbert A. Simon, *Organizations*. John Wiley and Sons, Inc., New York 1958, p. 4.

type of organization did not give sufficient emphasis to the problem of interrelationship or integration of activity within the organization. It is also noted that the neoclassical theory did not move in this direction. Its approach appeared to be aimed at interjecting human motivations, aspirations, desires, and limitations into the mechanistic traditional models. None of the approaches explored provides a basis for an integrated, systematic structural functional organizational model.

In the past decade, a body of literature on organizations and organizational theory has given increased attention to the notion that the most useful way to study organizations is to consider them as systems. The reflected modern view of organizations tends to treat the organization as a system of mutually dependent parts and variables, and the enterprise is thought of as a social system within the broader, more inclusive system of society.[24]

Talcott Parsons' definition of organization expresses this new view:[25]

> It seems appropriate to define an organization as a social system which is organized for the attainment of a particular type of goal; the attainment of that goal is at the same time a performance of a type of function on behalf of a more inclusive system, the society.

Modern organization theory and general systems theory are closely related, with organization theory a special element of general systems theory. Systems theory and organization theory are both concerned with the investigation and performance of the organization as an integrated whole. Scott suggests the interrelationship between general systems theory and organization theory as follows:[26]

> Modern organization theory leads, as it has been shown, almost inevitably into a discussion of general systems theory. A science of organization universals has strong advocates, particularly among biologists. Organization theorists in administrative science cannot afford to overlook the contributions of general system theory. Indeed, modern organization concepts could offer a great deal to those working with general systems theory.

Based upon this discussion, it appears appropriate to pause briefly in the expansion of modern organization theory to develop some operational definitions and phrase concepts. The selected terminology will then serve as building blocks for the systems theory of organizational structure to be presented.

Systems Defined

The term "system" has been introduced at several points without offering a precise definition of the term as utilized in this book. The following definition structured by Johnson, Kast and Rosenzweig is accepted as the basis for all further discussions of the term "system" in an organization context.[27]

> A system is an organized or complex whole; an assemblage or combination of things or parts forming a complex or unitary whole.

It should be realized that the term system covers an extremely broad spectrum of concepts. Possibly the concept becomes clearer when we think of systems examples that affect our lives. There are mountain systems, river systems and the solar system as part of the physical surroundings. Our body itself is a complex organism including the skeletal system, the circulatory system and the nervous system. Daily contact is made with such phenomena as transportation systems, communication systems (telephone, telegraph, etc.) and economic systems. From these examples it becomes clear that the word system connotes plan, method, order, and arrangement. Hence the term has become pervasive through utilization by scientists, researchers and organization men.

It is interesting to note that the antonym of systematic is chaotic. A chaotic situation might be described as one where "everything depends on everything else," but where the connecting system is not understood.[28] Two major goals of any subject area including organizations are: complete explanation and outcome prediction; a chaotic scheme cannot be tolerated. Therefore, there would appear to be considerable incentive to develop bodies of knowledge that can be organized into a complex whole, within which subparts or subsystems can be interrelated. These views lead to a second concept that requires explanation — General Systems Theory.

General Systems Theory

In defining the concept of General Systems Theory, this paper accepts the following explanation by Kenneth Boulding:[29]

> General systems theory is concerned with developing a systematic, theoretical framework for describing general relationships of the empirical world. A broad spectrum of potential achievements for such a frame-

[24]Op. Cit., Johnson, Kast and Rosenzweig, p. 63.
[25]Talcott Parsons, "Suggestions for a Sociological Approach to the Theory of Organizations," Administrative Science Quarterly, September 1956, p. 238.
[26]William G. Scott, "Organizational Theory: An Overview and an Appraisal," Journal of the Academy of Management, April 1961, pp. 7–26.

[27]Op. Cit., Johnson, Kast and Rosenzweig, p. 4.
[28]Ibid., p. 5.
[29]Kenneth Boulding, "General Systems Theory: The Skeleton of Science," Management Science, April 1956, p. 197.

work is evident. Existing similarities in the theoretical construction of various disciplines can be pointed out. Models can be developed which are applicable to many systems, whether physical, biological, behavioral, or social. An ultimate but distant goal will be a framework (or system of systems of systems) which will tie all disciplines together in a meaningful relationship.

Boulding also explains that areas such as social psychology, biochemistry, astrophysics, social anthropology, economic psychology, and economic sociology have been developed in order to emphasize the interrelationships of previously isolated disciplines. More recently the literature indicates areas of study and research that have developed which call on numerous subfields. Examples would include cybernetics, the science of communication and control, which calls on electrical engineering, neurophysiology, physics, biology and other fields. Operations research is often pointed to as a multidisciplinary approach to problem solving. Information theory is another discipline which employs numerous subfields. And, important to this book, organization theory embraces economics, sociology, engineering, psychology, physiology, and anthropology.

Boulding further notes that:[30]

> In order that the interdisciplinary movement may not degenerate into undisciplined approaches, it is important that some structure be developed to integrate the various separate disciplines while retaining the type of discipline which distinguishes them. One approach to providing an over-all framework (general systems theory) would be to pick out phenomena common to many different disciplines and to develop general models which would include such phenomena.

General systems theory could provide a useful framework within which to carry out specialized activities. Furthermore, it allows researchers to relate findings and compare concepts with similar findings and concepts in other disciplines. The relationship between general systems theory and a systems theory for organizations follows.

Modern Organization Theory

Modern organization theory appears to focus primarily upon human social organization. The developmental theory is multidimensional in its consideration of organization subsystems and their relationships. As has been noted, traditional management theory placed primary importance on the hierarchical job and task pyramid with its emphasis on vertical relationships. The modern theory considers any total defined system as composed of numerous units

and subsystems which interact and communicate with each other through patterned relationships. Not only hierarchical, but cross and horizontal relationships, are considered as being extremely important. For example, Henry A. Landsberger states:[31]

> The function of horizontal relationships is to facilitate the solution of problems arising from division of labor, and their nature and characteristics are determined by the participants having different organization subgoals but interdependent activities that need to intermesh.

It is also worthy to note that the traditional view of authority in organizations emphasized certain relationships but exluded others. The modern view of authority considers authoritative relationships as an integration of the formal structure and a number of modifying processes. Golembiewski states:[32]

> . . . authoritative relations are conceived as "integrative," that is, as having "traditional," "functional," and "behavioral" component overlays. In the application of the integrative conceptual approach . . . the crucial issue is the increase in congruence of the several overlays so that they substantially reinforce one another.

Thus it can be determined that modern organization theory considers the system and its components from many viewpoints and is concerned with the integration of subsystems and modifying processes. Johnson, Kast and Rosenzweig expand the concept by stating:[33]

> . . . separate components of the enterprise become a viable, operating system by virtue of organization. All man's more complex relationships are established in a systematic arrangement through the process of organization, or organizing. Thus organization concepts are vitally important to systems concepts. The organizing function is the means or bonding agent, by which separate human and material resources are fused together to form an integrated, operating system.

These introductory concepts concerning General Systems Theory and Modern Organizational Theory in a systems context, lead directly to the examination of an organization from a systems approach.

Organization Objectives

The functional objective of administration in a complex organization is to coordinate the activities of the various operational units and optimize the goals of the total enterprise.

[30]*Ibid.*, p. 198.

[31]Henry A. Landsberger, "The Horizontal Dimension in Bureaucracy," *Administrative Science Quarterly*, December 1961, p. 300.

[32]Robert T. Golembiewski, "Authority as a Problem in Overlays: A Concept for Action and Analysis," *Administrative Science Quarterly*, June 1964, p. 23.

[33]*Op. Cit.*, Johnson, Kast and Rosenzweig, p. 65.

Therefore, the administrator must understand his organization, not as a number of isolated parts, but as a system; he must have knowledge of the relationship between the parts and be aware of their potential interactions. In essence, the organization administrator maintains the objective of bringing individual, often diverse, functions together into an integrated, organized system with all the parts working toward the common organizational mission. Considering the growing specialization, size, and intricacies of organizations, the problem of meeting the objective of integration has increased and this factor will be even more important in the future. Prior to the adoption of the systems approach to public fire safety organizations, the objective of coordinated integration of activities, units, and individuals must be viewed relative to structural concepts.

Structural-Functional Concepts for Systems Organizations

In the organization framework, the structural elements or parts of the system are comprised of the single individual, the informal group arrangement, the formal organization chart, and finally the environmental systems which have a direct impact upon the organization as a total system. There are also numerous subsystems which are established to perform specific organizational functions. These subsystems under a general organizational framework might include the following units: research and development, budgeting, resource allocations, repair and improvement, data processing, equipment and facilities, project programs, service programs, utility programs, training programs and design programs. The mission of the organization is going to dictate whether one or more of the subsystems are included in the organization's framework. The peculiar nature of the public fire safety systems organization under consideration may mean that other unidentified subsystems will be added.

One point concerning the systems organization structure must be clarified and emphasized. There continues to be a systems hierarchy interrelating the many subsystems. The typical organization structure chart will remain recognizable. Herbert Simon makes this point when he says:[34]

1. Organizations will still be constructed in three layers; an underlying system of physical production and distribution processes, a layer of programmed (and probably largely automated) decision processes for

governing the routine day-to-day operation of the physical system, and a layer of nonprogrammed decision processes (carried out in a man-machine system) for monitoring the first-level processes, redesigning them, and changing parameter values.

2. Organizations will still be hierarchical in form. The organization will be divided into major subparts, each of these into parts, and so on, in familiar forms of departmentalization. The exact basis for drawing departmental lines may change somewhat. Product divisions may become even more important then they are today, while the sharp lines of demarcation among purchasing, manufacturing, engineering, and sales are likely to fade.

There appears to be general agreement in the literature concerning systems concepts with Simon's viewpoint of future organizations. However, a point must be stressed. The notion of systems does appear to specifically include layering of the organizational structure. The nature of the administrative and management layers may differ somewhat from the Simon concept based upon the required number of subsystems necessary to meet the organizational mission.

Furthermore, the layering mentioned by Simon connotes a horizontal structural base that cuts across the typical department arrangements of line and staff organizations. The systems concept this book would like to emphasize will develop from tasks, projects, programs, and services, while authoritative levels will be vested in administrative and management personnel whose influence will cut across traditional departmental lines. The focus of the systems organization in a public fire safety context will turn to the descriptive patterns of men, equipment and information flow throughout the organization. Identifying information-decisions systems will provide a useful means of analysis and synthesis. This latter concept will be fully developed in Chapters IV, V, VI, and VII.

Another fundamental step in developing the systems approach to organization is to consider the interrelationships between the various elements, or parts of the system. In interrelating the various subsystems, there should be a comprehensive framework, or general system of reference. Bakke has set forth a useful criterion for looking at the interrelationships between the various parts in an organization, as follows:[35]

---

[34]Herbert A. Simon, "The New Science of Management Decision," New York: Harper and Row, 1960, p. 49.

[35]E. Wight Bakke, "Concept of the Social Organization," in Haire, Mason "Psychology and the Study of Business: Joint Behavioral Sciences in Social Science Research on Business: Product and Potential." New York: Columbia University Press, 1959, pp. 35–36.

1. The parts should be recognizable as variables essential to the achievement of end-result characteristics of an organization or its parts (such as flexibility, stability, etc.).

2. The parts should be related to the whole by reference to a common characteristic (or characteristics) having a necessary and logical functional relation to the performance of the organization's function.

3. The parts should be so defined as to indicate their logical and necessary functional relationship to each other and to the whole, and not merely to suggest their usefulness as a set of categories for classifying variables.

4. Major parts should be capable of subsuming all elementary parts necessary to the explanation of organizational behavior.

5. The parts should have a necessary relation to the behavior of all participants in the organization.

6. The kind and pattern of interaction among the parts should indicate an unbroken continuity of reciprocal relations from individual participants, through systems of activity, to the surrounding environment.

Bakke talks about the fusion process, which attempts to reconcile or fuse these various parts and bring them into harmony with each other. The fusion process, in effect, maintains the objectives of the organization in face of the divergent interests of individuals, groups, other organizations, and the organization itself.

A further fundamental consideration of the systems approach to organization relates to the information and communication processes. Basic to the integration of the various parts to a system is the concept of a communication, or information network. Communications not only stimulate action with the organization but also provide the coordinating mechanism for relating the parts of the system into a synchronized pattern. A number of years ago Karl W. Deutsch recognized that organizations are composed of subsystems which communicate with each other, receive and transmit messages with the world outside a given system and store essential information to the successful operation of the organization.[36] He further stated that "communication networks constitute a configuration representing the total system."[37]

It appears appropriate to inject at this point the idea that a cybernetics model is primarily concerned with communication and information flow in complex systems. Although cybernetics has been applied primarily to mechanistic engineering problems, its model of feedback, control, and regulation has a great deal of applicability for biological and social systems as well.[38]

Another fundamental characteristic of organizational systems is their ability to remain dynamic, grow and adapt. A well planned systems organization can handle problems associated with growth and adaption. It should be realized that every system is subject to forces which make it necessary to adapt to a changing environment. Therefore, maintaining organization vitality is an important part of the systems concept. It appears that the organizational systems can remain dynamic to change through feedback information from each subsystem internal to the basic system and total external systems that are peripheral to the basic organizational structure. The feedback structure is part of a decision-making process and part of the complex management information components that interconnect all of the subsystems. The specific nature of both components, decision-making and management information systems are discussed in detail under Chapter IV.

A final support point concerning the structure of systems organizations relates to a concern over properly locating decision points within the organization. This statement implies that the decision-making process takes place at more than one level in the organization. Under the systems concept there may be several decision nodes within the administrative and management structural layers. The common decision points are found at the administrative level, the resource level and the operations level. Under complex organizational arrangements, a decision structure may be found at each subsystem level. When this condition occurs care must be taken to insure that decisions are communicated to all other interacting elements of the total system.

The foregoing discussion has been aimed at presenting foundation concepts relating to systems theory and organization. However, the systems concept of organization has been treated in very broad terms. The following subsections are intended to apply the basic concepts and theory to the specific application of public fire safety organization.

A Systems Organization for Public Fire Safety

The conversion of a fire department organization from a traditional line and staff type of operation to an integrated systems operation involves several significant considerations. These considerations appear to include: the structural framework of the organization, the identifica-

---

[36]Karl W. Deutsch, "On Communication Models in the Social Sciences," Public Opinion Quarterly, 1952, p. 356.

[37]Ibid., p. 360.

[38]Op. Cit., Johnson, Kast and Rosenzweig, p. 66.

tion of the structural components, the man-machine support complex, plus the function of the components and the integrated activity of the components. To expand each considera-tion to the full potential that it deserves will require extensive explanation. Therefore, the topic considerations are segmented for clarity of understanding and reference. The total Public Fire Safety Systems Organization is drawn together through the final chapter of the book.

In order to accomplish the objective of ex-plaining fully the systems organizational con-cept applied to public fire safety, chapters have been structured to present the significant components as subsystem units. This chapter is confined to exploring the basic structural framework of the organization. The following chapter covers the potential application of computers to the support of the organization mission. Four chapters concentrate on the ad-ministration and management functions so es-sential to a workable system. The final chapter ties the developed units and subsystems into a total integrated communicative system.

The Specialized Systems Organization Structure

Chart II-2 depicts the perceived transition that takes place from the traditional line and staff type fire department organization to the Public Fire Safety Systems Organization. Sev-eral major concepts should be established con-cerning the organizational chart. Therefore, the following concepts are presented as "key points" to obtaining a full understanding and appreciation of the Public Fire Safety System Organization.

1. The organization chart shows a definite pattern of hierarchical arrangements. However, the traditional pyramid has been flattened out. Vertical lines remain necessary to demonstrate evolvement of the organization and to portray subsystem unity.

2. Two major levels are evident in the sys-tems structure. The top structure is designated the administrative level. A second level is designated the management level. The essen-tial difference between the two levels relates to policy making functions, total systems planning and total systems coordination. At this stage of development, it seems sufficient to note that the administrative level is concerned with the total system, while the management level is con-cerned with identified subsystems within the total organization. The perceived differentia-

tion between Administration and Management is the subject of Chapter IV.

3. A major departure from traditional or-ganization is the introduction of a Master Planning Council at the administrative level and two major committees, the Resource Allo-cation Committee and the Operations Com-mittee at the management level. In keeping with the systems concept of integrating com-ponents of the system, the committee structure is introduced to improve channels of communi-cation, to improve the decision-making process, and to enhance the coordinating mechanism within the organization.

4. Vertical lines connecting designated ele-ments of the system really detract from the systems concept. The interconnections are of the step-down design, demonstrating a quasi-chain of command type structure. Actually the system should be thought of as an evolu-tionary process. There is a total system which subdivides into subsystems which further di-vides into sub-subsystems, etc. The chart is presented in a conventional hierarchical form simply to illustrate the individual functional elements with clarity. It should be remembered that the several horizontal and vertical con-nectors between elements have not been intro-duced into the framework at this time. The complex nature of the organizational structure is explored in depth in Chapter VIII.

5. There is a significant change in descrip-tive titles and subsystem headings from the traditional chart. Most notable is the point that the fire chief is not positioned at the apex of the organization. The Fire Chief by title re-mains as the director of the service subsystem concerned with fire suppression and rescue work. Some might view this new structure as nothing more than a highly sophisticated ad-ministrative overlay to the normal structural-functional arrangement of a public fire de-partment. This type of observation would be considered to be superficial. The whole con-ceptual framework of the organization has been changed, not just the administrative structure. Titles are intended to be descriptive of the unit function. The functions have been drawn together into subsystem areas that would most closely act together in accomplish-ing the objectives of the system.

6. Subunits under the Major Project Sys-tems display the numerical categories of 1, 2, or 3 combinations of these numerals. The numbers indicate potential levels of service. In other words, the system is structured to adapt readily to variable service needs. The

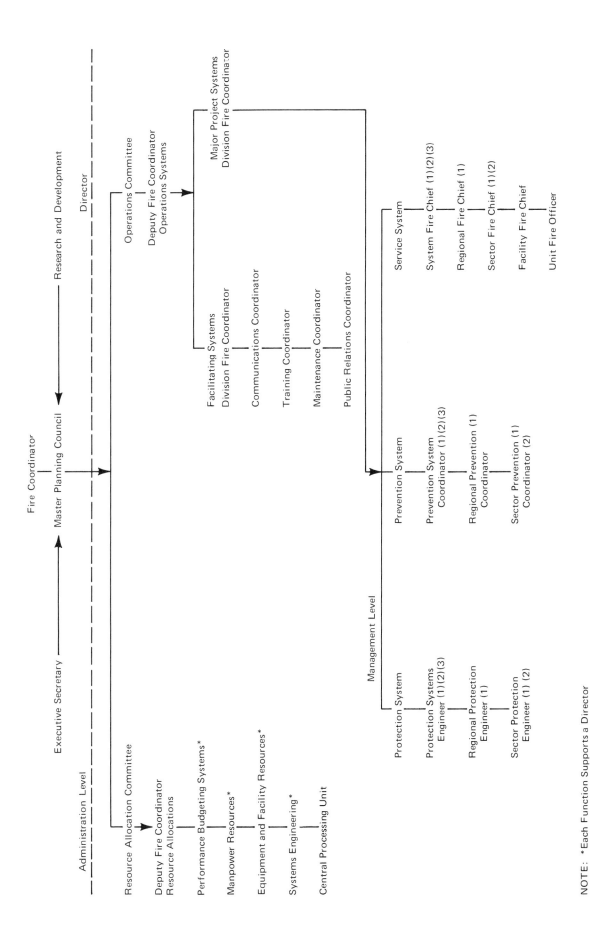

CHART II-2 A PUBLIC FIRE SAFETY SYSTEMS ORGANIZATION

NOTE: *Each Function Supports a Director

55

organization arrangement provides for a basic subsystem service (level 3), a subsystem service with geographical sectors (level 2), and a subsystem service with both sector arrangements and geographical regions (level 1), under a broad public fire safety system. This concept is so important to the dynamic flexibility of the system that a complete explanation covering this aspect of the total system is provided at the end of the chapter.

The Administration Level

The administrative level of the proposed public fire safety system organization represents the highest level of decision-making and policy formulation. Decisions made at this level should only be reviewed by an individual or group outside of the defined Public Fire Safety System. This point alone distinguishes the administrative level from the management level. Management level personnel may be capable of making decisions and developing policy for an identified subsystem within the fire safety system but such decisions and policies have the effect of recommendations since they are subject to review by the Master Planning Committee or the Fire Coordinator. The administrative level is also distinguished by its ultimate level of responsibility. In other words, the Fire Coordinator as an individual and the Master Planning Committee as a group, retain ultimate responsibility for the performance and maintenance of the total system. This total area of responsibility cannot be delegated to the defined management level.

A further area of differentiation exists between the administrative level and the management level. The management level is charged with the implementation of the administrative decisions and policies. No actual implementation of direct or indirect service is performed by the administrative level beyond the preparation of organization policy criteria, directives, rules and regulations, and the transmittal of prepared documentation to the designated management level functions.

The administrative stress is on policy development and implementation. The policy process closely coordinates the functioning of the Public Fire Safety System with the larger urban environment (system). The mechanics of the administrative policy process are detailed in Chapter IV.

Fire Coordinator

The position of Fire Coordinator is established as the central administrative position for the defined Public Fire Safety System. The perceived role of the Fire Coordinator in the organization differs considerably from that of the position of Fire Chief under most existing forms of local government. It is intended that the Fire Coordinator accomplish exactly what his title implies. He coordinates the allocation of resources, activities, and output services, associated with the handling of a defined fire problem complex in the responsible geographical jurisdiction. The position charge is a very broad one; it is not restricted to the internal arrangement of the Public Fire Safety System. Rather, it implies an encompassing view of fire safety within a total environmental context.

The coordination function is necessarily restricted to organizational administration. Under this concept the Fire Coordinator does not assume the role of directing fire suppression forces. The suppression element is delegated to the System Fire Chief under the Operating Subsystem. Based upon the systems theory concept, it does not appear feasible or practical for the top administrator in the organization to attempt the responsible and diverse role of both administrator and fire chief. The functional scope and responsibility of this position should be more evident as the description of the complete Public Fire Safety System develops in subsequent chapters.

Following are listed some of the broad areas of responsibility and functional performance for the position of Fire Coordinator. The specific scope and detail of this position is developed under Chapter III.

Policy Formulation

1. The preparation of policy statements concerning organization performance levels to be provided for defined geographical jurisdictions by the responsible Public Fire Safety Systems Organization.

2. The preparation of policy statements concerning the implementation of the Public Fire Safety Systems Organization and the projected level of service at designated future time periods.

3. The establishment of policy relation statements with external urban subsystems. This would involve defining mutual support areas, joint funding areas, mutual aid agreements, and personnel representation on committees with mutual interest problems.

4. Policy formulation in accordance with state and local legal requirements.

5. The structure of organization policy through the establishment of procedural-operational rules and regulations.

Administrative Planning

1. The establishment of a formalized plan of organization for the jurisdiction level of service to be provided.

2. The establishment of short range plans (one year or less) and long range plans (5 yr., 10 yr., and 20 yr.) based upon projected growth or recession patterns in resources, services, and responsible jurisdictional areas.

3. Coordination of planning development with external planning groups.

4. Program planning and evaluation based upon problem identification.

Administrative Coordination

1. Coordinate the study areas, the investigation areas, the report areas and the agenda areas of the three identified administration and management organization committees.

2. Coordinate the mission and objectives of the Public Fire Safety System through the Chairmanship role of the Master Planning Committee.

3. Coordination of the internal and external subsystems through membership on external committees, commissions and study groups.

4. Coordination of the research and development areas through a direct liaison relationship with the Director of Systems Research and Development.

Administrative Control

1. Administrative control of the organization is essentially established through techniques of administration by exception. Each exception is reported to the Fire Coordinator within a specified time period. The identified exceptions can then be corrected to maintain control of the system within the limits established. Deviations from the standard might signify the need to reevaluate existing criteria.

Administrative Communications

1. It is vitally important that the Fire Coordinator establish lines of communication between elements of the external urban system. The systems concept applied to organizations is intended to facilitate avenues of communication.

2. The organization position of Executive Secretary is one line of communication between the Fire Coordinator and each planning level. The Executive Secretary serves as both the recording and correspondence secretary for each organizational committee. In this manner, the secretary is in a position to reflect upon the formal and informal nature of each group.

3. The Fire Coordinator serves as editor for special study reports by the respective organizational committees. This function provides both an element of continuity and authority to all system level documents.

4. In accordance with administrative control, the Fire Coordinator receives a report of "conditions by exception" from several functional areas of the system.

5. The Fire Coordinator communicates to the internal system through two basic published items. One is the published *Directives of the Fire Coordinator*. Sequential directives represent the official policy document updating that governs the day-to-day operations of the organization. A second document is intended to be more informal. It would follow the pattern of an administrative letter to all personnel. Such a letter might include: news items, new programs, personnel changes, equipment purchases, reflections on outside meetings and research areas. The intent of such a document is to keep the organization correctly informed of current events.

6. The Fire Coordinator broadly communicates with both the internal organization, the external organization and the public through a monthly and annual administrative report. Such a report might identify statistical trends, identified problem areas, and areas of significant accomplishment.

The Executive Secretary

The position of Executive Secretary is established at the administrative level to insure communication continuity between the administrative level and the management level. The Executive Secretary functions to maintain complete, accurate and consistent documents, records and transcripts of the Master Planning Committee, the Resource Allocation Committee and the Operations Committee. The Executive Secretary also serves the Fire Coordinator for handling administrative correspondence and documents. This position also carries the responsibility for briefing each separate committee on the scope of activities of the remaining committees. The objective is to avoid duplication of committee effort including record keeping.

Research and Development

A Research and Development unit is established at the administrative level to work directly with the Fire Coordinator and the Master Planning Committee. The Research and Development unit broadly performs in the following areas.

1. The Director is responsible for informing the Master Planning Committee of research studies conducted external to the system.

2. The Director would evaluate and report upon technological developments by the equipment industry.

3. The Research and Development group would study problem areas identified by the Master Planning Committee, the Resource Allocations Committee and the Operations Committee.

4. The Director would have responsibility for studying and analyzing the statistical data developed within the organization.

5. The Director would supervise research contracts awarded to outside groups.

The Master Planning Council

The Master Planning Committee is structured for the primary purpose of relating the Public Fire Safety System to the jurisdictional environmental system. This statement emphasizes that the Public Fire Safety System is very much a part of the larger urban system. To be viable in the public interest, the Public Fire Safety System must be sensitive to outside environmental groups and urban subsystems. Specifically, the committee must relate the Public Fire Safety System to responsible planning groups, jurisdictional utility authorities, the governmental administration unit, the area human relations council, the consumer affairs group, and higher levels of government.

The Master Planning Committee under the guidance of the Fire Coordinator, is concerned with providing a coordinated effort between external systems and internal subsystems. This coordinated effort should be designed to produce a defined level of public safety services. The committee should be sensitive to both internal and external research and development. Furthermore, the committee of the whole evaluates subcommittee reports and study documents from both the Resource Allocation Committee and the Operations Committee.

On the basis of external and internal information, the committee would be broadly charged with policy development on matters relative to the structure and operation of the system. The Master Planning Committee attempts to project the requirements for identified services on both a short-range and long-range planning schedule. In other words, this committee works out the planning coordination, and control for policy implementation.

Composition of the Master Planning Committee

The committee structure is aimed at providing a representative body of people who can reflect on both relevant conditions of the external urban system and the internal Public Fire Safety System. The individuals selected to compose the committee structure are chosen with the objective of maintaining identifiable communication links between the administrative level, the management level, and external related systems.

Chairman: Fire Coordinator

Secretary: Executive Secretary

Membership: Deputy Coordinator Resource Allocations
Deputy Coordinator Operations Systems
Director of Research and Development
Division Coordinator Facilitating Systems
Division Coordinator Major Project Systems

Ex-officio Members: City or County Attorney
Union Representative
Water Superintendent
City or County Planning Engineer
Mayor, City Manager or the equivalent at the County level
Representative of the Human Relations Council
Representative of Consumer Affairs
Rotating Representative from Facility Areas

The Management Level

Several writers in the management field are quite explicit in drawing a distinction between the administrative policy formulation level and the management process level of an organization. Frederick Hooper states the distinction clearly when he says,[39]

> By management we mean management as distinct from the framing of policy: that is, the complex of operations which, in a business extends from immediately below the directors when acting corporately as a board, down to and including the lower supervisory levels.

Under a systems mode of organization, it is generally accepted that policy formulation, in the hierarchy of organization, outranks management. But, Fred Brown points out:[40]

> Management and policy formulation depend on each other. Bad policy carried out by effective management is the essence of oppressive dictatorship. Poor management in contrast, can subvert and negate good policy.

Therefore, the objective is to bring good policy and effective management together to successfully accomplish worthy purposes. Under the systems organization framework, the bridge between the administrative level and the management level is crossed through the interaction of the three major committees.

The management level under the systems concept operates according to the following operational definition.[41] "Management is the manner in which resources are used to accomplish prescribed objectives. Its keynotes are economy and balance."

Management resources, management balance and the economy of organization through sound management practices are achieved through two major organization subsystems. These subsystems are identified as the Resource Allocation Support System and the Operations Support System. The broad scope and objective considerations of each support system are advanced under the following topic headings. Detailed considerations of each major support system are advanced under Chapter VI — *The Management of Facilitating Systems*, and Chapter VII — *The Management of Major Project Systems*.

Resource Allocation Support Subsystems

The Resource Allocation Support System is concerned with the activities associated with the allocation of present and future resources — money, men, and equipment — to the support and service systems. The elements of this subsystem are identified as:

1. Performance Budgeting Unit
2. Manpower Resources
3. Equipment and Facility Resources
4. Systems Engineering

Each subsystem element is identified separately to lend clarity to the total system. However, to retain the concept of organization flexibility, mergers can be effected between one or more of the elements. The following subsections present an overview of Resource Allocations. The details of this subsystem implementation are presented in Chapter V.

Performance Budgeting

Economic reality and balance is a fundamental concept of the systems approach. An economic balance is traditionally achieved through a careful auditing procedure over financial income and expenditures. The audit control remains under the systems application to organization.

Actually, what this component adds is a performance audit and analysis. Under the proposed budgeting system, support and service areas are broken down in terms of work loads or units of performance, creating units of measurement which are then used to calculate the labor and material inputs required to achieve the objective output of a given program.[42] Program information budgets emphasize whole elements or whole programs instead of details. To this extent program budgeting is compatible with Program Performance Budgeting Systems (PPBS).

A program type budgeting system is considered a minimum requirement for managing the economic aspects of the proposed Public Fire Safety Systems Organization. The evaluation merits of the more sophisticated PPBS financial system should be evaluated by the systems design engineer. A PPBS program appears almost essential for the community with a population over 500,000. Compatability with local budget arrangements should serve as an important criterion in deciding between a

[39]Frederick Hooper, *Management Survey*. Baltimore: Penguin Books, Inc., 1960, p. 11.

[40]Fred Brown, ed., *Management: Concepts and Practices*. Washington: Industrial College of the Armed Forces, 1967, p. 3.

[41]Col. Frank A. Osmanski, *Military Command and Business Management*. Washington: Industrial College of the Armed Forces, 1958 (M58–94), p. 147.

[42]International City Managers Association. *Planning and Budgeting in Municipal Government*. Chicago: International City Managers Association, 1969, pp. 22–23.

program budget and a program performance budget. The merits and implications of PPBS are explored in Chapter V.

Manpower Resources

This subsystem is concerned with establishing the basic service force and allocating this force to the specialized requirements of the total system. The management process for this subsystem entails recruitment, selection, employment, scheduling, promotion, and retirement of the systems personnel. This element of the total system has responsibility for balancing the work force among both the operations systems and all related support systems. The systems type of organizational arrangement tends to minimize one major problem associated with professional personnel:[43] "their tendency to associate their activities with specialized areas rather than with the optimal performance of the overall operation."

Equipment and Facility Resources

This subsystem actively considers both the existing and future requirements for: building facilities (i.e., fire stations, training facilities, maintenance facilities), specialized fire apparatus, routine equipment and communications equipment.

Systems Engineering

The total Public Fire Safety Systems Organization is elaborate, detailed, and requires a considerable depth of understanding to integrate the process functions of each subsystem. Systems engineering supplies the technical assistance for all subsystems design. The technology consists of preparing, implementing and reviewing an integrated flow analysis for all of the systems components.

Actually, it is the personnel of the Systems Engineering group that expands and adapts the basic design components proposed in this book to a real-world organization. Once the system has been implemented at some defined geographical level, the function of Systems Engineering is to maintain a sensitivity to all system components and to identify requisite adjustments as supply and demand on the system change. This would certainly include changing major project systems levels and splitting total systems into two or more self-contained systems. A major objective of this subsystem group is to keep the total system manageable, viable and responsive to changing patterns of development.

[43]*Op. Cit.*, Johnson, Kast and Rosenzweig, p. 56.

Central Processing Unit

The systems concept is associated with modern management. The trend towards automation is an essential part of the systems concept and therefore becomes a function of modern management. The Central Processing Unit (CPU) represents the machine automated element in the total system.

The CPU is placed schematically under the Resource Allocation Support System because its automated data processing function so closely complements the management efforts of these subsystem categories. Resource allocations, by their very nature, involve statistical analysis, accounting procedures and basic data handling. The CPU subsystem brings advanced technology and automation to the Public Fire Safety System Organization.

Resource Allocation Committee

The planning, integrating, controlling and communicating activities of resource allocations are directed by the Resource Allocation Committee.

The Resource Allocation Committee is concerned with obtaining financial and material resources from external systems and matching this resource to the identified demands of the system. The committee charge is to organize and adjust the total system to meet expanding or diminishing needs. To meet this need the committee functions to coordinate the defined elements grouped under resource allocation with the administrative level and the elements of the operations system.

Composition of the Resource Allocation

The committee structure is aimed at achieving a balance of input from each major component of the system. Committee recommendations serve as policy recommendations for the administration level in all resource areas. The Committee is very instrumental in planning and controlling organizational effectiveness.

Chairman: Deputy Fire Coordinator
Resource Allocations

Secretary: Executive Secretary

Membership: Director — Performance Budgeting Systems
Director — Manpower Resources
Director — Equipment and Facility Resources
Director–Systems Engineering
Deputy Fire Coordinator — Operation Support System

Ex-officio Membership: Director — Research
and Development
Division Fire Coor-
dinator — Facili-
tating Systems
Division Fire Coor-
dinator — Major
Project Systems

Operations Support Systems Subsystems

The Operations Support System is designed
to implement activities associated with the
mission of public fire safety. From a pure systems viewpoint, this support system utilizes
the allocated resources of information, manpower, equipment, finances, and facilities to
accomplish the defined performance tasks.

The Operations Support System breaks down
into the following two major support subsystems. Facilitating subsystems and Major
Project subsystems are key elements to providing efficient and effective public fire safety.
The following points outline the major features
of these subsystems. The detailed management
functions associated with each subsystem are
detailed under Chapter IV.

Facilitating Subsystems

A facilitating subsystem is defined as an organizational unit to provide a direct service
to the major project system. The facilitating
subsystem is composed of unit subsystems that
demonstrate a specialized expertise capable of
enhancing the performance of each major
project system. The elements of the facilitating subsystem are identified as follows. Each
unit is directed by an individual with the title
of coordinator.

Communications

Communications commands a special definition under the framework of a Public Fire
Safety System. Under the Public Fire Safety
System, communications relates to all these
features associated with emergency fire alarm
systems. In other words, this element in the
system provides for radio, telephone, detection,
and telegraph types communications facilities.
Communications can best be described as the
nerve center of the total system. Under the
systems concept advanced in this book, communications become electronically sophisticated and highly automated. The electronic
communications equipment is closely integrated with the Central Processing Unit.

Training

The training subsystem has the objective of
providing and evaluating a total education and
training program for the Public Fire Safety
System. This means that the Education and
Training program involves the systems internal
personnel and external system personnel that
interact with the Public Fire Safety System. It
should be noted that a number of the desired
educational programs may be provided by
higher government or geographical level Public
Fire Safety Systems. For example, statewide
training programs might provide an important
segment of the desired training activity.

Maintenance

The maintenance subsystem is charged with
the scheduled maintenance and unscheduled or
emergency maintenance of all systems components. The Maintenance Coordinator is concerned with measuring the efficiency and effectiveness of the maintenance program. Therefore, this program has an ongoing integrating
activity with every other component of the
total system.

Public Relations

The Public Relations Coordinator is charged
with establishing and maintaining an information flow between the public fire safety system
and the public. Through information, an image
of public fire safety is formed in many ways.
One important effort of this subsystem is to
portray the public fire safety system level of
effectiveness and efficiency.

Major Project Systems

Each major project subsystem provides an
interacting public and private service. These
functional services are established and implemented in accordance with the described objectives of public fire safety. While each project
subsystem is presented in the three subsystem
areas of: protection, prevention and service,
stress should be placed on realizing that each
element is highly dependent on the remaining
two elements. It would appear almost impossible to meet the organizational mission unless the major project subsystems relate to each
other in a planned and harmonious atmo-
sphere. The basic charge of each Major Project
System is outlined below. The detailed content of each functional element is explained
under Chapter VII — *The Management of Major
Project Systems.*

Prevention

Fire Prevention refers to the organizational operations, duties and activities concerned with ignition prevention, the reduction of fire casualties, and the reduction of modular fire loss in buildings. To achieve these objectives, the fire prevention subsystem is mainly involved in educational programs, survey programs and investigation programs.

Protection

Fire Protection refers to organizational operation duties and activities concerned with the design and engineering of components to extinguish or control fires and fire effects. The substantive effort of the protection system involves technical applications applied to buildings and the fire control features of those buildings.

Service

The Service Subsystem relates to the organizational operations, duties and activities concerned with direct public emergency services which emphasize fire suppression and rescue work. Functions of the service system are not limited to emergency efforts. Based upon the flexibility of objectives and the level of service implementation, members of the service system may be assigned duties associated with the total operations area. This last point has far-reaching implications for the objective performance of the total system. Again, the details associated with the Service Subsystem are presented in Chapter VII.

Operations Committee

This specific committee is structured to perform the following functions:

(1) Act as a sensor committee of the whole to measure and evaluate changes in the Facilitating Subsystem functions and in the Major Project Subsystems of Protection, Prevention and Service.

(2) Maintain control over the objective effectiveness of the Major Project System.

(3) Serves as the information collection source for all operational subsystems for report purposes.

(4) Coordinates the measurement channel for evaluating the effectiveness of both internal and external project areas of the Protection and Prevention Subsystems.

Composition of the Operations Committee

Chairman: Deputy Fire Coordinator — Operations Systems

Secretary: Executive Secretary

Membership: Division Fire Coordinator — Facilitating System
Division Fire Coordinator — Major Project System
Communications Coordinator
Training Coordinator
Maintenance Coordinator
Public Relations Coordinator
Protection System Engineer
Prevention System Coordinator
Service System Fire Chief
Rotating Facility Representative

Ex-officio Membership: Director of Research and Development
Deputy Fire Coordinator
Resource Allocations

Implementation of the Public Fire Safety Systems Organization

Adaptation to specific requirements is a basic concept associated with the systems approach to organization. If the system is well designed, it should be adaptable to the variety of conditions encountered in providing public fire safety for a selected jurisdictional area. One might question how this is to be accomplished with such an extensive organizational framework supporting close to two dozen separate elements. The reader whose perception takes into account the small community volunteer fire department type of public fire safety might feel that the organization described would possibly fit a large metropolitan complex but certainly not the average sized American community. Again, if the system has been properly tailored, the organization framework presented should adapt to all situations that accept *the proposed objectives* of public fire safety. The established systems approach *may not adapt to localities that do not prescribe to the objectives set forth*. This view raises a fundamental concept upon which the total Public Fire Safety Systems Organization is structured. For the organization to be understood, the principle of the organization must be understood.

The principal reason for organizing a public fire safety department is to provide a given legal and/or geographical jurisdiction with a degree of fire prevention, fire protection, fire suppression and related emergency public services commensurate with that jurisdiction's needs, desires and economic capabilities. In other words, a service is to be performed within certain defined limits. A corollary to this principle suggests that the demand for a level of service may change over time. Therefore, the organization should be able to adapt to changing levels of service without major reorganization efforts.

The concluding portion of this chapter details a method for implementing and adapting the proposed Public Fire Safety System Organization to selected public areas. The process involves two sets of dependent variables: (1) size of the service area as measured by population density and dispersion, and (2) the degree of service to be rendered according to the established problem, the performance level desired, and the economic capability to support services. The following material will concentrate on the size of the service area as the control variable. A selected performance level will be only indirectly alluded to at this time. The variable set associated with the problems of performance and economy will be expanded upon in the administrative structure chapter.

The Implementation Level

The Public Fire Safety Organization complex is designed to be implemented at one of three service area levels. These levels are actually related to the size of the population and governmental dispersion. The three areas are arbitrarily defined according to the following parameters.

Population Category:
  Level one system — greater than 500,000 population
  Level two system — 250,000 to 500,000 population
  Level three system — 100,000 to 250,000 population

Governmental Dispersion:
  1. A City
  2. A County
  3. A Region (i.e., two or more identified jurisdictional areas)
     a. Two or more cities with adjacent defined areas to achieve one of the population categories.

b. A city and a county to achieve one of the population categories.
c. Two or more counties to achieve one of the population categories.

The pronouncement of these categories requires supportive documentation. The Committee for Economic Development's Research and Policy Committee has long been concerned with the ways in which organization and structure affect the ability of governments to manage the public's business.[44] In recent years, the Committee has issued a number of statements that propose policies for improving government at all levels. One study, *Reshaping Government in Metropolitan Areas*, is timely and significant to all units of local government, including public fire safety. First, it examines the impact of governmental structure on the lives of citizens and demonstrates that the existing organization complex of metropolitan government can be a serious impediment to the solution of problems of the central city and the suburbs. Second, it recognizes that there are increasing problem areas including fire, police, sanitation, highways, water supply, and commuter transportation, that spill beyond the boundaries of local communities and that these problems can only be dealt with by a larger, metropolitan-wide jurisdiction. However, within this context there is also a demonstrated requirement for a plan of action that will be sensitive to smaller units of government and which will allow citizens of local communities to exercise degrees of control and manage their own affairs. The need for local government service structure reforms at all service levels is underscored by the following quotation:[45]

The bewildering multiplicity of small, piecemeal, duplicative, overlapping local jurisdictions cannot cope with the staggering difficulties encountered in managing modern urban affairs. The fiscal effects of duplicative suburban separation create great difficulty in provision of costly central city services benefiting the whole urbanized area. If local governments are to function effectively in metropolitan areas, they must have sufficient size and authority to plan, administer, and provide significant financial support for solutions to area-wide problems.

Based upon this statement, it almost seems paradoxical that today there appears to be a growing support for decentralization which rests upon the same assumptions. The advocates of decentralization see it as a means of

[44]Committee for Economic Development. *Reshaping Government in Metropolitan Areas*. New York: Committee for Economic Development, 1970, p. 7.

[45]*Ibid.*, p. 16.

humanizing government, giving the voter greater access to public services, more control over the bureaucracy which manages his affairs, and a more important role in decisions in which he has a stake. The case for decentralization, however, should not ignore the economic, technological and social arguments which favor a centralized system. The Committee for Economic Development further identifies the case for local government centralization:[46]

---
[46]*Ibid.*, p. 17.

Small-unit governments are poorly equipped to take advantage of economics of scale and technological innovations; hence, they often find it more difficult to respond to the growing and disparate needs of their citizens. Proponents of centralization argue that the interests of the disadvantaged are best served by a larger rather than smaller unit of government. They point to the economic weakness of the ghetto, historic conservatism of America's small communities, and the growing dependence on the federal government for social progress.

It appears clear from the arguments that what is needed is a *system* of local government administration that recognizes both forces,

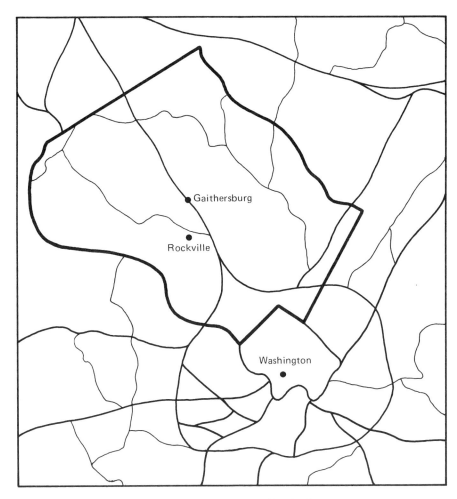

A. Montgomery County, Maryland
Potential for Level 1 System

ILLUSTRATION II-3 POTENTIAL EXAMPLES OF PUBLIC FIRE SAFETY SYSTEM STRUCTURES

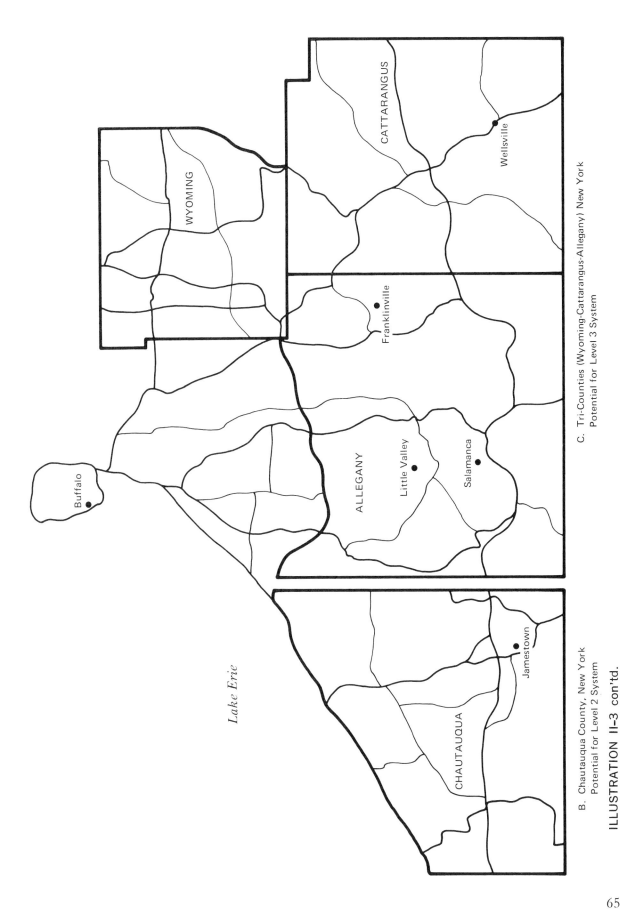

C. Tri-Counties (Wyoming-Cattarangus-Allegany) New York
   Potential for Level 3 System

B. Chautauqua County, New York
   Potential for Level 2 System

ILLUSTRATION II-3 con'td.

centralization and decentralization. The system should permit a genuine sharing of power over functions between a larger unit and a smaller unit. It must recognize a larger government unit to permit economics of scale, area-wide planning, and equities in finance. It must recognize a smaller government unit to permit the exercise of local power over matters which affect the lives of local citizens.

The perceived Public Fire Safety Systems Organization is both sensitive and responsive to these identified needs. Homogeneous areas within a total defined system have the opportunity to assume different risk levels for their jurisdiction through prorated financial support to the Major Project Subsystems. Rotating facility representatives on the Operations Committee assure that local views are considered in the decision-making process. Finally, jurisdictional representatives are encouraged to sit as ex-officio members on the Master Planning Committee.

To achieve the ends outlined in this book, it is proposed that county governments — because they are less limited in area, population and fiscal resources — be utilized, where acceptable, as the primary basis for consolidation. As mentioned, in predominantly rural areas, two or more counties might be consolidated into one system with each county retaining its identity as a region of the total system and individual towns as Sectors of the System. Illustration II-3 depicts several counties selected from the states of New York and Maryland to demonstrate possible applications of the systems structure presented in this book.

A central concept related to the structure presented needs to be clearly understood. It would initially appear that an aggregate population of approximately 100,000 would be required to formulate an economic base capable of supporting the organization system outlined. Also associated with the minimum size level is the notion that to meet the objectives of public fire safety outlined in this book requires an extensive support structure to service the major project subsystems. In turn, the major project subsystems outlined are essential to supplying the service components necessary to meet the objectives.

Chapter I established that some fire departments perceive their role to be one of providing fire suppression operations after a fire is discovered. The people of American cities and towns that continue to accept this philosophy of protection are also accepting an undefinable and uncalculatable risk to life and property. A speculative risk may be acceptable to some geographical areas. In conclusion, it should be recognized that the proposed Public Fire Safety Systems Organization is not particularly appropriate for areas that exhibit little or no concern for the type of fire protection they receive.

Chapter 2

Bibliographical Entries

Books

Bakke, E. W. "Concepts of the Social Organization," in Haire Mason. *Psychology and the Study of Business*, (Joint Behavioral Sciences in Social Science Research on Business: Product and Potential) New York: Columbia University Press, 1959.

Blau, Peter, and R. Scott. *Formal Organizations*. San Francisco: Chandler Publishing Company, 1962.

Brown, Fred, ed. *Management: Concepts and Practices*. Washington: Industrial College of the Armed Forces, 1967.

Etzioni, Amitai. *Modern Organization:* Englewood Cliffs: Prentice-Hall, Inc., 1964.

Gerth, H. H., and C. W. Mills. *From Max Weber: Essays in Sociology*. New York: Oxford University Press, 1946.

Hooper, Frederic. *Management Survey*. Baltimore: Penguin Books, Inc., 1960.

International City Managers Association. *Planning and Budgeting in Municipal Government*. Chicago: International City Managers Association, 1969.

Johnson, Richard, F. Kast, and J. Rosenzweig. *The Theory and Management of Systems*. New York: McGraw-Hill Book Company, 1967.

Likert, Renis. *New Patterns of Management*. New York: McGraw-Hill Book Co., 1961.

March, James and H. Simon. *Organizations*. John Wiley and Sons, Inc., New York, 1958.

Pfiffner, J., and F. Sherwood. *Administrative Organization*. Englewood Cliffs: Prentice-Hall, Inc., 1960.

Simon, Herbert. *The New Science of Management Decision*. New York: Harper and Row, Inc., 1960.

Webster's New Collegiate Dictionary. G. & C. Merriam Co., Publ., 1961.

Publications of the Government, Learned Societies, and Other Organizations

Committee for Economic Development. *Reshaping Government in Metropolitan Areas*. New York: Committee for Economic Development, 1970.

Osmanski, Col. Frank A. *Military Command and Business Management*. Washington: Industrial College of the Armed Forces, (M58-94), 1958.

Periodicals

Boulding, Kenneth. "General Systems Theory — The Skeleton of Science," *Management Science*, April 1956, p. 197.

Culliton, J. "Age of Synthesis," *Harvard Business Review*, September–October, 1962, p. 368.

Deutsch, Karl. "On Communication Models in the Social Sciences," Public Opinion Quarterly, 1952, p. 356.

Golembiewski, Robert. "Authority as a Problem in Overlays: A Concept for Action and Analysis," *Administrative Science Quarterly*, June 1964, p. 23.

Hall, R. "The Concept of Bureaucracy, An Empirical Assessment," *American Journal of Sociology*, July 1963, p. 33.

Landsberger, Henry. "The Horizontal Dimension in Bureaucracy," *Administrative Science Quarterly*, December 1961, p. 300.

Parsons, Talcott. "Suggestions for a Sociological Approach to the Theory of Organizations," *Administrative Science Quarterly*, September 1956, p. 238.

Scott, W. "Organizational Theory — An Overview and An Appraisal," *Journal of the Academy of Management*, April 1961, p. 7.

Shepard, H. "Superiors and Subordinates in Research," *Journal of Business*, October 1956, p. 261.

Chapter III

The Man-Computer Complex Applied To Public Fire Safety Systems Organization

Introduction

In structuring the proposal for this book it was perceived that a discussion concerning the future impact of computer technology on public fire safety systems organization would culminate the entire presentation. However, it became quite evident that computers would play a vital, if not indispensable role, in the structural-functional relationships within the restructured public fire safety organization utilizing the systems approach. The administration and management of a systems organization cannot be intelligently discussed without reference to computer support. Therefore, a decision was made to reorder the discussion of computer applications to the public fire safety systems organization.

An objective of Chapter III is to establish the potential utilization of the computer to the administration and management of public fire safety systems organization. The core of material to be presented represents computer application without the technical details. A few technical concepts are introduced in order to establish uniform definitions and to outline the capabilities and limitations of computer applications. A number of basic references are cited in the footnotes and the bibliography for readers requiring more depth and understanding concerning the fundamentals of computer application.

Problem Overview

In the previous decade, computer systems have developed as a crucial and essential component in the operations of military, business, local and national governments. The concept of a computer system has progressed from a theoretical idea to a concept of toleration by the average citizen, and to a concept of dependence by the technically informed individual. Yet today, there is still a certain awe about the nature, scope, and operation of computers. The capabilities and limitations of computers still require appreciation. A second objective of this chapter is to present a basic understanding concerning the application of computers to some of the specialized problems associated with public fire safety systems organization.

The potential utilization of computers for the specialized task of supporting the administration and management of public fire safety systems organization is limited only by the lack of individual imagination and the economic cost considerations. Therefore, it is believed the technical capability in relation to both the software requirements and the hardware requirements for computer systems is currently available to meet the demand of public fire safety systems organizations. There is every indication the developmental capability of the computer systems will exceed our conceptual ability to utilize these systems to support the operations and administration of public fire safety system organization problems.

The economic structure of a computer system involves both the software and the hardware capabilities of the system which entails expensive factors. The efficiency of a computer system is directly dependent on utilizing the maximum capability of the equipment on a nearly continuous basis. There appears to be four efficient and effective reasons for the consideration of a computer system.

The first reason may be the economic trade-off between labor costs and machine costs to accomplish a defined processing task. Only when electronic data processing provides an output at less cost than is possible with a manual or semiautomated operation, does the computer system become economically feasible. Second, the element of time required for task completion represents one of the prime factors for the consideration of a computer application. Electronic data processing systems are now available with a capability of completing the most elementary numerical tasks at one-millionth to one-billionth of the time required for human task completion. As a defined task becomes more complex, the performance time differential between the human individual and the computer increases exponentially. Therefore, a computer system demonstrates a great advantage when the time frame from the occurrence of a stipulated event to the outcome of that event is crucial to the effective operation of the system. Administrators and managers often require real time information. This simply means that there is the necessity for information on an event as it happens or as it is unfolding. Computers provide the means to make this real time concept possible.[1]

A third reason for a computer system relates to the consideration of the problems involving the processing and evaluation of a large number of variables almost simultaneously. In the comparison and analysis of data, concentration limits develop concerning the number and complexity level of the variables a man's mind can comprehend and manipulate into meaningful relationships. The capability of computer systems to perform complex mathematical operations; to retain and compare a large number of variables in a multiple array of sets and matrices, appears to be almost limitless today.

Finally, computers can be utilized to simulate real-world events. Many problems that cannot be solved analytically can be solved by an empirical process in which a model of the real-world system is studied. A fire safety example might be structured as follows: What are the most effective and most economical sets of fire protection features to be provided at the time a building is constructed? Provisions are often made for relatively expensive fire safety components within a structure. Then attempts are made to estimate or wonder if these items, singularly or in combination, will perform effectively. The usual procedure is to wait until a fire actually becomes an experiment to determine the performance of the components. With a computer system and simulation procedures, a simulation model of the components under consideration could be developed to relate variables mathematically and process the relationships in a computer to simulate a variety of conditions.

This example of computer utilization identifies one of the presently perceived roles of computers in relation to the broad spectrum of public fire safety systems organization. More specifically, computers appear to offer capabilities necessary to formulate the integrated concepts associated with a systems approach to the organization of public fire safety. Computers can expedite the information flow so essential to the comprehensive nature of the systems approach.

A great deal of literature expounds on the utility of computers in a generalized systems framework. Basic considerations of computers in the administrative and management process will be advanced in subsequent chapters. Now it becomes necessary to be explicit concerning the application of computer techniques, capabilities and limitations to the systems organization concept for public fire safety. However, for such a discussion to be meaningful, it is first necessary to establish a general frame of reference for understanding the functional utility of the computer. The following subsections are aimed at providing this foundation.

The History of Computers

The conceptual framework of Electronic Data Processing had its genesis in the ENIAC (Electronic Numeric Integrator and Calculator), the first electronic digital computer, developed by Dr. John W. Mauchly and Mr. John P. Eckert at the University of Pennsylvania in 1945.

---

[1]Richard A. Johnson, Fremont E. Kast, and James E. Rosenzweig, *The Theory and Management of Systems.* New York: McGraw-Hill Book Company, Inc., 1963, p. 199.

This device permitted man to peer over the threshold into an entirely new era of human potential. Today's space missions illustrate how the computer is achieving the brilliant scientific role that was predicted for it shortly after the ENIAC solved its first nuclear physics problem in two weeks — a problem which by previous conventional methods would have taken in excess of one hundred man-years to solve.[2]

Despite this obvious achievement, there soon developed a disparity between the business community and the scientific community. Business leaders developed an early blame mechanism against the computer for failures from the ineptness of programmers, systems designers, and users.[3] Studies have shown that public administrators have developed similar attitudes. The basic reason appears to be one of recognizing educational backgrounds. This recognition has an important parallel for public fire safety. Basically, it must be recognized that the majority of the present-day, top-level executives did not have computers in their earlier years, since the development of computers has been relatively recent. This recognition would be especially true for present-day fire administrators. From the age of mechanical calculator computation there has been a rapid transformation of computational equipment by five orders of magnitude without the intervening steps which would normally have allowed time for humans to adapt gradually to the changes.[4]

Despite the lack of recognition by certain elements of the business community concerning the computer, man possesses a significant new tool that will have a marked effect on the total organization, the administrative and management process, and the effectiveness and efficiency of operations. Few organizations can escape the effects and utilization of the computer; public fire safety is not viewed as one of these exceptions.

In its evolution, the digital computer has already passed through three "generations."[5] The first generation of computers which lasted from 1944 until about 1960, used vacuum tubes as the active electronic circuit elements. These early computers were characterized by their large physical size, a small amount of memory capability, and slow input-output devices. Circuit packaging, the great number of vacuum tubes (5,500 in UNIVAC I), and the air conditioning required to dissipate the heat were the prime causes for the large size of these computers. Various types of internal memory devices were used: cathode ray tubes, mercury delay-line tanks, magnetic drums, and, eventually, magnetic cores.[6]

In the second generation computer, which was in its prime from 1960 until 1966, the physical size diminished, the amount of memory increased, and the concept of hierarchy of memory became a necessary and common feature of larger computer systems. The reduction in physical size resulted primarily from the use of transistors as the active electronic circuit elements. This permitted a less voluminous type of circuit packaging, and reduced or, in some cases, eliminated the need for integral air conditioning. The principal type of internal memory became the magnetic core. Other types of memory, such as thin film, started to appear. Despite the accelerated speed of input-output devices, the internal memory was usually the limiting factor of second generation computer operations.[7]

The third generation computers are even smaller in physical size and have a vastly increased amount of internal memory. Any computer is sometimes part of a family of computers offering flexibility to the user to increase (or decrease) computer capacity and capability without significant changes in programming. Communications media are a significant part of these computer systems. Speed of computation is now as much as 100,000 times that of the first generation computers. The further reduction in size and increase in speed were accomplished primarily by the use of integrated circuits in lieu of discrete element circuits.[8]

What Is a Computer?

A computer is "a machine that manipulates symbols in accordance with given rules in a predetermined and self-directed manner. In a more technical reference, an automatic computer is a high-speed, automatic, electronic, digital data-processing machine."[9] Some pertinent information concerning the adjectives involved in the above quotation would appear helpful in understanding the equipment, or "hardware" utilized in electronic data processing.

[2]Statement prepared by the faculty of the Department of Defense Computer Institute. Stated in Fred Brown, *Management: Concepts and Practice*. Washington: Industrial College of the Armed Forces, 1967, p. 195.

[3]*Ibid.*, p. 195.   [4]*Ibid.*, p. 196.

[5]William R. Corliss, *Computers*. Washington: Division of Technical Information, U.S. Atomic Energy Commission (20545), 1967, p. 13.

[6]*Op. Cit.*, Fred Brown, p. 196.

[7]*Op. Cit.*, William R. Corliss, p. 13.   [8]*Ibid.*, p. 14.

[9]Ned Chapin, *An Introduction to Automatic Computers*. Princeton: D. Van Nostrand Company, Inc., 1957, p. 4.

The electronic computer is developed primarily to provide a faster means of computation in scientific problems than was possible by mechanical calculators. The computation of older type calculators was limited by movement of mechanical parts, thus imposing a relatively low upper limit on ultimate speeds of calculation. A significant principle for electronic computers is stated in the following manner: "that the flow of electrons, acting as signals in the circuitry of the equipment, is susceptible to direction and control. Numbers and alphabetic characters are symbolized by electronic pulses or other manifestations. The controlled movement, or flow, of these symbolic signals provides the basic framework for electronic computers."[10]

Another one of the important adjectives is "highspeed," since speed in computation was one of the prime goals of computers. Speed relates to the operational processing time of the computer as measured in fractions of a second. Computational speed is now as much as 100,000 times that of the first computers. Therefore, the speeds obtained to date by electronic computers are fantastic and promise to increase even more in the future. Increasing computational speed plus larger and larger storage, or memory, devices make the electronic computer an extremely versatile tool for use in any data processing system. The functional elements of a public fire safety systems organization are deeply involved with data handling and data processing. This would imply that the computer has a data processing role to play in the organizational framework.

The term "digital" is used in contrast to the term "analog." Analog describes an important group of computing machines which use a physical analog as an approach to the problem being studied. A digital computer counts discretely, but an analog computer measures continuously. The general purpose digital computer, the object of concern, can store a variety of programs which makes it suitable for many different applications. The program is stored as information accessible to the computer, but without any fixed or mechanical relationship to it. For different applications, the program is changed without alteration in the physical aspects of the computer.[11] The analog computer in contrast, solves problems by translating the physical conditions being studied, such as liquid flow, air tempera-

ture, or a power sources voltage into proportional mechanical or electrical quantities to be manipulated by the computer's internal devices and circuits. It should be noted that the digital computer is based on symbol manipulation and counting with a binary numbering system. Most of the applications of computers to public fire safety will relate to the digital computer. One possible application of the analog computer to fire safety problems would be in the area of municipal water supply analysis. This application is discussed in Chapter VIII.

The term "automatic" refers to the self-controlling aspects of electronic computers which have internally stored programs, or lists of instructions, that determine the sequence of operation in a processing or computational routine.[12] These instructions are predetermined in the sense that human effort is required to plan and set forth in detail all the steps involved in any processing job. Once the program is designed, it acts as the control element in the data processing systems. During processing the program itself can be modified, again according to predetermined rules, and hence provide directions according to the situation which input data represents. It is necessary to point out that it is this characteristic which parallels the feedback-control concept of production through automation that has led to describing electronic data processing as office automation.[13] The point will be further clarified by example in a later chapter subsection. The concept of internally stored, self-adjusting programs for controlling operations, sets the electronic computer completely apart from predecessor equipment. In this respect, the computer is not just an additional step in the long line of increased mechanization. It provides a new dimension for data processing and allows much more sophisticated and imaginative systems of information flow. Chapter VIII attempts to relate the computer function to the information flow requirements of the perceived public fire safety systems organization.

A discussion of computers within the framework of public fire safety systems organizations must consider two additional terms that by definition will play an important part in potential computer applications. The terms to be defined and understood are "real-time data processing" and "batch processing." The normal computer processing technique is to utilize "batch processing." This term refers to a processing technique where facts or data are

[10]*Op. Cit.*, Johnson, Kast, and Rosenzweig, p. 243.
[11]*Op. Cit.*, Fred Brown, p. 197.

[12]*Op. Cit.*, Johnson, Kast and Rosenzweig, p. 242.
[13]*Ibid.*, p. 243.

collected manually or electronically over a period of time and then merged with a master file in a processing run.[14] Such processing might take place on a biweekly, weekly, or daily time frame. For example, fire incident reports are completed as an event happens. The event data might be converted to computer input form and placed in storage. At one of the time intervals cited above, the computer would process the "batch of information" and print out a summary report according to some predetermined pattern. Batch processing takes place where there is not an immediate need for data retrieval.

"Real-time processing," in contrast, involves updating a master data file or what is currently termed a description file concerning a current situation with every change in the event no matter how frequent. The concepts concerning real-time data draw heavily upon Military Defense programs. Therefore, it appears appropriate to turn to Donald G. Malcolm's article "Exploring the Military Analogy: Real-time Management Control" for a structured definition of "Real-Time."[15]

> The term real-time control, communication, and information system, has evolved as a system design concept. By this is meant that the information is transmitted instantaneously, without conversion, into a centralized computer, which processes it, compares it with predetermined decision criteria and issues instructions to men and/or machines for corrective or purposeful action. This may be thought of as "real-time control." Further, the computer by means of direct output informs affected parties of this information as it is developed. This is "real-time communication." Lastly, suitable condensations of the above information are prepared, transmitted and displayed to higher levels of management for broader system decisions. This is "real-time management information."
>
> The meaning of the word "real-time" lies in the fact that information is used as it develops and that elements in the system are controlled by the processed information immediately, not after the fact or by making periodic forecasts of the expected future state of the system.

Real-time control, communication and information systems require sophisticated computer equipment and programs. In many cases real-time action can only be accomplished with very complex computer support. Is there a need for real-time functions in the public fire safety systems organization? The answer is affirmative. Examples can be cited for the advantage of real-time structures in the functional areas of fire alarm and communications

systems, command and control, water supply and inspections, and administration by exception. Examples of the need for real-time information systems in several of these areas are advanced in Chapters IV–VIII. The following example concerning water supply will give the reader an appreciation of the need and potential for real-time data.

Adequate water supply is crucial to effective fire control. A fire officer must be aware of existing water supply in terms of volume and pressure in the vicinity of a fire. This knowledge traditionally comes from water supply tests that were conducted prior to the event. A less exact approach is to simply estimate the potential quantity of water available by a cursory examination of area water pipe sizes. Both techniques leave much to be desired. The fire officer presently must rely on past information or speculative information that is often incorrect. He has the need for specific information dealing with water supply adequacy right at the time of the fire — real-time information.

Considering the water supply example, data concerning pipe arrangements, supply sources and consumer consumption can be kept entirely on magnetic storage of a computer memory. As the supply and demand of the water supply system change for consumer requirements, so does the adequacy of the system change for fire suppression. Under a real-time concept, the data information concerning flow and pressure points would be constantly updated to reflect current conditions. At the time of fire in a particular locality of the city, a readout of existing water supply availability would be requested. The computer readout would give the fire officer a reflection of water supply adequacy as it exists "now." This example is rather straightforward. Other real-time functions concerning water supply might include starting pumps, altering valve arrangements, and giving printout warnings when supply conditions drop below some predetermined level.

The last point concerning warning signals when a water supply system drops below some predetermined level introduces the need to advance another term for clarification. The term to be defined is "management by exception." This is simply a means of cutting down the amount of detail usually brought to the attention of managers by selecting only those items that require action.[16] For example, in an inventory control situation minimum and

[14]*Ibid.*, p. 258.

[15]Donald G. Malcolm, Alan J. Rowe, and Lorimer F. McConnel, eds., *Management Control Systems.* John Wiley and Sons, Inc., 1960, pp. 187–280.

[16]Robert R. Arnold, Harold C. Hill, and Aylmer V. Nichols. *Introduction to Data Processing.* New York: John Wiley and Sons, Inc., 1967, p. 12.

maximum quantities can be established for each item. In a public fire safety systems organization such an inventory process might be developed for fire hose. As inventory balances are reviewed automatically, only those items that are overstocked or understocked are called to management's attention. After a large fire a considerable amount of hose might be out of service during the cleaning and drying process. If this amount of hose out of service reached some minimum acceptable level, a computer printout would signal a management decision to redistribute resources. Higher level administration by exception techniques will be advanced in Chapter IV.

Hardware-Software Packages

The introductory statements covering computers briefly referenced the concepts revolving around computer hardware and computer software. The full range of parameters concerning each term could be fully explained in no less than a complete textbook. The objective of this subsection is to provide a funda-

mental distinction to each concept. While distinctions between "hardware" and "software" are developed in this subsection, stress should be made that both elements form a computer package and that one is highly dependent upon the other.

In basic form, "computer hardware" refers to the physical features of the computer. The hardware is the device or devices that form a computer assembly. In a more precise fashion hardware has been defined as "A colloquialism applied to the mechanical, electrical and electronic features of a data processing system."[17] A generalized description of the Digital Computer is offered to illustrate both content and scope of computer hardware systems.

Illustration III-1 depicts the five components of a computer system in the *Block Diagram*.[18] All digital computers have five things in common.[19] First, there is an input

[17]*Ibid.*, p. 312.

[18]William R. Corliss, *Computers*. Washington: United States Atomic Energy Commission, 1967, p. 13.

[19]*Ibid.*, p. 14.

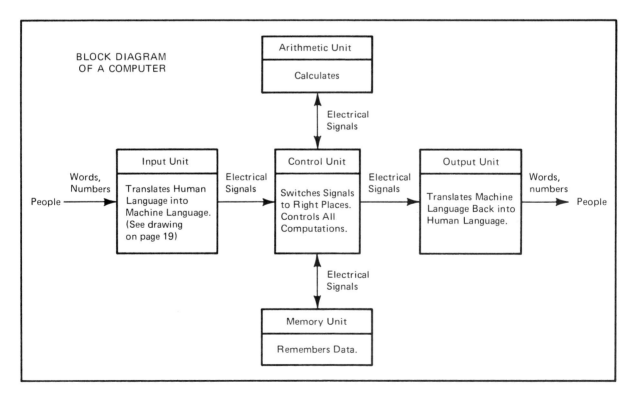

ILLUSTRATION III-1 FIVE COMPONENTS OF A COMPUTER SYSTEM

Reference: William R. Corliss, *Computers*. Washington: United States Atomic Energy Commission, 1967, p. 13.

unit that digests human produced information and instructions about what to do with this information. The input for the computer is punched cards and tapes. Once in the computer, information and instructions are sent to a second component, the memory, to await recall by the computer control unit, which is the computer's taskmaster. In other words, the memory section is a storage area for the instructions that direct the computer through the steps of a problem and for the data that are used in that problem. Supporting the memory is the control section which directs and coordinates the activities of the other sections. The control unit makes sure that data are channeled to the right places and that the fourth major component, the arithmetic unit, makes the right calculations. It is the arithmetic and logic section that performs all of the mathematical operations and makes all necessary comparisons. The decision-making capability of the computer is the result of the numeric comparisons made in this section.

Finally, when the computations are complete, the output unit transforms the computer's electrical signals into written records that people can read. The input and output sections in the central processing unit are linked with input and output peripheral devices, which handle the data entering the computer and the information coming out of the computer.

For efficiency, the five computer components must be able to converse with one another rapidly and in the same electrical language. In the electronic digital computer, pulses of electricity flow among the five units at nearly the speed of light. The pulses carry numbers and symbols in the binary language.[20]

In terms of talking about computer application to public fire protection, further considerations must be advanced relative to the hardware implications of the "input"-"output" sections of the computer. The prime concern of relating computers to a systems framework of public fire safety is to focus on what we expect out of the system and thereby create the requirements for input. The input-output scheme needs to be translated into the entire computer network. The faculty of the Department of Defense Computer Institute states:[21]

Input and output are generic terms used for a number of elements. Input or output data are intelligence such as represented by a set of numbers. The physical substances upon which data are written or coded are designated as input or output media. Input media might be paper with information printed thereon. Input and output devices are the physical units that handle the media. A card reader, for example, is an input device, and a printer is an output device.

Relative to input information, it should be recognized that computer problems always originate in someone's head. Human thoughts are converted into the computer's electrical pulse trains, that is, from human language to machine language. For example, if the decimal number 3 is to be inserted into the working innards of a digital computer, someone first has to write the numeral 3 on a printed form, which then goes to a key punch operator, who operates a machine that punches holes in a card or paper tape. The number 3 has now moved from a mental abstraction, to a written abstraction — the figure 3 — to still another abstraction, a hole, whose position on a piece of paper can be sensed and turned into computer language.[22]

In a computer data is represented in many electronic components such as transistors, switches, magnetic cores, wires and so on by the presence or absence of electronic signals or indications, much as the presence or absence of holes in a punched card represents.

Each component in a computer has only two possible states: on or off. For example, transistors are in either a conducting or nonconducting state; magnetic materials are magnetized in one direction or in the opposite direction; relays and switches are open or closed; and voltage is present or absent.[23] With this limited number of possibilities for each component part, the computer must accept large numbers, letters, and words as input; must store and process them and must produce them as output. Because of these design characteristics, the computer must use a two digit number system known as the binary system.[24]

The base in the binary system is 2, as there are only two discrete symbols, 0 and 1, which are used to represent various binary quantities. The binary notations 0 and 1 are commonly referred to as bits. This means coding into BInary digiTS (bits). Considering the bits concept, the 0 is described as no bit and represents an "off" condition. The 1 is described as a bit and represents an "on" condition.[25]

[20]*Op. Cit.*, William Corliss, p. 13.

[21]*Op. Cit.*, Fred Brown, p. 202.

[22]*Op. Cit.*, William Corliss, p. 18.

[23]*Op. Cit.*, Arnold, Hill, and Nichols, p. 183.

[24]*Ibid.*, p. 183.   [25]*Ibid.*, p. 183.

DECIMAL AND BINARY EQUIVALENTS

Decimal Digits	Binary Notation							
	128	64	32	16	8	4	2	1 = Value of each bit.
1								1
2							1	0
4						1	0	0
8					1	0	0	0
16				1	0	0	0	0
32			1	0	0	0	0	0
64		1	0	0	0	0	0	0
128	1	0	0	0	0	0	0	0

TABLE III-2 DECIMAL AND BINARY EQUIVALENTS

Reference: Robert R. Arnold, Harold C. Hill and Aylmer V. Nichols. *Introduction to Data Processing.* New York: John Wiley and Sons, Inc., 1967, p. 184.

The position value of bit symbols is based on the progression of powers of two. Table III-2 illustrates the manner in which a binary digit doubles its value each time it moves one place to the left. The lowest order position in the binary system is called the 1 bit. The next position is called the 2 bit; the next 4 bit; the next the 8 bit; the next the 16 bit; and so on. Each of these can have only one of two conditions, "0" or "1". Thus, the binary system is just another way of expressing quantities.[26]

If a computer is to process data, the data must be made available to the computer in a form that it can utilize — binary code. Many methods and devices are used to provide input to electronic computers. Included are punched cards (Illustration III-3), punched tape, magnetic tape, documents encoded with magnetic characters, and printed characters designed for optical scanning.

Reading takes place as the input medium physically moves through an input device. Data is sensed or read and is converted to a form that is compatible with the computer system. The data is then transmitted to main storage.

All standard input-output devices have certain common characteristics. They are auxiliary machines connected directly to the electronic data processing system, and under control of the central processing unit. Most input-output devices are automatic. Once started, they continue to operate as directed by the stored program. These devices can transmit data to or receive data only from the main memory unit.[27]

In addition to the standard input-output devices, remotely located recorders are emerging as an important technique. Although separated from the computer, these devices can be operated on-line; that is, they may transmit input data directly to a computer as the data is recorded at the point of origin. Traditionally, input has been regarded as the weakest link in computer systems because of the time required to record, convert, and read data for input. On-line transaction recorders, and other innovations such as optical character recognition and magnetic ink character recognition, are alleviating the "input bottleneck" by making it possible for data in machine-sensible language to be read directly into a computer.[28]

An understanding of digital computers is better secured if the functions and some of the physical characteristics of the memory are understood. The most common form of memory used in central processing units today is magnetic cores. The cores are small and donut-

---

[26]*Ibid.*, p. 184.

[27]*Ibid.*, p. 190.   [28]*Ibid.*, p. 202.

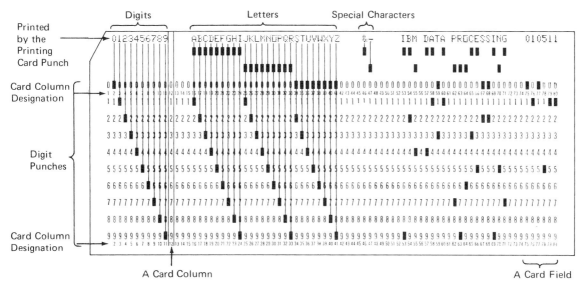

A typical punched card. By using combinations of two holes, the decimal numbers, the alphabet, and several punctuation marks can be fed into computers and converted into electrical signals. By using combinations of three holes in each column a great many mathematical symbols can be introduced. Punched cards were first used for large-scale data processing by Herman Holierith in the Census of 1890.

ILLUSTRATION III-3 A TYPICAL PUNCHED CARD

Reference: Robert R. Arnold, Harold C. Hill and Aylmer V. Nichols. *Introduction to Data Processing.* New York: John Wiley and Sons, Inc., 1967, p. 190.

shaped and are made of a ferrite material. A "one" or "zero" of the binary digit system may be stored in each core, depending on which of two ways it is magnetized.[29]

These cores are arranged in groups to store data. There are two ways these groups may be arranged in computers. The terms "fixed word length" or "character" are used to designate the machines using one of these two ways. A "character" machine might have six cores per group making up one character, assuming that the character can be coded into six BITS. Each of these characters is a memory cell in the computer and each has its own unique address. The address is the location number of the cell and is used to tell from where to extract data or where to put data into the computer's memory. The "fixed word length" computer has a larger group of cores making up one word in a memory location or cell. An example would be a thirty-six-bit word length.[30]

A computer solves problems by doing operations specified by a group of instructions. These instructions are called a computer program and are stored in a computer's memory. The subject of computer programs will be further expanded under the title "software." The computer automatically steps through the program instructions in sequence, performing the procedures specified by each instruction.

The computer needs what are referred to as "peripheral devices" to become a useful tool. These peripheral devices all have one thing in common. They either feed data into the central processing unit or receive information from it. With some exceptions, these devices can be classified into two broad categories carrying the titles of auxiliary memory units and input and output devices.[31]

The auxiliary memory units are able to hold large amounts of data which can be transferred rapidly into the central processing unit. Magnetic drums and disks are examples of auxiliary memory. The outside magnetic coating of a drum can be magnetized to represent binary characters. When the drum is rotated at high speed, the stationary "read" and "write" heads are able to read what is on the drum or write new data on the drum. The disk file works similarly, except that the magnetic storage surfaces are a series of disks stacked so that the read and write heads can get between them.[32]

The magnetic tape unit is another example of auxiliary storage. With a tape unit and an unlimited number of reels of tape, the computer can have unlimited storage capability.

---

[29]*Ibid.*, p. 191.   [30]*Ibid.*, pp. 206–212.   [31]*Ibid.*, pp. 206–212.   [32]*Ibid.*, p. 194.

Since the data are stored on the tape sequentially, to get to any stored item the tape must be run through the tape unit from the beginning until the item is reached. With the disk and drum, however, any item can be selected by its location designation and read without searching from the beginning of the file. Thus, magnetic drums or disks have great applicability to random access uses of computer storage and retrieval.[33]

It seems appropriate at this point to introduce the concepts of "on-line" and "off-line" computer work. A computer's arithmetic unit can assimilate information, data and instructions, much faster than a punched card reader can feed it. To circumvent a possible bottleneck, modern computers first translate the data on punched cards and paper tapes into magnetized spots on a metal tape using an "off-line" unit; this is, a unit on a side circuit. This unit is classified as a reading machine. During this process, most of the computer parts, the "on-line portion," work on other problems. The magnetized spots — moving past magnets — activate electric "readers." When the control and arithmetic units are ready for the next problem, the information is "read off" the much faster magnetic tape. Since computer time rents for as much as several hundred dollars an hour, time is truly a savings feature, and ways to make savings like this are important.[34]

It has been noted that the input and output devices commonly used with computers are card readers and punch machines, line printers, paper tape readers and punches. Magnetic tape can also be considered an input and output medium since it is used for this purpose. In the same manner paper tape and cards also are a form of auxiliary memory, but more human intervention is necessary in handling them between each output or input operation. This makes cards or paper tape relatively inefficient as auxiliary memory. The line printer prints, in readable form, information that has been produced by the computer. The combination of the central processing unit (and some of these peripheral devices) of the central processing unit comprise the equipment making up almost every computer installation.

Before leaving the computer hardware subsection, a few words are in order concerning "Source Data Collection." "Source Data Collection" involves the capturing in machine readable media (such as paper tape or punched cards) data at the time it is generated by people or machines. A key concept is that such capture should be a by-product operation, not requiring additional human intervention. The need for capture stems from the fact that human reorigination of data input is increasingly expensive and constantly error-prone. An example of source data collection is that in a typical organization, about eighty per cent of the actions affecting pay records are originated in such Special Orders on a typewriter which simultaneously produces a punched paper tape capturing all or part of the Special Orders for subsequent machine handling of the various pay records.[35]

Equipment is currently available to capture the outputs of typewriters, adding machines, calculators, cash registers, time clocks, etc. In fact, most commonly used business machines can be so adapted, and it has been demonstrated that decentralized organizations such as the perceived public fire safety systems organization can profit from these source data collection techniques.

Software

"Software" is an equally important concept in the discussion of computers. Actually the term "software" has two connotations. They complement each other but one is more limited in scope than the other. In a limited sense "software" means the programming process.[36] A more inclusive definition states: "Software is the programs and routines used to extend the capabilities of computers, such as compilers, assemblers, routines and subroutines. Also, all documents associated with a computer, e.g. manuals, circuit diagrams."[37]

The Department of Defense Computer Institute describes the programming process in eleven phases: "(1) Stating the problem; (2) Analyzing the problem; (3) Defining the problem; (4) Developing the program logic; (5) Constructing a flow chart of the program logic; (6) Coding the program instructions; (7) Preparing a machine-sensible program; (8) Constructing a test deck; (9) Debugging the program; (10) Preparing operator procedures; (11) Completing all of the necessary documentation."[38]

Some reflections are necessary on the above points. When the problem has been stated, analyzed, and defined, the programmer must develop the logic — the method by which the

[33]*Ibid.*, p. 197.   [34]*Ibid.*, pp. 206–212.

[35]*Ibid.*, pp. 206–212.
[36]*Op. Cit.*, Fred Brown, p. 205.
[37]*Op. Cit.*, Arnold, Hill, and Nichols, p. 317.
[38]*Op. Cit.*, Fred Brown, p. 205.

computer will handle the problem. This phase of the programming process is often very tedious and time consuming, since the programmer must determine precisely what will take place in the program and the sequence in which these events must occur.

At this stage the program flowchart is prepared. This is a graphic display of exactly what is to be accomplished by the program, and it will be used as an outline for the writing of the machine instructions. After the flowchart is completed, the programmer faces the task of coding these elements into machine instructions. These instructions will dictate to the computer precisely how it is to accomplish the task and, thus the instructions constitute a computer program. Several languages are normally available to the programmer. These languages are referred to as machine languages, assembly languages or higher level languages. A further discussion of program languages will be advanced. When finished, the program is put into a machine readable form such as punched cards.[39]

The eleven programming phases apply to any programming process whether it be a scientific research application, a fire department administration or management problem, or a large scale fire safety command and control requirement. The first three phases are required because the initial statement of the problem by the user may be incomplete. A dialogue usually ensues between the person desiring the processing and the programmer to develop a refined problem statement. In other words, administrative and management elements of the public fire safety systems organization must be able to converse with the programming section in order that specific problems can be refined and the proper program written. This chapter is designed to improve this communication process but it does not attempt to render all the expertise necessary for administrative and management assistance to the programmer.

The programmer must know, for example, the exact nature of the data to be processed by the computer. He must know the format and sequence of the information and if the data contain alphabetic characters. If the data are numerical, how large are the numbers? He must also determine precisely the form in which the results of the program are desired — on punched cards, magnetic tape, or a printed page.

The disposition of errors in the input data is another problem which must be discussed. The program must be able to recognize an error situation and make the necessary corrections or reject the erroneous data for human correction.[40]

The programmer also prepares test data to be used with his program. The "test deck" is a set of data similar to that which the program will encounter. The program and the text deck data are then tried on the computer. This phase is called "debugging" since its purpose is to determine if there are any errors, or "bugs" in the program. Usually, several errors are found and the programmer corrects these mistakes. In many cases, this debugging phase is the most time-consuming part of the programming process.

When the program has been tested sufficiently, it becomes what is known as a "production program." In addition to instructions for the computer operator, the programmer must be sure that there is full documentation of the program. This means establishing the record of all the phases of the programming process, including completed flow charts and written descriptions of the program.[41]

The above narrative represents a broad view of the programming process. The amounts of time and cost required to accomplish these tasks vary widely, of course, depending on the complexity of the problem and the ability of the programmer. The "in-house" capability of the public fire safety organization personnel could have a significant bearing on the time and cost question.

Some broad and introductory comments need to be advanced concerning "Programming Languages." In reality, the task of programming a computer can be thought of as a communication task. The basic requirement is for a man to communicate to the machine a great deal of his own personal ability, creativeness and knowledge, so that the computer can follow through the extensive, sometimes unbelievable complex, problem solving procedures. The communicative medium must be translated into the language that the computer can itself recognize.

The most basic language in relation to the computer is machine language. Machine language is the language composed of the binary digits in combinations that constitute the computer's vocabulary or instruction repertoire.[42] This language in effect arranges the bits in each of the computer's memory locations into the pattern or instructions that will tell the machine what to do. The directions conveyed

---

[39]*Ibid.*, pp. 205–210.

[40]*Ibid.*, pp. 205–210.   [41]*Ibid.*, pp. 205–210.

[42]*Ibid.*, pp. 205–210.

must be expressed in terms of the limited set of commands that the computer can recognize and obey. The data that the computer is to manipulate must be described by referral to the locations in the computer's memory that hold the individual items. Fortunately, machine-language computer programming is seldom accomplished directly today, even though the ultimate result of any type of programming is a machine-language program ready for the computer to use.

The next level of programming languages is assembly languages. The principal difference between the use of these languages and machine language is the vocabulary and the character set available to the programmer. Using assembly languages does not require arrangement of the binary digits of the computer's instructions into the pattern that has specific meaning to the computer. The use of assembly languages for programming has done much to expand the power of the programmer. However, the programs cannot be used immediately by the computer. Instead, the assembly language program must be translated into the language of the computer. Fortunately, the computer itself can be programmed to do that translation. The process is called the assembly process and the computer program that causes the machine to accomplish it is called an "assembler." Perhaps eighty per cent of the computer programs in use today were written originally in an assembly language.[43] Each language is applicable to a specific computer, and the programmer must know a great deal concerning the computer on which the program will be run. Hence, these languages are called machine-oriented languages.

The third class of programming language to be considered is the class called higher level languages. These languages are also referred to as machine-independent or procedure-oriented languages.[44] When a programmer uses one of these for writing his computer programs, he no longer has a specific concern about the computer. He can express his problem-solving procedures in terms of the problem itself, in terms of some mathematical notation, or even in terms of near-English expressions. The underlying theory of these languages is that once a person knows how to use one of them, he can write programs that will operate on several different computers. Because the languages are applicable to more than one computer, there are fewer of them than there are assembly languages.

The development of programming languages has progressed rapidly over the last decade. FORTRAN IV (FORmula TRANslation), COBOL (Common Business Oriented Language), and ALGOL (Alogorithmic Language) are examples of widely used approaches. There have been numerous suggestions for standardization in order that program packages may be used on a variety of computers. Some progress has been made but much remains to be done.[45]

NPL (New Programming Language, now PL-1) was designed to meet the need for a language that could be used for both business and scientific applications. The absence of arbitrary restrictions allows the programmer to devote most of his effort to problem description and to express with freedom the procedure for its solution. The objective was to develop a language which would enable programmers to write more diverse application programs than heretofore possible.[46] It should be noted that most of the computer applications envisioned in this book can be adequately programmed in either FORTRAN IV or PL-1.

Another phase of software development directly applicable to systems organization techniques is presented by compilers or translators which are similar to assembly programs but usually are far more complex. The trend in business has been to make the language used by the programmer as simple as possible, thus requiring a more complex compiler or translator program to develop the machine-language instructions. This is often referred to as an object program.[47] For scientific computations which may be carried out only once, the efficiency of the object program is not critical. Numerous programs are likely to be compiled and it is more important that the compiler program itself be as efficient as possible. For the general type of data processing requirements found in public fire safety organizations, it is considered that compiling time is not so critical. What does become important is the concern that the object program must become as efficient as possible because it is used repeatedly. For example, the goal in fire incident record data processing is to have standard, efficient programs for the everyday tasks of sorting and merging the fire records. This point is enlarged upon in Chapter VIII.

Time-Sharing

The concept of time-sharing with computer installations may be very important to public fire safety under the systems organization con-

[43]Ibid., p. 207.   [44]Ibid., p. 208.

[45]Ibid., p. 208.   [46]Ibid., p. 209.   [47]Ibid., p. 209.

cept. Therefore, a definition and scope statement on time-sharing appears appropriate at this point. Time-sharing is defined as "the use of a device for two or more purposes during the same overall time interval, accomplished by interspersing component actions in time."[48] Time-sharing of computers is generally accomplished from remote terminals and is based upon the fact that such terminals, and the personnel associated with them, act quite slowly as compared with computer processing speeds. The computer in effect uses this extra time to do processing for other users. Such systems are characterized by (1) being communications-oriented, (2) the use of large random access disks or drum files to hold users' programs and files, and (3) very complex software operating systems which act as a traffic control for multiple users doing discrete and nonconnected work during the same time interval.[49] The performance of such systems ideally gives each user the impression that the computer is working for him alone — very much in the same way that a user of a telephone system is served. The user gains the services of larger and faster hardware than he could afford alone and an extensive software library resulting in a reduction of overhead costs. He must balance these against a greater degree of operating discipline, higher communications costs, etc. In terms of reliability, the user has no more or less control than if he had his own system. It may be expected that time-sharing techniques will afford computer use to many who could not otherwise afford such service.

The concept of time-sharing computer services within the framework of public fire safety systems organizations may be viewed from two points. First, the fire group could feasibly share most of its computer requirements with other municipal services thus cutting the overhead cost obligation and making the utility of computers more attractive. Second, considerable attention is paid in this book to the premise that the organization base of public fire safety needs to be broadened to accommodate public fire safety on a systems approach. The broad organization base (i.e., County or Regional Concept) opens up the opportunity for more shared service capability. Time-sharing of a computer on a county or regional base would appear to have much merit.

The Application of Computers to Administration and Management Requirements

The previous material of this chapter has been advanced with one thought in mind. That thought was to present an overview of computers with just enough detail so that computer applications could be appreciated within the context of the proposed public fire safety systems organization. With the stage set, the objective now turns to a more specific appreciation of computers in relation to the organizational structure of public fire safety. Emphasis is placed on computer utility within the spheres of public fire safety administration and management.

It is readily apparent that functional elements of public fire safety handle immense amounts of records and reports. Like many units of government, the present Fire Service has often been characterized by its "record mill." The vast amount of time devoted to records is a problem not fully explored in Chapter I. In a study conducted by the author titled "The Perceived Involvement of Fire Department Officers: Operational and Management Functions"; it was determined that on an average, fire department officers considered that they spend thirty per cent of their working time in record maintenance.[50] In some of the larger population cities, fire officers in the line companies reported they spent as much as seventy-five per cent of their time to complete assigned records. Record handling and record management is obviously an important concern to elements of public fire safety. Much of the present problem can be solved through modern techniques of data processing. To implement the full concept of a systems approach to public fire safety, it is almost essential that the combined functions of data processing and records management be viewed from the point of computer assistance. Therefore, the following subsections are aimed at structuring some of the basic concepts of data processing, data management and record document preparation through the utilization of computers.

Computer Assisted Data Processing

In the broadest sense, data processing refers to the recording and handling procedures that are necessary to convert data into a more refined or useful form. In traditional management concepts these tasks were referred to as

[48]Bureau of the Budget, *Automatic Data Processing Glossary.* Washington: U.S. Government Printing Office (1962), p. 53.

[49]*Ibid.*, pp. 53–55.

[50]Harry E. Hickey, *The Perceived Involvement of Fire Department Officers: Operational and Management Functions.* Albany: The International Fire Administration Institute, 1970, pp. 9–20.

record keeping or paperwork.[51] Data tasks were accepted as a routine clerical activity. With the advent of more sophisticated electro-mechanical and electronic business machines in the past few years, the terms "paperwork" and "record keeping" have been replaced by the phrase "data processing." Of particular significance to the systems approach for organization is the realization that the objectives of data processing now extend far beyond the routine handling transaction documents and records of other types. Data processing has assumed new importance. It now fills a greatly expanded need for information that is required in the administration of enterprises — in this instance public fire safety.

There has been a tendency in the literature to focus on the term "data" as a reference to primarily accounting functions. This seems unnecessarily restrictive in terms of modern systems approach administration. Actually, data can include any facts, figures, letters, words, charts, or symbols that represent an idea, object, condition or situation.[52] Thus data can include such diverse records as manpower rosters, inventory figures, personnel records, fire incident statistics, apparatus status displays and water supply analysis plotted on logarithmic paper. Concepts relating to data collection and data analysis will be covered throughout the entire paper. The focus at this point is on automated techniques associated with data collection and assessment.

It should be pointed out that a distinction is often made between data and information, namely, that data is the raw material from which information is derived.[53] According to this concept, the significant characteristic that separates data from information is usefulness. Thus a compilation of data may, in itself, be of little value unless it provides knowledge leading to the achievement of some objective. The conversion of raw data to information is a primary function of data processing within the systems concept. There is an increasing focus on the internal organization need for data to be compiled in informative reports for use in analyzing progress, determining policy, solving problems, and planning actions of the future. Providing administrators and management personnel with timely information to facilitate greater control and improved decisions is an increasingly important function of data processing. The requirement for improved data handling has dictated a need for improved

data processing techniques. Other factors such as the volume of data, clerical costs, line and staff commitments, accuracy requirements and promptness in converting data into information can also be sighted as forcing organizations to improve the data processing program. The public fire safety systems organization is not an exception.

Aside from the sheer volume of data, one might ask what there is about processing data that consumes so much time and effort and creates such a need for mechanical and electronic computer support. It should be observed that from the time of origin to the time of arrival in a final, more useful form, data may go through a number of operational steps referred to as the "data processing cycle."[54] This cycle may be roughly divided into the following steps:

1. Origination of the Data — The raw material for data processing originates on various organization forms, often referred to as source documents. These original documents are especially important for two reasons: a) they provide verification of all transactions, and b) they are the basis for all further actions.

2. Recording Data — The basic function of this step is the recording of data in some form that permits its convenient handling in whatever system is being used. The manual entry into a journal or register is being replaced by using a typewriter equipped with a paper tape punching device. Thus the original data is automatically recorded in a form that can be processed by machines capable of reading punched paper tape.

a. Editing — This is the process of selecting significant data and eliminating that which does not need to be recorded for further processing.

b. Coding — As a means of further reducing the amount of data to be recorded and processed, abbreviated codes are often used to condense the data being expressed.

c. Classifying — Classifying is the process of identifying one or more common characteristics to be used as a means of systematically grouping data into classes. For example, fire incident data may be classified into response data, direct loss data, indirect loss data and life loss data.

d. Conversion — Conversion is a means of transforming data from one recorded form to another. For example, data recorded on punched cards may be converted to punched paper tape, or vice versa, by the use of special equipment designed for this purpose.

e. Copying and Duplicating — These are processes by which facsimiles of data can be

[51]*Op. Cit.*, Arnold, Hill, and Nichols, p. 1.

[52]*Ibid.*, p. 1.   [53]*Ibid.*, p. 2.

[54]*Ibid.*, p. 4.

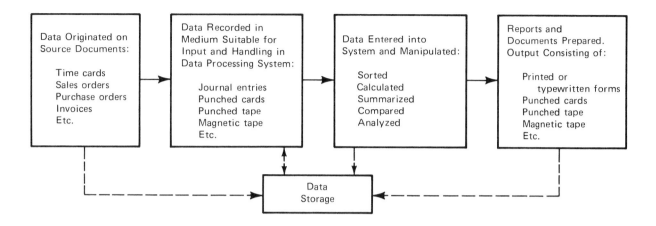

ILLUSTRATION III-4 STEPS IN THE DATA PROCESSING CYCLE

Reference: Robert R. Arnold, Harold C. Hill and Aylmer V. Nichols. *Introduction to Data Processing.* New York: John Wiley and Sons, Inc., 1967, p. 4.

prepared for distribution to more than one user or for use in different steps in the processing cycle.

f. Verifying — This essential function assures that all parts of the recording process have been accomplished without error, and that accurate data is entered into the processing system.

3. Manipulation of Data — If the original form of data were suitable for all purposes, less processing would be necessary. Seldom, however, can the real objective of a transaction or situation be attained without converting data into a more useful form. The conversion is accomplished by means of one or more of the following procedures.[55]

a. Sorting — Sorting is the process of arranging or selecting data according to (1) order or rank or (2) common characteristic. Sorting according to order or rank, known as sorting in sequence, takes place when data is arranged in numeric or alphabetic sequence. Sorting, according to common characteristic, known as sorting by classification, takes place when data is arranged in similar groups.

b. Calculating — Calculating refers to the arithmetical processes of multiplication, division, addition, or subtraction which are necessary to convert data into a more significant form. The calculation of the frequency of residential fire occurrences would be an example of the calculating function.

c. Summarizing — Summarizing is the process of condensing data so that the main points are emphasized. Summarizing generally involves listing or tabulating data and totaling each list. The summary of fire loss information for a year would be an example in this category.

4. Comparing and Analyzing — These are the processes used in determining such factors as the nature, proportion, relationship, order, similarity, or relative value of data.[56]

a. Report Preparation — The processed information that results from the data processing cycle is known as "output." This could include documents such as the fire unit monthly report; or finished reports such as the administrator's annual report. The means by which the processed information is finally recorded is known as the "output medium." Depending on the type of processing system being used, output media could consist of typewritten documents or reports, printed forms, punched cards, punched paper tape, magnetic tape, or other special forms.

b. Data Transmission — Transmitting is the process of transferring data from one point to another during the processing cycle or of delivering the final results to the user. Many methods may be used ranging from the very simple to the highly complex. Data in

[55]*Ibid.,* p. 5.

[56]*Ibid.,* p. 6.

written, punched card, or other form may be transported by hand or by some mechanism such as a teletypewriter. The latter service is probably the most familiar example of wire communication. This method enables data in typewritten or punched tape form to be transmitted between units in the same building or city — or thousands of miles apart. The concept is very important to the realization of a public fire safety systems organization on a sector or regional basis.

c. Data Storage — Upon completion of the processing cycle, or possibly at a point of intermediate results during the cycle, data must be stored so that it is readily retrievable. The storage of data could be a matter of monumental proportions in a Level 1 Fire Safety Organization. Storage techniques already referred to, depend on the type and volume of data involved.

It should be noted, before going further, that all or part of the above functions have to be performed whether they are done manually, by mechanical means, by punched cards machines, or by electronic computer. In spite of the vast differences in these methods, however, the procedures and objectives of data processing remain basically the same.

Electronic Data Processing

The most recent development in data processing is the electronic computer, which has attracted great interest because of its vastly superior capacity to perform computation and other functions at incredible speeds. Performance speed in a computer results from the fact that processing in a computer is accomplished by the movement of electrical impulses through the computer's circuitry rather than by the movement of mechanical parts. Through instructions programmed into the computer by means of magnetic tapes, punched paper tapes, or punched cards, thousands of complex operations can be completed in a second. This rapid processing is essential to the efficient and effective handling of command, control and communications within the public fire safety systems organization.

Prior to establishing some of the possible specific uses of electronic data processing under the systems approach to public fire safety organization, it appears appropriate to summarize the principal advantages of EDP over other data processing methods. The unique advantages of EDP are:[57]

1. The speed of processing is many times faster than that attainable in punched card or other mechanical systems.

2. Once data is entered into the system, the processing is continuous. There is no need to handle or transport data between each operation.

3. More compact equipment and storage results in a saving of space.

4. Accuracy is generally greater than in other systems.

5. The superior speed, capacity, and versatility of the electronic computer makes possible the completion of tasks never attempted under other systems because of the impossibility of completing them in time for the results to be useful.

An associative principle of EDP also needs to be introduced. An important extension of EDP is IDP (Integrated Data Processing). The term integrated data processing is interpreted in various ways in the literature. Broadly defined, integrated data processing is a method by which data is initially recorded in a form that allows it to proceed through the entire processing cycle with a minimum of human effort and without again having to be manually copied.[58] More specifically defined, IDP describes the process by which data is initially recorded by some manual method, and is simultaneously recorded in a form that is acceptable for further processing by machines.[59]

This is accomplished by means of attachments to more conventional devices such as calculators, electronic accounting machines and special typewriters that make possible not only the preparation of original documents but also the simultaneous production of punched tapes or cards. These tapes or cards are used to insert the data into other devices such as punched card machines and electronic computers. They may be used also to transmit the data to some distant point by data transmission equipment. Machines that can communicate in this manner are referred to as common-language machines.[60] These techniques produce an integration of functions which eliminate the recopying that otherwise would be required to convert source data to a form that is suitable for further processing.

Applications for Public Fire Safety

Chapters IV through VIII in this book are an attempt to precisely state many data requirements and information requirements for

[57]*Ibid.*, p. 10.

[58]*Ibid.*, p. 11.   [59]*Ibid.*, p. 12.   [60]*Ibid.*, p. 12.

the administrative structure, the resource systems and the operation system under the proposed framework of a public fire safety systems organization. However, computer support to the structural-functional elements of the systems is perceived to be so vital that some examples at this time may be appropriate. The following items are also presented with the intent of identifying and supporting the need for a systems engineering component with the accompanying Central Processing Unit within the organizational framework.

EDP applications are presented with the view of solving the current fire department paper work problem and providing certain requisite information on an instantaneous retrieval basis for specialized operational functions. Certain support areas have been developed as examples, and the integration of these support areas into the total organizational scheme should be remembered.

Clerical Work

A major activity of any organization is the recording of transactions, events, inventory and personnel. Each of these basic categories of course applies to public fire safety. *The Fire Company Journal*, the *Fire Report Journal* (or register — the terms may vary by existing fire departments) and the Attendance Register are examples of constantly maintained records that require varying amounts of clerical time.[61] In active fire companies the time devoted to this routine clerical chore can be considerable; some would describe it as excessive.[62] The events mentioned could be typed directly onto tape with a verifiable copy routed for the officer in charge. The daily tapes could be committed to input storage. Daily summaries could be prepared by the data processing section based upon a pre-prepared program with a printed copy going to the designed functional units on a scheduled basis. The manpower attendance information could be sorted out for the payroll unit in personnel. Today the payroll processing job turns out to include more than just multiplying hours worked times rate-per-hour and writing a check for the resulting amount. For example, records must be kept of such items as year-to-date earnings, year-to-date withholding tax, year-to-date social security payments, vacation, and sick leave. Numerous deductions must be taken into ac-

count: life, medical, and accident and health insurance; savings bonds, credit union; and others. When all the items are considered, there is a significantly large number of steps involved in what appears to the uninitiated as a relatively straightforward task. The computer is ideally suited to this type of manipulation of many facts and variables.

On the more sophisticated side is the real-time application of measuring and reporting on duty strength. The shift roll call could be immediately typed into computer storage. Within a minute after all units report roll call, company officers, sector officers, regional officers and the Major Project Systems coordinator could determine the systems strengths and weaknesses. Adjustments or reassignments could be made without delay. In fact, the computer could be programmed to make adjustment assignments automatically.

It is important to note that information placed in storage can be recalled almost at will. The "almost" term is inserted to emphasize that equipment and program characteristics reflect on information availability. If the facts revolving around a particular incident or event are required, the search and print capability of the computer is phenomenally faster than a manual search and copy.

Inventory control represents another potential area for saving clerical requirements. Examples of inventory applications involve keeping records of all apparatus, hose and minor equipment along with routine building inventories and personal equipment inventories.

A current, and in most cases a precomputer era approach to the inventory tasks, might be one of keeping items in the Kardex type of visible-tip records. In an EDP system such records would be replaced by magnetic tapes. Requisition and/or periodic check information could be fed into the computer, where the transaction and the update are carried out and a list of the activity is produced. The ultimate in this approach would be the use of a special file computer assembly, on line at all times, in order that random access to the status of each and every item may be available immediately. Such an access requirement can be envisioned as a valuable resource at the time of large scale emergencies.

It should be stressed that the clerical type data problem is not confined to the paid Fire Service, as might be implied from the foregoing examples. Volunteer fire departments with large membership roles and involvement with a large number of events are taxed by the

[61]International City Managers Association, *Municipal Fire Administration*. Chicago: International City Managers Association (1969), pp. 284–288.

[62]*Op. Cit.*, Harry E. Hickey, p. 9.

burden of records management.[63] The public fire safety systems organization contemplated in this book is designed to alleviate a considerable portion of this burden. However, to achieve this goal attention must be focused on a system-wide data collection and analysis base which can support EDP equipment.

Special Information Storage and Retrieval Programs

Almost every functional element of the proposed public fire safety systems organization requires data to be collected, stored, and retrieved in some form. The following examples are offered as an insight to some of the requirements and applications. The functional element data handling process is considered to be a bit more intricate in terms of both "hardware" and "software" requirements than was advanced under the more pure clerical operations.

A viable fire prevention program designed and implemented in accordance with the objectives outlined in Chapter I is going to be sufficiently complex to almost require computer support. Data banks could be compiled on buildings to be surveyed, their frequency, and their location. On the basis of this information, the computer could print out survey schedules and assignments. Once a survey is completed, the data elements associated with a building could be stored on tape. The input data could also be utilized to update the frequency of survey files for future assignments on a follow-up or cycle basis.

Probably most important is the concept that the survey information could be made available almost instantaneously in the event of an emergency for tactical size-up operations. Key information could be displayed on a CRT (Cathode Ray Tube) in the first responding emergency unit. Since it is perceived that the building data would be updated frequently, the responsible fire officer should have current and accurate information on which to base his decisions. Furthermore, with computer assistance and the right peripheral hardware, floor plans may be shown with selected areas enlarged for grasping specific details.

Another striking example of storage and retrieval computer support lies in the area of training programs. The personnel record of each fireman can be updated after each event according to his involvement. In other words data input would include his time involvement in the basic skills areas such as rescue, ventila-

tion, forcible entry, hand-line operation, pump operation, etc. On a cycle training program areas could be identified where men are not getting adequate experience for minimum skill maintenance. On the basis of predetermined levels of involvement and/or officer competency ratings, personnel could be assigned to special training classes. Such a proposition would allow for training programs geared more to the individual than is normally offered. To maintain the kind of involvement records perceived on a manual basis would require record keeping times that could be considered prohibitive in large fire departments.

Computers and Management by Exception

The concept of management by exception has already been established in this chapter. Now it is appropriate to cite an example concerning how this concept could be implemented into the public fire safety systems organization with computer support. The main Administration functions, Resource Management Funtion, and the Operations Management, set criteria for operational procedures, objective plans and performance standards. The organizational components are expected to function according to established criteria. However, when one or more elements of the organization, or in fact the total system, deviate from the criteria pattern by some prescribed amount, the system can be considered out of balance and must be corrected. Components out of balance must be reported to the responsible management or administration level. In essence the concept means that as long as the system components move according to a prescribed plan there is no requirement for deviant notification.

The current problem of false alarms in the Fire Service can be utilized as an example of exception reporting. Due mainly to resource limitations, a fire department is often forced to tolerate a few false alarm situations. Yet at some point in the crescendo of false alarm events a toleration level is exceeded and appropriate actions must be taken. The computer can be programmed to flag this toleration point based upon the incident reports. For instance, when a certain fire alarm box has been falsely pulled a certain number of times within a given span of time, the computer can print out the events when they happened and the associated history of other boxes in the area to identify event patterns. A daily, weekly or monthly data search could identify the false

---

[63]*Ibid.*, p. 10.

alarm problem areas. A lack of identification would carry the assumption that the false alarm problem was within the upper range previously established. Verification checks could also be called for on certain identified boxes.

Similar checks and printouts could be established for other event areas and parameters such as the frequency of fires in certain prescribed areas, the frequency by construction, by occupancy classification, etc. The capabilities for management by exception reports is almost limitless in terms of computer technology. There is obviously a limit regarding the cost obligation to achieve some sophisticated reporting schemes. The systems engineering group should be able to advise administrators of these constraints. The important concept to be engendered is the realization that managers and administrators do not have to be weighted down with voluminous amounts of pure printout data unless they want the "dump approach." The data can be selectively printed out to simply focus on problems, or trends, that could create a problem, if not arrested at some defined point. Finally, it is also important to realize that this report capability within the time span of a day or a week would simply not be possible without computer support.

Computers and the Coordination of Complex Operations

Communications and command procedures become extremely complex for fire departments under large-scale emergency conditions or where there is a significant group of simultaneous emergency events. There are records to support the assumption that fire department alarms offices can become easily overtaxed, resulting in delays or in a complete breakdown of the communications system altogether.[64] Neilsen and Ryland have demonstrated how the speed and flexibility of a computer can be utilized to establish more effective control over alarms, dispatching, and communications in general.[65] In a study of the Los Angeles Communications systems, they noted that

> the present system requires numerous steps to deploy the firefighting force — each step manually executed, each consuming precious time, but each vital to the success of a mission. Consequently, the overall objective is to simplify and automate the predetermined command and control procedures.

Such a command and control procedural unit must have specified operational requirements.

One of the main design components of a command and control unit should be to maintain the status of the various fire and emergency units. Dispatch personnel must be able to rapidly determine the location and status of all fire department units especially during periods of high activity which simply means that the dispatcher must have immediate means of finding the availability and location of each unit and of contacting it. As much as possible, therefore, the system should maintain unit status information with a minimum of personal attention from dispatch personnel. Therefore, it is necessary that a change in mobile equipment status should be entered into the system automatically or directly by the unit concerned.

Supplemental requirements of a command and control unit establish that dispatch personnel should no longer need to identify assignments manually from the street index and running cards and then determine the availability of the needed fire units. Unit assignments should be identified and dispatched according to the type, magnitude, and location of the incident. The dispatch function needs to identify company move-ups and fill-in-units. Also the system should automatically establish communication links, including land-line voice, radio voice, and teletype, to the dispatched units. The accomplishment of these tasks within a reasonable time frame are considered impossible without the automated support of computer systems.

Neilsen and Ryland report that the LAFD Command and Control System will permit any individual dispatcher to receive emergency calls, dispatch appropriate assignments, and handle other command and control functions in a fraction of the present time frames.[66] It is noted in their communications scheme that single-point dispatcher operations require that all sources of information and all communication links be instantly available to each dispatcher. The total communication-control system design is perceived for rapid and multiple access based upon the use of a digital computer and other peripheral data processing equipment with associated input-output consoles. A dispatch console will contain a cathode ray tube (CRT) display (Illustration III-5), a microfilm display, a color-coded unit status display, an input keyboard, and radio and telephone communications controls. This type

[64]Edward H. Blum, *Urban Fire Protection: Studies of the Operations of the New York City Fire Department.* New York: The New York City Rand Institute (R-681), January, 1971.

[65]D. J. Neilsen and H. G. Ryland, "Computer Command — Control," *Fire Journal,* May 1968, p. 43.

[66]*Ibid.,* p. 44.

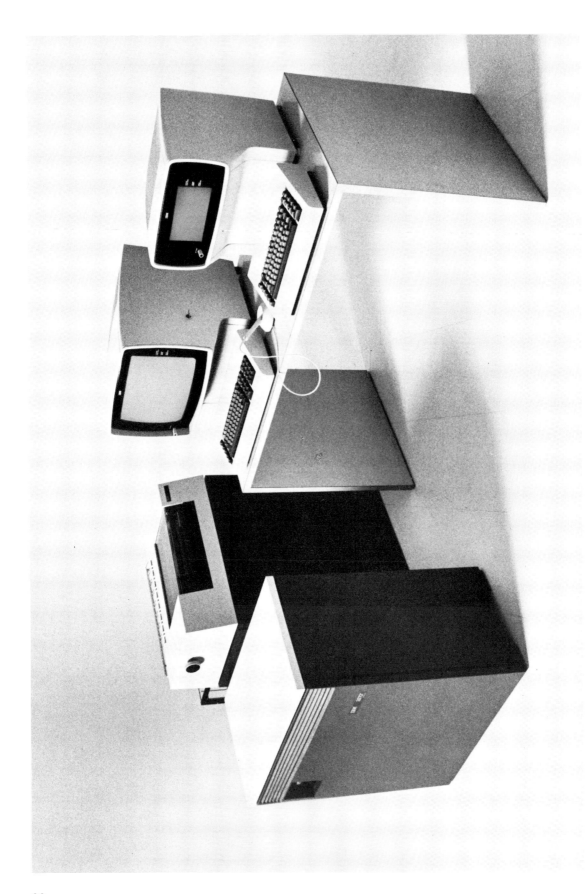

ILLUSTRATION III-5   DATA DISPLAY DEVICE

of system calls for real-time information.

An even higher level real-time support would be advantageous in the command and control complex. This need exists in the area of water supply adequacy. At best, most fire officers are dependent upon water supply information gathered during flow test programs. Even then the tests normally are limited to one- or two-point evaluations in a rather large heterogeneous area. The resultant figures do not lend themselves well to large-scale operations where pumper units are committed to several fire hydrants. Furthermore, localized consumer consumption demands might be considerably different at the time of the incident in relation to the test period. Therefore, the officer in charge is forced to make decisions on information that may not reflect current conditions. Technically, this problem can be overcome with the use of computer support. A real-time Hardy-Cross Analysis program could compute instantaneous flow and pressure availability at desired points on the water systems. The readout could be displayed on the command CRT, in the responsible officer's vehicle, or in a field command and control unit. The same program could be utilized to adjust demand pressure-volume relationships through the opening and closing of electro-mechanical valves, and adjusting the driving power for stationary pumps.

Policy — Strategy — Decision-Making — Education

This subtopic to the general area of data processing encompasses several points. However, the broad points utilized to suggest appropriate areas of computer support have a commonality among the title words. Management techniques employing simulations, gaming, modeling, statistics, probability theory, queuing theory, and Monte Carlo Techniques are representative of analysis methodology utilized to develop organizational policy, planning, strategy, decision-making theory and education of systems organization personnel. Each of these techniques is also aimed at developing rational decision-making through techniques employing quantitative analysis. Every evidence points to the realization that administrators and managers are moving into new areas for quantitative analysis support in the decision-making process. These analysis techniques would be incomprehensible without the capability of computer support. A modern public fire safety systems organization must be aware of these techniques and move forward toward their adoption if a viable organization is to be created.

Since World War II, under the labels of Operations Research, Management Science, and Systems Analysis, quantitative methods have been extended so that they can now be part of the mainstream of executive decision-making.[67] The point is that quantitative methods previously had been primarily used to provide data of various sorts of functional activities which executives then integrated intuitively while performing their functions of organizing, planning, and controlling. Recent developments in analytical methodology and the advent of electronic computers now permit quantitative methods to be utilized to provide answers when management asks "what would happen if" for highly complex situations. It should be emphasized that most decision situations will always require capable human judgments. However, the trend is toward facilitating the exercise of judgment by providing information of greater pertinence and with smaller volume.

Managerial activities are inconceivable without numerical data of some sort, and numerical data imply or require quantitative methods for collection, processing, or analysis. Often the necessary methods for collecting and processing data involve only simple arithmetic, and "analysis" may only mean comparing one number with another. Even disregarding such elementary procedures, the list of quantitative methods useful to managers is a long one.

It would appear appropriate to comment briefly on the sometimes confusing labeling of quantitative methods under the heads of Operations Research (OR), Management Science (MS), and the thrust area of this book, Systems Analysis (SA). These categories have so much in common that the distinctions are significant only for the purists. They all refer to the conscious formal application of logic and scientific objectivity to the problems of decision-making. The Systems Analysis purists maintain that Operations Research deals with decision situations which permit mathematical representation of the relationships between the controllable (choice) variables and a single, unambiguous criterion of preference.[68] That is, OR deals with relatively simple statistical systems. System Analysis is claimed by the purists to apply to complex situations involving more vague objectives and many criteria,

[67]*Op. Cit.*, Fred Brown, p. 155.

[68]*Ibid.*, p. 158.

usually some of which are nonquantitative, so that the mathematical techniques so useful to simpler situations are not applicable. Those advocating a broader use of the OR label argue that even though the pioneering applications performed under the OR label do deal with relatively unambiguous criteria and with situations that are admittedly optimization ventures, this does not imply that OR is restricted to such situations. Those performing studies under the label of Management Science maintain that MS covers complex decision situations as well as the simple situations ascribed by the SA purists to OR. Some of those who advocate MS designation have associated OR with studies of military and hardware systems, but some OR purists suggest that studies of hardware systems are in the province of systems engineering.[69]

The task of decision-making, viewed in the context of the entire decision-making process (see Chapter IV) presents many problems. The following general categories of decision-making problems are common. They are offered to sharpen the relationship between offered examples of computer application and decision-making tools.

1. Insufficient range of feasible alternatives.
2. Too many alternatives.
3. The outcomes of a possible action known only imperfectly, especially in terms alternative to the established objectives.
4. The possible range of outcomes known, but specific outcomes uncertain.
5. Presence of many pertinent but conflicting criteria, rendering evaluation (choice) difficult; in addition, objectives may be vague.

The above and related categories will be discussed in later chapters as each point reflects on administrative and management concepts associated with public fire safety. However, each point should be remembered as the respective subject areas bearing on quantitative decision-making are reviewed.

Tools and Techniques

For distinctiveness and comprehension, the several techniques of analysis for this subsection will be covered by topic heading. However, the reader should not assume that problem-solving techniques fall into neat categories which lend themselves to solutions through straight-forward cookbook approaches. Combinations of several techniques may be appropriate in given instances. The analyst must de-

fine the problem carefully and then fit the most appropriate technique into the problem-solving process. Tailoring the techniques to the problems, plus the use of good judgment, appear to lead to the best possible solution.

Some of the techniques to be described have proven worthwhile in the areas of administrative and management decision-making over a period of years. Some have not been applied fruitfully in real situations as yet. Still others fall in between these extremes, having had limited application in practical situations. In each case, the movement from conceptualization to actuation could not be fully realized without computer support to handle the analysis functions.

Some of the techniques to be described have proved worthwhile to administrators in the decision-making process over a period of years. Some have not been applied to any great extent. Still other techniques fall in between these two extremes, having had a moderate amount of application in practical situations. It will be important to ascertain the usefulness of particular techniques in implementing the systems concept to public fire safety.

Systems Analysis

This whole text revolves around the systems concept of organization as defined in Chapter II. Contained within the broad structure of systems theory is the specific branch of systems analysis. The quantitative aspects of systems analysis needed to be evaluated in relation to the decision-making process.

The analysis of systems could be construed as an extremely diffused organizational activity. Indeed, systems analysis has special connotations in systems engineering, systems and procedures work, and operations research or management science. In recent years, however, the term has taken on special meaning because of its use in large-scale, complex decision problems at the national level, particularly in the Department of Defense.[70] The present quasi-military nature of public fire departments makes a parallel analogy appropriate.

In the case of the Defense Department, the term applies to the process of evaluating alternative courses of action in allocating resources to meet national security objectives. Then within the constraints of accepted (at least temporarily) objectives, various programs are proposed to accomplish designated tasks. A similar relationship could be representative

[69]Ibid., p. 159.

[70]Ibid., p. 212.

of public fire safety. The resources change from weapon systems to suppression systems. With the objectives defined, alternate courses of providing resources to suppress fires according to acceptable loss limits could be effected through program planning. Therefore, systems analysis includes the process of setting objectives as well as that of evaluating alternative proposals. Technical feasibility may be of prime importance at this stage; the immediate goal is to develop alternative means of achieving the objective(s). As more alternatives become feasible, the systems analysis process may involve choosing the most appropriate fire station location, or a mix of responding fire units from several stations in terms of technical superiority in meeting specified requirements. Under the broad view of systems analysis both quantity and quality are considered.

Given the unlimited resources of fire apparatus and manpower, the task would be accomplished at this stage. However in the real world, the resources of equipment and manpower are scarce and costs become an important consideration. Systems analysis involves a thorough scrutiny of cost-effectiveness trade-offs. For instance, at what point do costs become prohibitive (Fire safety economic objective 6) regardless of the increasing effectiveness of suppressing fire at some defined modular level? In other words, at what point should society start to accept the risk? The answer is to balance these factors within an overall systems analysis approach to goal setting and resource allocation.

More detailed management science tools and techniques can be used to carry out the quantitative steps in systems analysis. Computers facilitate the use of detailed, comprehensive calculations to ensure a thorough consideration of all the relevant variables. Alain C. Enthoven states that qualitative approaches are important also: ". . . analysis cannot supplant decision-making. Policy decisions cannot be calculated."[71]

Systems analysis stresses the importance of developing a balanced approach to decision-making — quantifying where appropriate and mixing in value judgments at the proper time. Enthoven supports this point in the following quotation.[72]

All of this is to suggest that although analysis in support of decision makers at the national policy level must be honest, in the sense that the quantitative factors are selected without bias, that the calculations are accurate, that alternatives are not arbitrarily suppressed, it cannot be objective in the sense of being independent of values. Value judgments are an integral part of analysis; and it is the role of the analyst to bring to light for the policymaker exactly how and where value judgments enter so that the latter can make his own value judgments in the light of as much relevant information as possible.

Systems analysis is primarily a managerial approach to decision-making wherein overall-system effectiveness is related to resource allocations in a process of careful, searching evaluations. Program-planning-budgeting and cost-effectiveness analysis are two approaches to the task; other more specific tools of the systems analysis techniques follow. It is important to stress that systems analysis in either a broad or a limited connotation is incomprehensible without computer techniques to carry out the quantitative steps in the analysis process. The computer is necessary to facilitate the use of detailed, comprehensive calculations and to ensure a thorough consideration of all the relevant variables.

Linear Programming

One of the most potentially useful of the operations-research techniques to problems associated with Public Fire Safety Organization is linear programming. It is both an approach to the formulation and statement of the problems for which it is suited and a set of mathematical procedures for making the calculations leading to selection of the best course of of action. It has been defined as:[73]

. . . a technique for specifying how to use limited resources or capacities of a business to obtain a particular objective, such as least cost, highest margin or least time, when those resources have alternate uses. It is a technique that systematizes for certain conditions the process of selecting the most desirable course of action from a number of available courses of action, thereby giving management information for making a more effective decision about the resources under its control.

Linear programming might be applied to public fire safety with good results in the determination of:

1. The best inventory strategy for apparatus and hose.
2. The effect of changes in bid proposals and equipment specifications.
3. The mathematical optimization of locating fire stations.
4. The most effective interface relationship between private fire suppression equipment and public fire suppression equipment.

[71]Alain C. Enthoven, "Systems Analysis in Decision Making," *Military Review*, January 1953, p. 15.

[72]*Ibid.*, p. 14.

[73]Robert O. Ferguson and Lauren F. Sargent, "Linear Programming," New York: McGraw-Hill Book Company, New York, 1958, p. 3.

5. The lowest level of inservice companies to provide a defined level of response over a twenty-four-hour time span.

6. The determination of the cost differential to benefit ratio for each of the stated examples.

The above list is only a representative example, but it does point out functional areas where linear programming might be useful. There appears to be some common characteristics in each one of these problem areas. First, various functions are in competition for the allocation of a given and fixed number of resource units. Next, the cost of allocating a given number of units of a resource to a given function is proportional to the number of units allocated. Such a situation could have a solution in which the total cost of the overall function is a minimum, or conversely, the effectiveness level is maximum. In addition to these considerations, in each instance the administrator must consider a large number of factors which may affect his decision. Also, these factors are interdependent, so that the administrator must consider them individually and in relation to each other. Finally, the choice must be made for one solution or course of action from among many obvious alternatives and, perhaps, some others which are not so obvious. Without linear programming techniques, these decisions must be based on experience, feel, intuition, and hope.[74]

Once a linear program problem has been set up properly on the computer, slight modifications can be made with little additional programming effort. Thus, once large-scale, complex problems have been defined and variables specified, relationships can be developed which allow reasonably quick assessment of the impact of changes in pertinent variables. For example, a linear program might be developed around the optimum number of men to be assigned to a given engine company so that not more than ten per cent of fire duty time was on a standby basis. The manpower could be varied with given risk factors to achieve the desired results under a defined set of conditions.[75]

The above pertinent points concerning linear programming are well summarized by Alan S. Manne.[76]

In all likelihood, the most important thing to be derived from the Linear Programming calculation is not the optimal product mix itself, but rather the implicit values of the individual bottlenecks. This seems typical of problems of economic choice. We are interested in finding optimal solutions to a problem under carefully defined given conditions — precisely so that we can find out what it would be worth to us if those conditions could themselves be altered . . . If linear programming provided nothing but a more reliable framework for estimating incremental costs and values, this alone would justify its importance to management.

Linear programming does have certain recognizable constraints. The fact that this method treats all relationships as linear functions limits the realism of the analysis. Linear programming cannot deal effectively with more than one set of conditions at a time. Optimal solutions to real problems involving simultaneous changes in several variables are extremely difficult to compute. Even with large-scale computer equipment, computational constraints for real situations do develop. Thus, it should be recognized that problems often must be simplified in order to reduce them to a form that can be handled by analytical techniques and available computational facilities. When this is done the application of the results to overall system may not be appropriate.

Quadratic and Dynamic Programming

The two named techniques have been developed in order to offset some of the disadvantages inherent in linear programming. For example, quadratic programming, like linear programming, is an algebraic technique, but one that can handle problems with nonlinear relationships. This allows development of a mathematical model yielding a more complete description of the system under study. In other words, more than one variable in a set can be changed on each computer run. For example, it would allow for computation problems in municipal water supply analysis where the delivery quantity, the delivery rate and the water density of application varied logarithmically as the area of the risk varies on a linear base. Such a technique might be useful to tactical command and control operations.

The intended objective of dynamic programming is that of facilitating solutions to sequential problems. It is a method of solving multistage problems in which the decisions at one stage become the conditions governing the succeeding stages.[77] The potential for multistage decisions processes in public fire safety

[74]*Op. Cit.*, Johnson, Kast, and Rosenzweig, p. 292.

[75]*Op. Cit.*, Edward H. Blum, pp. 11–16.

[76]Alan S. Manne, *Economic Analysis of Business Decisions.* New York: McGraw-Hill Book Company, New York, 1961, pp. 19–20.

[77]Richard Bellman, *Dynamic Programming.* Princeton: Princeton University Press, 1957, p. vii.

command and control situations appears large. An officer in charge of a large-scale event often is required to make rapid cascading decisions. Through simulation (to be discussed) or through a real-world situation, programs could be developed that given a set of criteria would respond with an evolutionary course of events leading to a desired outcome. Coupled to a cathode ray reading tube, a dynamic program readout could provide fire officers with necessary assistance to the decision-making process on the imagined or real fireground.

Dynamic programming is still in a state of development and has not been applied widely to real problems.[78] However, it does have considerable potential and may provide a frame of reference for analysis of large-scale, complex operations.

Statistics and Probability

Mention has already been made in Chapter I concerning the potential role of statistics and probability theory in relation to identifying quantitatively factors related to organizational objectives. A few additional concepts are now presented to illustrate how statistics are so much a part of the decision-making process. Furthermore, a complete statistical program for public fire safety would not be economically possible without the support of computer analysis. A large variety of statistical calculation requirements are currently available as canned software packages. In most cases pre-programs eliminate the need for extensive outlays for new programming effort.

One of the most firmly established analytical techniques for modern management revolves around the use of statistical inference. Quite often textbooks on management consider the term statistics primarily in terms of data, or at most, in terms of descriptive statistics. However, modern statistics techniques provide a useful tool for the decision-making process, primarily in the realms of estimation and hypothesis testing. This connotation is supported in the following quotation by E. Bright Wilson, Jr.:[79]

> It is the purpose of statistical analysis to provide methods of treating data so that the maximum information can be obtained with a predetermined risk of drawing false conclusions. No method of analysis can extract more information from a set of data than is contained therein, and no method, statistical or otherwise, can draw conclusions from experimental data with zero

risk of error. The use of statistical methods is based on a reasonable assumption that accepted principles of logic and probability should produce correct answers more often than guessing.

The use of sampling techniques in public fire safety must increase; in some cases it is the only approach to obtaining data for improving decision-making, and in other cases it is the only feasible approach in terms of time requirements and/or money requirements. An appreciation of the fire problem as it relates to certain variables such as occupancy, structures and social conditions can only be developed through statistical analysis.

Administrative decisions relating to public fire safety resource allocations involve assumptions concerning the probability of future events. Therefore, it is important to understand the nature of probability theory and its application in decision-making. For example, the probability of fire losses under certain sets of conditions must be related to the important aspects of these outcomes (i.e., whether the loss is acceptable to the community) in order to provide meaningful information on the requirements for manpower and equipment resources in future years. When a sequence of events is involved, each with a probability distribution for various outcomes, the problem can become very complex. In such cases it is imperative that a systematic approach be employed which takes into account every pertinent facet of the problem. The statistical parameters of such complex situations would not be comprehensible without the rapid analytical capability of computers.

Game Theory

Game theory involves analysis of the choice of strategies in competitive situations. It appears to have had a major impact on the development of linear programming, as well as starting a new way of thinking about competitive decision-making.[80] The literature indicates that up through 1969 game theory applications have been few in number and limited in scope because of the unmanageable complexities that arise once the number of contestants exceeds two and the rules allow more than trivial freedom of action. The well-known game of monopoly is often cited as an example of simple game theory.

Today numerous groups are working on game theory applications to real administration problems. The approaches utilized in applying

---

[78]*Ibid.*, p. viii.

[79]E. Bright Wilson, Jr., *An Introduction to Scientific Research.* New York: McGraw-Hill Book Company, 1952, p. 57.

[80]C. West Churchman, Russel L. Ackoff, and E. Leonard Arnoff, *Introduction to Operation's Research.* New York: John Wiley and Sons, Inc., 1957, p. 519.

game techniques to complex situations can provide managers with valuable insight relative to complex situations. The process of analyzing data relevant to organizational events thus forces administrators to consider all possible alternatives for both their own and the opponent's strategy. The necessary formal thinking process insures consideration of the total problem.

Game theory often utilizes other sophisticated and unusually mathematically oriented methods for understanding variable relationships and for evaluating alternate courses of action.[81] Associated with the game approach to the administration and management of organizations are such techniques as Monte Carlo, Decision Tree or fault tree, simulation, and network analysis. Depending upon the literature reference, some authors would treat one or more of these topics as separate entities from Game Theory.

This author wishes to follow the approach of Johnson, Kast and Rosenzweig in considering that alternate approaches to problems are very much like playing a game whether the end-result is certainty, uncertainty or some point in between.[82] It is also important to note that each of the techniques referenced employ the combination of variable analysis. This variable analysis is often sufficiently complex as to require computer techniques to achieve end-results within reasonable time spans. However, it is equally important to realize that some simple, and often rewarding, game situations can be developed and analyzed without computer support. The following techniques should be reviewed with these points in mind.

Simulation

Simulation techniques represent an important part of the game process in decision-making. The term simulation means "to obtain the essence of, without reality."[83] In other words, concrete or abstract experiences can be created and tried without carrying the exercise to fulfillment in the real world. The alternate response routes for a fire department pumper from the station to a given building can be simulated with a map. Several routes under several conditions can be tried before selecting the apparent best route. This example represents a very simplified concept of simulation. In the normal management or research

sense, simulation can be used in the application of operations research techniques to specific problems.

Two basic types of large-scale systems simulation have been developed. In one case, the decision-making process is programmed into the simulation in order that the entire system may be run automatically on a computer complex without involvement of human decision-makers. Complex transportation systems can be constantly simulated based upon flow directions and peak-load conditions. A fire department response of several vehicles could be evaluated on a real-time basis with this type of transportation simulation process. This technique is often called systems simulation.[84]

A second type of simulation exercise requires recurrent decisions on the part of outside decision-makers, the effect or results of those decisions being generated by a simulated system which again is normally programmed on a computer. This approach often utilizes role players in the decision process. A basic example applied to public fire safety might include a game approach to locating fire stations plus the allocation of men and equipment to staff these stations. The objective might be to keep the response time of apparatus to a minimum for all segments of the city. The role players could include citizen group representatives, the mayor's office, the fire and police commissioners, the urban planner, and a labor representative. Once the competitive decision-making takes place, the computer would evaluate the results in relation to a set of predefined parameters. The game output would indicate how close the players came to making optimum decisions. This example also leads to another technique that can be employed where there is the need to establish probabilistic events in the simulation exercise. The supportive approach is called the Monte Carlo Technique.

Monte Carlo Technique

A particular application of random sampling called the Monte Carlo Technique can serve to obtain a satisfactory solution to many problems that involve the interactions of a number of probabilistic events, and where some representation must be made of combination techniques. Basically, the technique is a process for developing data through the use of some random-number generator.[85] For variables which are difficult to evaluate, the Monte

---

[81]*Ibid.*, p. 520.

[82]*Op. Cit.*, Johnson, Kast, and Rosenzweig, pp. 289–305.

[83]*Ibid.*, p. 299.   [84]*Ibid.*, p. 301.   [85]*Ibid.*, p. 298.

Carlo Technique can be used to generate respective values from the proper statistical distribution. In other words, as a support to simulation, a sample of values can be generated and used to represent observations in the real world. In the specific case of a public fire safety system, the Monte Carlo Technique might be utilized to generate the probable fire incidents in a given sector of a city over a defined time span. This generation would be based on the combination of conditions such as occupancy, construction and private protection that might affect the loss condition. This is an example where the use of the Monte Carlo Technique can be used to simulate certain aspects of problems which cannot be approached through rigorous mathematical analysis.

Logic Diagramming

Network analysis, decision trees, critical path methods and PERT (Program Evaluation Research Task) are examples of a broad area called Logic Diagramming.[86] By means of geometric symbols and interconnecting lines, bars, or arrows showing the significant operations, occurrences, sequences, and interrelationships, the logic diagram can display the characteristics, constraints and time-phased logic of a problem situation. Logic diagrams can take many forms according to the analytical requirement and the predisposition of the users.

The decision tree (a modified version is called the fault tree) is considered to be the prototype for the preponderance of logic diagramming.[87] It is a linear means for representing alternatives, objectives, and consequences of a series of decisions. The decision tree diagram is a good initial procedure to follow in systematic problem solving because it can represent the dead end or "disjunctive" paths as well as the continuing or "conjunctive" paths that may be taken.[88] The decision tree diagram demonstrates that the process of finding the preferred solution to a problem is something like going through a maze in which more than one route may lead to the end objective. Further, it is possible to assign a ranking order of value to the various routes. The diagramming of more than one route is done to gain an overview of several alternatives

so that selection of the one thought to be best can be made on a comparative basis. When this selection has been made the less promising alternate paths can be pruned from the tree. The process of selecting the desired path to follow amount to converting to a "Critical Path Method" or a PERT Network.

Logic diagramming has a distinct potential as an analytic technique for public fire safety systems organizations. The area of communications can be singled out as one area for possible application. The receipt of an alarm is actually the starting point. The processing of the alarm would be handled on a flow diagram (called a network) consisting of all the activities and events that must be accomplished (i.e., establish location, unit assignment, verification of units in service, keying of units for multiple alarms, filling empty companies, and returning units to prior status) showing their planned sequence of accomplishment and interdependencies. An extension of this concept might include elapsed time estimates for activities and identification of activity paths in the network which are critical to controlling a fire before a potential flashover takes place. This exercise could represent a possible and worthy objective.

Summary

Kenneth Boulding states, "One of man's most pervasive activities is problem solving."[89] The scientist and the manager can come together to define the problem and designate the information and analysis which would be pertinent to that problem. An inspired goal for public fire safety administrators might be to become imbued with the scientific approach. Only then will management science be capable of achieving its potential within the framework of the perceived public fire safety systems organization.

Systems concepts, by emphasizing wholeness and integration of the various elements to be analyzed, provide a framework for achieving mutual understanding. Relationships rather than parts are stressed in order to ascertain how the elements fit together. The penetrating analysis of the complex system can be significantly enhanced by computer support application. This chapter has attempted to demonstrate that most of the applicable analysis methods are sufficiently intricate to make the analysis process a real chore without the aid of computer support. To retrace some earlier

[86]*Op. Cit.*, Fred Brown, p. 106.

[87]Guy A. Best, Director of PERT Orientation and Training Center, Department of the Air Force, in Fred Brown, *Management: Concepts and Practice*, 1967, p. 108.

[88]*Ibid.*, p. 107.

[89]Kenneth Boulding, "General System Theory: The Skeleton of Science," *Management Science*, April 1956, p. 198.

steps, it can be stated that the computer fulfills one very important function in the scientific method. The scientific method can be summarized as a systematic, orderly approach to problem solving which includes defining the problem, formulating the hypothesis, collecting relevant information, analyzing the information and drawing conclusions.[90] The computer fits into the area of information and data associated with research. It is also important to note that the computer does not complete the final step in the drawing of conclusions. The computer does not make the final decisions. The computer simply provides more meaningful relationships of data to enable the administrators and managers to make intelligent decisions.

Public fire safety personnel need to become aware of the parallels that are evident between decision-making and problem solving. While the scientific method normally is considered an integral part of good research, it also can be considered an integral part of good administrative decision-making. In fact, the terms decision-making and administration have been considered synonymous by some writers.[91] A systematic, orderly, comprehensive approach to decision-making includes defining the problem, setting forth the available alternatives, analyzing them in light of environment (competitive and internal aspects), and choosing the most appropriate course of action. Public fire safety has been grossly negligent in approaching its problems from a comprehensive standpoint. The systems approach, utilizing the scientific method, and with potential computer support for problem analysis promises to open new modes of management capability to public fire safety. The public fire safety systems organization role can be examined as it interfaces with the rest of the community. The essential concept is to replace "bad experience" and "rule of thumb" techniques with a stress on scientific management.

This point leads to a further conclusion. The terms operations research and management science have followed in the wake of the term scientific management. While these more current approaches stress quantification, model building, and mathematical analysis, they still fit under the overall umbrella of the application of scientific method to general organization or administration problems. Thus any accepted definition of management science must be broad when considering the application of scientific method to managerial decision-making. Many tools and techniques lie within this broad framework.

In further summary, this book recognizes that one of the most important of these tools is the concept of a model used to represent the operational system under study. The development of models requires the explicit treatment of system variables and forces an integrated approach to the overall situation. The introduction of electronic computers to management science has allowed analysts to use approaches heretofore considered unfeasible to research.

The identity of research and administrative techniques has advanced the total framework of systems analysis to include such areas as: linear programming, quadratic and dynamic programming, and various forms of network analysis. These techniques especially provide administrators and managers with an opportunity, through their systems support function, to deal with large-scale, complex problem situations. Some problems can be well defined and a state of relative certainty assumed. Other problems involving uncertainty require somewhat different techniques of analysis. Statistics and probability are appropriate tools in many cases. In addition, Game Theory provides an approach to administrative strategy, but the theory has not proved applicable in many real-world situations. Monte Carlo Techniques can be useful in problems of uncertainty to simulate a certain randomness that may be a part of any systems model under study.

Because applications of typical mathematical analysis require explicit determination of all relevant variables in the system, simplifying assumptions often must be made in order to carry out analytical solutions. This type of problem currently is in evidence with several of the fire station siting models that have been or are under development by various research organizations. Because of the complexity of the situation and the lack of objective criteria, the variable analysis appears to be oversimplified in many cases.

Simplifications of the order described cut down the usefulness of the techniques since the results may not be applicable in real life. To offset this problem, simulation techniques are being proposed with the goal of describing systems and developing workable solutions on the basis of trial-and-error methods. Rather than striving for an optimal solution which

[90]Herbert A. Simon, *The New Science of Management Decision*, New York: Harper and Row, Publishers, 1960, p. 2.

[91]Richard A. Johnson, Fremont E. Kast, and James E. Rosenzweig. *The Theory and Management of Systems*, 2nd ed. New York: McGraw-Hill Book Company, 1967, p. 281.

may not be applicable because of simplifying assumptions made in structuring the problem, simulation focuses on describing the system as it exists in order to model it realistically. The obvious advantage of such a model is that policy changes can be evaluated in terms of their impact on the simulated system, thus allowing a laboratory for testing administrative and managerial decision-making without committing the resources of the organization. Time spans for such modeling can only be compressed with the support of a computer to generate events, quantify decision inputs and print or display output data for evaluation and retrial.

The science of management in general, and the simulation exercises in particular, can be useful, if not essential to the systems concept. Emphasis has been placed on model building because it appears to be one of the most useful tools for forcing decision-makers to structure the operation under analysis as an integrated system tied together by a series of set matrices. Emphasis has also been placed on the realization that the use of computers in symbolic system simulation allows treatment of large-scale complex systems. Thus the analyst can develop a model around a group of subsystems, their interrelationship, and the total system. Such an approach provides a framework for more detailed analytical examination of various segments of the total system. This book is attempting to establish the realization that a public fire safety organization is a complex system within a larger urban system. The public fire safety organization framework and mode of operation must blend in with the broader urban community system. Public fire safety systems can only be fully understood as a subsystem of other systems. The computer is but one tool to aid and assist in the process of understanding.

Chapter 3

Bibliographical Entries

Books

Arnold, Robert, Harold Hill, and Aylmer Nichols. *Introdduction to Data Processing.* New York: John Wiley and Sons, Inc., 1967.

Bellman, Richard. *Dynamic Programming.* Princeton: Princeton University Press, 1957.

Brown, Fred, ed. *Management: Concepts and Practices.* Washington: Industrial College of the Armed Forces, 1967.

Chapin, Ned. *An Introduction to Automatic Computers.* Princeton: D. Van Nostrand Co. Inc., 1957.

Churchman, C. West, Russel L. Ackoff and E. Leonard Arnoff. *Introduction to Operations Research.* New York: John Wiley and Sons, Inc. 1957.

Ferguson, Robert O., and Lauren F. Sargent. *Linear Programming.* New York: McGraw Book Company, 1958.

International City Managers Association. *Municipal Fire Administration.* Chicago: International City Managers Association, 1969.

Johnson, Richard, F. Kast, and J. Rosenzweig. *The Theory and Management of Systems.* New York: McGraw-Hill Book Company, 1967.

Malcolm, Donald G., A. J. Rowe and L. F. McConnell. *Management Control Systems.* New York: John Wiley and Sons, Inc. 1960.

Manne, Alan S. *Economic Analysis of Business Decisions.* New York: McGraw Book Company, 1961.

Simon, Herbert. *The New Science of Management Decision.* New York: Harper and Row, Inc. 1960.

Wilson, E. Bright, Jr. *An Introduction to Scientific Research.* New York: McGraw-Hill Book Company, 1952.

Publications of the Government, Learned Societies, and Other Organizations

Blum, Edward H. *Urban Fire Protection: Studies of the New York City Fire Department.* New York: The New York City Rand Institute (R-681), January 1971.

Bureau of the Budget. *Automatic Data Processing Glossary.* Washington: U. S. Government Printing Office (1962).

Corliss, William. *Computers.* Washington: Division of Technical Information, U. S. Atomic Energy Commission, 1967.

Hickey, Harry E. *The Perceived Involvement of Fire Department Officers: Operational and Management Functions.* Albany: The International Fire Administration Institute, 1970.

Periodicals

Boulding, Kenneth. "General Systems Theory — The Skeleton of Science." *Management Science,* April 1956, p. 197.

Enthoven, Alain. "Systems Analysis in Decision Making," *Military Review,* January 1953, p. 15.

Neilsen, D. J., and H. J. Ryland, "Computer Command — Control," *Fire Journal,* May 1968, p. 43.

Chapter IV

The Administration Process of the
Public Fire Safety Systems Organization

Introduction

Organization administrators have a set of unique characteristics that set them distinctly separate from organization managers. This is a bold statement. The concept is not shared by a large segment of the community of public administrators. However, the separateness thesis existing between administrators and managers appears to have such significant implications for the systems approach to organization as to require its adoption in this book. The first objective of this chapter is to substantiate this distinction and to demonstrate its relevance to the concept of a Public Fire Safety Systems Organization.

One word in the last sentence has to be singled out as "key" to the thrust of this chapter. The term is *Public*. The discussion is limited to an organization that specifically serves the public interest. Felix Nigro indicates that when the sources of policies and objectives of the government programs are analyzed, it is apparent that public affairs are conducted in a quite different environment from those of a private business.[1] It should be recognized early in this discussion that the constraints and pressures constantly felt by one administering in a public realm is somewhat different from that of one administering in the private sphere. The public sector offers constraints and pressures peculiar to the governmental situation. The governmental framework in this discussion will be limited to the local government level.

[1]Felix A. Nigro, *Modern Public Administration*. New York: Harper and Row, 1965, pp. 14–15.

The environment of the public fire safety administrator might include such diverse demands and requirements as follows: First, there is the response to an executive group of local government. The public fire safety administrator must respond to and be cognizant of the demands of the Mayor; or the city manager; the form of council; the local political organizations; various other forms of organized interest groups such as the insurance industry; citizen pressure groups such as the local chamber of commerce; and at times the general public, especially when there is a large-loss fire.

In other words, the public fire administrator directly relates to persons outside the organization structure on a daily basis. The management level in the public fire safety organization, by contrast, is somewhat shielded from these outside influences at the defined support, operating and implementing levels. However, this chapter will demonstrate that, at the functional planning and directing levels, the external factors tend to have an impact on the actions taken in the development and execution of public programs.

The public fire safety administrator must be a politically sensitive person. The term politics has often been considered "a dirty word" in the connotation of public fire departments. To divorce the fire department from political sensitivity would be to place the fire department in a vacuum — out of touch with reality. There is a distinction between political awareness and political corruption. A fire chief who is appointed because he is the mayor's son-in-law is an entirely different proposition from the fire administrator who is engaged in policy-making and power struggles that take place every day in the human activity of the community. Albert Lepawsky makes the observation that a political approach in an organizational context simply means that "the administrator is being shrewd and engaging in 'horse-trading'."[2] In contrast, the management level does horse-trading also but the framework and level of activity are different. The administrator works in the external organizational environment as well as the internal organization structure. The operating management levels almost solely are confined to the inter-organization type of activity.

Wallace S. Sayre establishes an important premise on this subject area. He notes that politics does not have to foster a bad connotation within organizations.[3] He indicates that it is unfortunate that a dichotomy exists between administration and politics. There appears to be an overt anxiousness to keep partisan influence out of the daily work of public administration. What political scientists have feared were the spoilsman and the evil consequences of handing out government jobs and rewards for supporting a political party, or a political candidate in power or seeking power. This type of "playing politics has been condemned because it stood in the way of administrative reform."[4] The reformers have wanted administration separated from politics in this sense. The writings of such notable political scientists as John M. Pfiffner, Frank P. Sherwood, Harold Laswell, and Wallace S. Sayre, seem to be saying that other writers have gone too far in arguing the separability of administration.[5]

Today, the same determination exists to keep out the spoilsman, but the broader definition of politics now holds sway. This broader view equates administrative policy-making with the reality of politics. Thus, administration must be regarded as a part of the political process (regardless of the level of government). Wallace S. Sayre again summarizes this point very well.[6] "The exercise of discretionary power, the making of value choices, is a characteristic and in-creasing function of administrators . . .; they are thus importantly engaged in politics." Future subsections of this chapter will deal with the administrator's relationship outside of the public fire safety system. How the fire administrator relates to the broader community systems is the story of how the administrator becomes politically involved. It is doubtful that the public fire safety administrator can comprehend the objectives outlined in this book and structure a program to meet these objectives without becoming involved in the power struggles of the community.

There are other very important distinctions between the administrative process and the management process. The following points are intended to focus on the differential functions between administration and management in relation to the organizational framework provided in this book. The distinctions, while not pure in reality, are sufficiently homogeneous to support the necessity for a dichotomous treatment.

The Functions of Public Fire Safety Administrators

The broad function of the public fire safety administrator in today's complex urban environment is to coordinate the activities of the various internal and external resource systems with the several operational systems in a manner that will optimize the structured objectives of the organization. The administrator must understand the organization, not as a number of isolated parts, but as a descriptive and viable system; he must have knowledge of the relationship between the parts and be aware of each component's potential interactions. Essentially, the fire administrator must bring the individual elements, which may have diverse individual goals, together into an integrated organized system with all the parts working toward the common organizational mission. Management does not bear the responsibility of this broad charge.

With the growing specialization emphasized in the Fire Service, the growing size of fire departments and the functional intricacies of the fire-protection organization, the problem of integrating support and operational activities has increased rapidly over the past few years and it appears that organization component integration will become even greater in importance in the near future. The realization prompts the establishment of the following further distinctions.

[2]Albert Lepawsky, ed., *Administration, The Art and Science of Organization and Management*. New York: Knopf, 1955, p. 41.

[3]Wallace Sayre, "Premises of Public Administration: Past and Emerging." *Public Administration Review*, XVIII, No. 2 (Spring 1958), p. 104.

[4]*Ibid.*, p. 4.

[5]James C. Charlesworth, ed., *Theory and Practice of Public Administration: Scope, Objectives, and Methods (Monograph 8 AAPS and ASPA)*. Philadelphia: The American Academy of Political and Social Science, pp. 1–63.

[6]*Op. Cit.*, Wallace Sayre, p. 105.

Fred Brown states,[7] "it is generally accepted that policy formulation, in the hierarchy of organization, outranks management." It is further recognized that policy formulation is the responsibility of the highest holder of authority in the organization. This highest authority is labeled administration. It is this administrative authority level in the organization that makes the final decisions. The management levels lie below the pinnacle of the organization. Furthermore, managers are considered as advisors to the decision-making process; the responsible authority for decisions is retained at the administrative level. Finally management is the executor of the policy framework.

Before extending this discussion it is important to note that management and policy formulation depend on each other. Bad policy carried out by effective management is considered the essence of oppressive dictatorship.[8] Poor management, in contrast, can subvert and negate good policy. Therefore, one can state with conviction that good policy and effective management together mean a more successful accomplishment of objective purposes.

Traditionally, one of the most well-known and simplified breakdowns of the functions of an administrator is that of Luther Gulick. Gulick's premise can be summarized by the letters POSDCORB which stand for planning, organizing, staffing, directing, coordinating, reporting, and budgeting.[9] Despite its classic nature, POSDCORB retains an important message even for the systems concept of organization. The functional elements cannot be ignored or subverted even though the organization philosophy has changed.

Gulick clearly stated three decades ago that each of the functions in POSDCORB did not follow each other in the chronological order presented. However, under traditional organizational theory it appears that a notion of sequence was implied. Under the systems concept the functions might require reordering for purposes of emphasis but it is more important to realize the interdependence of each function to the remaining functions. The functions by name only are subject to a variety of interpretations. It is the interpretation of the functions that have been altered under the systems

concept more than the inherency of the function itself. To understand this relationship change between terms it is necessary to demonstrate the change in operational definitions.

The traditional meaning of the POSDCORB term is very well synthesized by Fred Brown. Each of the following operational definitions are quoted directly from Brown's book *Management: Concepts and Practice*.[10]

> Planning is the process of looking ahead and selecting among the alternatives which affect the future of the enterprise.

Essential to this definition is the concept that the administrator is faced with the never-ending process of forecasting events, deciding future directions, and communicating the future tense to those who will effectuate them. Planning at the administrative level involves the organization as a total entity.

> Organizing consists of setting patterned relationships by the administrator among the various specialists and operators who will be working toward fulfilling the enterprise's objectives.

The subject of organization has many ramifications. The significant facets of public fire safety organization have already been covered in Chapter II from the viewpoint of several schools of thought. Organization is a thread that weaves throughout the entire book. The dynamics and responsiveness of the organization will continue to be subjects of this chapter and the remaining chapters.

> Staffing is concerned with the people who perform the work.

The administrator has the broad responsibility of formulating his personal staff support. Within the organization at large, the administrator must establish staff needs, and oversee the selection, training and placement of the most suitable people in the most appropriate positions. In this board area the administrator must provide the mechanism for staff appraisal, provision for supplemental education and training, grooming of experience, plus the promotion and relocation of staff to reflect the changing requirements of public fire safety and the changing capabilities of the individuals.

> There are many angles from which to examine the directing function within the organization. Involved here are the concepts relating to leadership attributes and how this leadership quality is demonstrated by the administration.

It is necessary to recognize that leadership is exercised directly through interpersonal relationships; it may also be exercised indirectly

[7]Fred Brown, ed., *Management: Concepts and Practice*. Washington: Industrial College of the Armed Forces, 1967, p. 2.

[8]Department of the Air Force, *The Management Process*, *Air Force Manual 25-1*. Washington: Superintendent of Documents, 1954, p. 2.

[9]Luther Gulick and Lyndall Urwick, eds.. *Papers on the Science of Administration*. New York: Institute of Public Administration, 1957, p. 13.

[10]*Op. Cit.*, Fred Brown, pp. 6–8.

through the chain of command, by delegation, or through the establishment of organizational policies, methods, and procedures. In the overall sense, the administrator directs by first activating the organization and then guiding it, and on a regular basis overseeing its performance.

> Coordination refers to the synchronization of efforts which otherwise might not be harmonious.

The chain of supervision from the administrator down through the management levels serves as a technique for the vertical coordination of the organization. Traditionally, horizontal coordination in the organizational complex was left to the discretion of managerial levels. Much has been written on the encouragement of voluntary coordination to effect the proper relationships between organization units to provide necessary communication channels between units on the organizational chart.

> Reporting is one of the essential procedures by which control is exercised by the "administrator" in the organization.

Control is considered to involve a determination as to whether enterprise objectives and standards are being attained. Also, it involves the taking of corrective steps by the administrator if these goals are not being met. Reports of performance traditionally have represented the information tool utilized by administrators for measuring achievements against goals. The report has been so extensively used in the organization that many levels of operations have been characterized as a "paper mill." Public fire departments are no exception to this indictment. The main intent of the reporting process should be to demonstrate exceptions and deviations from expectation so that proper attention may be given to corrective actions.

> Budgeting narrowly reflects on the process of acquiring and allocating financial resources.

In an overview sense, the budget is an instrument of planning, coordinating, control and reporting on achievements. The budget more than any other item mentioned brings the administrator into the political arena. He serves as salesman and competitor for a piece of the annual "budget pie."

The reviewed terms take on new meaning, new emphasis, new ordering and new implications under a systems concept of organization. Therefore, it is imperative that new operational parameters and definitions be assigned to the established terminology. The change in perspective is essential to understanding not only the administrative position in the Public

Fire Safety Systems Organization but also to grasping the scope and nature of the organization itself.

Identified Administrative Functions Under the Systems Concept

This book is structured on the premise that coordination is the primary function of the administrator. Coordination is key to the integrated activity associated with the total systems. Coordination reorders the POSDCORB functions into a set of patterned relationships aimed towards achieving an improved organizational structure. Therefore, coordination can be defined as "the techniques and activities associated with linking together all structural-functional elements of the organization to achieve an established mission."[11]

Litterer suggests three primary means of systems type organization coordination.[12] First, there is the hierarchical arrangement of the organization structure. The structural framework illustrates the functional components that must establish coordinating links. A central authority of the administrative level actually places the functions in an integrated linking arrangement. To emphasize coordination in the Public Fire Safety Systems, the chief architect of administration is called simply the "Fire Coordinator."

The second element of coordination focuses on the administrative system which is intended to provide a further mechanism for coordination of activities.

> A great deal of coordinative effort in organization is concerned with a horizontal flow of work of a routine nature. Administrative systems are formal procedures designed to carry out much of this routine coordinative work automatically.[13]

It appears that many work procedures, such as memos with routing slips, help coordinate efforts of different operating units. To the extent that these procedures can be programmed or routinized, it is not necessary to establish specific means for coordination. For nonroutine and nonprogrammable events, specific units such as committees may be highly effective in providing horizontal integrating activities.

With the above concepts in mind, the administrative level of the proposed Public Fire Safety Systems Organization incorporates a

[11]Fremont E. Kast and James E. Rosenzweig, *Organization and Management — A Systems Approach*. New York: McGraw-Hill Book Company, 1970, p. 187.
[12]Joseph A. Litterer, *The Analysis of Organization*. New York: John Wiley and Sons, Inc., 1965, p. 223.
[13]*Op. Cit.*, Joseph A. Litterer, p. 230.

special structure to enhance functional coordination. Among other intended activities, the Master Planning Committee is formulated to coordinate the activities of each major functional area. This is accomplished through selective membership on the committee. It should be stressed that the aim of the organization system is not only for internal coordination but also the achievement of public fire safety coordination within the context of the larger urban system. In other words, the Master Planning Committee is the linking element for both the inter-organization and the intra-organization. As previously mentioned, the position of Executive Secretary is also structured with the idea of carrying coordination down the hierarchy to the resource allocation committee and the operations committee. By serving in the capacity of Secretary to each committee and responding directly to the Fire Coordinator, the Executive Secretary is in the position of maintaining a balance of information, of filling voids, and expounding administrative intent and as a carrier of advice between the committee structural levels.

A third type of coordination is through voluntary means. Litterer also states:[14] "The individual or group of individuals sees a need, finds a program, and applies it when deemed necessary." Much of the coordination reality may depend upon the willingness and ability of individuals or groups to voluntarily find means to integrate their activities with other organizational participants. Achieving voluntary coordination is one of the most important yet difficult problems of any administrator. Voluntary coordination requires that the individual have sufficient knowledge of organization goals and objectives, adequate information concerning the specific problem of coordination, and the motivation to do something on his own. The traditional line and staff organization associated with public fire departments does not lend itself well to voluntary coordination. The systems concept of organization appears to hold some brighter prospects for improving this type of coordination activity. This may be realized through a structure that allows the individual to perceive his role in the organization and how this role merges with the role of others.

Planning

Any given phase of organizational activity must start with planning. Planning in the broad sense is "the process by which the system adapts its resources to changing environmental and internal forces."[15] Under the systems approach, planning is a most dynamic function and must be carried out effectively in order to provide a solid foundation for the remaining managerial activities. This book considers that the purpose of the planning function in the public fire safety system is to provide an integrated decision system which establishes the framework for its activities. At the administrative level, the systems concept of planning considers the enterprise as an integration of numerous decision-making subsystems. The primary administrative planning function is to design an integrated system which will enhance organizational performance in line with established objectives.

Chapter I demonstrated that public fire safety must breed innovation, creativity and flexibility. With these expanded requirements for modernizing public fire safety and with the prospect of increasing employment of participants with higher educational levels and professional knowledge, it is imperative for management to develop effective means for integrating this knowledge into the planning function. The systems organization concept of planning provides the model for this integration.

After receiving informational inputs from the Resource Allocation Committee and the Operations Committee, the Administrator (Fire Coordinator) working with the Master Planning Committee has the responsibility for setting forth long-range, strategic plans for the organization. The level of implementation for the organization must be established and modified as necessary. Concurrently the objectives must be appraised and the goals set forth explicitly as guidelines to decision-making throughout the entire organization. Clearcut statements of expectation agreed to by the external members and the internal group members help focus the efforts of the administrator towards a common game plan. Planning, therefore, provides the organizational stimulus for effective decision-making throughout the enterprise.

In essence, the primary function of administrative level planning is implementation of the systems design, which involves (1) the establishment of goals, objectives, policies, procedures, and most importantly, the organizational relationships appearing on the Public Fire Safety Systems Organization Chart on a systematic basis for guidance of decision-

[14]*Ibid.*, p. 223.

[15]Richard A. Johnson, Fremont E. Kast and James E. Rosenzweig, *The Theory and Management of Systems.* New York: McGraw-Hill Book Company, 1967, p. 21.

making and planning at various organization levels, and (2) the provision for the flow of information to and from the two subordinate planning centers; the Resource Allocation Committee and the Operations Committee. With these ideas in mind, the Fire Coordinator defines more explicitly the planning function, sets forth a structure of plans, and then continues to examine, refine and implement the detailed system concepts of planning.

With this introduction, it is now necessary to define the planning function more specifically.

Definition of the Planning Function

Kast and Rosenzweig define the systems planing function as the "intelligent cooperation with the inevitable."[16] This definition, although short, does emphasize the futurity of planning. For our purposes, in the specific framework of of public fire safety, the following definition appears to be preferable.

Administrative planning for public fire safety is an integrative activity which seeks to maximize the total effectiveness of the fire safety system in accordance with established objectives.[17] This defines the planning process in terms of its system relationship. This still does not define the term "plan." The following definition is inserted to cover this important requirement. A plan is a predetermined source of action. Essentially, a plan is perceived to have three characteristics.[18] First, a plan must involve the future. Second, a plan must involve action. Third, there is an element of personal or organizational identification or causation; that is, the future course of action will be taken by the planner or someone designated by or for him within the Public Fire Safety Systems Organization. Futurity, action, and personal or organizational causation are necessary elements in every plan.

It appears important to note that decision-making and planning are closely related. A decision may be considered as basically a resolution of alternative choices. A decision is not a plan in that it need not involve either action or the future. Decisions, of course, are necessary at every stage in the planning process and are therefore inextricably linked to planning.

Planning is also a functional vehicle for changing the system. In our modern dynamic urban societies the major way in which the Public Fire Safety Systems Organization, as a subsystem of the total urban economic system, adapts to changing requirements is through planning. Under the systems concept the planning process can be considered as the vehicle for accomplishment of system change. Without planning, the system could not change and could not adapt to different environmental forces. In the systems organization, changes are dependent upon the rationality of the human decision processes. Thus for any socially oriented system, of which public fire safety is a subpart, the only vehicle for change, innovation, and adaptability is the human decision-making and planning process. Harold Guetzkow states that:[19] there is strong evidence to suggest that creativity and innovation in planning is enhanced by an organizational system which allows for diversity of ideas and inputs and does not attempt to structure human behavior totally. Yet if organizational planning is to be effective it must operate within an established system of individual and organizational relationships. Awareness of the total system, including the subsystem of individuals and groups, will help in providing a creative and innovative organization.

Planning, therefore, should be geared to obtaining, translating, understanding, and communicating information that will help to improve the rationality of current decisions which are based upon future expectations. Expectations are developed through the process of forecasting and predicting the future. However, it is generally agreed in the planning literature that forecasting is not planning. While forecasting provides a basis for understanding and formulating expectations, the Fire Coordinator must go beyond this orientation state and develop protection, prevention and service programs of action designed to optimize the company's overall performance.

Planning as an Integrated Decision System

Public Fire Safety Systems Organization planning must be considered as an integrative activity which should seek to maximize the total effectiveness of the entire system. Frequently, in a complex organization, it appears that a great deal of planning is carried on by specialized functional or staff groups without a

[16]Fremont E. Kast and James Rosenzweig, "Planning: Framework for an Integrated Decision System," *University of Washington Business Review*, April 1960, p. 39.

[17]*Ibid.*, p. 24. (Note: Adapted from Kast and Rosenzweig's Conceptual idea on the planning function.)

[18]Preston P. LeBreton and Dale A. Henning, *Planning Theory*, Prentice-Hall, Inc., Englewood Cliffs, N.J., 1961, p. 7.

[19]Harold Guetzkow, "The Creative Person in Organization," in Gary A. Setiner, ed., *The Creative Organization*. Chicago: The University of Chicago Press, 1965, p. 25.

system for the coordination of these efforts. Unless there is a clearcut understanding of what overall objectives and goals are paramount, some of the subgroup activities may be maximized at the expense of total organizational effectiveness. It must be stressed that all elements in the Public Fire Safety Systems Organization must be aware of the expectation and directions set forth by the Fire Coordinator and should understand the various premises upon which a course of action is founded. The means of achieving such understanding requires reviewing the planning function on an integrated systems approach.

A logical approach for an administrative oriented integrative plan should include the following steps.[20]

1. Appraise the future political, economic, and the sociological environment.

2. Visualize the desired role of the Public Fire Safety Systems Organization in the environmental context (i.e., the balance to be achieved between the elements of fire prevention, fire protection and fire suppression).

3. Perceive the acceptable loss levels for various sectors of the community [and the property classifications within the identified sectors.

4. Determine the changes in the needs and requirements of identified sectors of the community (i.e., alternative levels of protection based upon resource allocations or shifts in the risk problem).

5. Provide a system of communications and information flow whereby organizational members can participate in the planing process (i.e., the role involvement in the designated committee structure).

6. Develop and redevelop broad organizational goals, objectives and plans which pay close attention to the involvement and direction of each identified function in the organizational chart. (Note: the element directions are the subject of Chapters V and VI.)

7. Translate the broad planning effort into functional efforts on a more detailed basis — include time frames for accomplishment — paying close attention to: research and development requirements, the systems engineering required to achieve desired goals, fire prevention and fire protection subsystems, and distribution of suppression facilities to achieve objective performance.

8. Develop the mechanisms, criteria and guideposts for detailed planning and control within each of the functional areas, stressing that each functional area be related to the overall planning effort.

This approach, developed and understood throughout the organization, should provide an integrated decision-making system. The framework outlined above essentially represents the planning charge of the Master Planning Committee. The Committee would utilize these points to focus the efforts of the entire organization toward a common set of goals. This structure also makes it possible for the Master Planning Committee to evaluate administrative decisions, resource decisions and operational decisions in light of the overall master plan to determine whether a particular course of action would carry the Public Fire Safety Systems Organization toward or away from its desired future position. Again, in this way the total systems concept tends to facilitate the integration of all segments of the organization.

In summarizing this subsection, it should be realized that one of the primary purposes of an integrated planning concept is to provide goals and objectives based upon predetermined premises about the level of community safety to be provided and the internal Public Fire Safety Systems Organization resources available to meet the goals and objectives. The systems approach to planning better insures that the planning decisions made in one functional area are related to those in other areas. As the operational and support functions become more specialized in the organizational framework and as the changing environment requires more complex planning, the need for complete integrative concepts becomes even more apparent.

Control

The function of administrative control includes the measurement of functional unit output performance, the comparison of this functional output performance with some predetermined standard, and the adjustment of input performance to restore the system to its planned norm. This is accomplished in the systems organization through an information feedback loop. This generalized definition is intended to apply to all functional elements of the system with special emphasis on the three major project systems.

Administrative control should not be viewed as an end in itself; rather control is a means to an accomplished end. It is a means to add

[20]*Op. Cit.*, Johnson, Kast and Rosenzweig, p. 27 (Note: Modified from the text approach).

flexibility and effectiveness to the operation of the Public Fire Safety Systems Organization. The design of control in the subsystem functions should be consistent with the objectives of the larger network, preventive of imbalance in nature, and no more elaborate than is necessary to accomplish the organizational mission.

Definition of Administrative Controls

Administrative control is that function of the total system which provides direction in conformance to the established plan, in other words, the maintenance of variation from system objectives within allowable limits.[21]

An example of administrative control within the framework of the Public Fire Safety Systems Organization may serve to crystallize the definition. The objective criteria for fire suppression might be to limit all single dwelling residential fires to the room of origin. A boundary level object is established. The system continues to function according to an emergency service distribution and response plan until a fire exceeds the boundary of the room of origin. A corrective action (i.e., a control measure) should take place when an excessive loss is noted. Broadly speaking, the administrative role is to ensure that the corrective procedures are implemented. The example is oversimplified, the control network is somewhat more complicated and there is a definite need to examine the full range of control implications.

Therefore, by definition and example, it should be observed that control is maintained through a network of information which serves as the medium of control.[22] When the information network of the Public Fire Safety Systems Organization is dormant or static (i.e., incident reports lay in a pigeonhole) items become of little value to the control concept. On the other hand, information passing between functional elements in a prescribed manner represents the vital flow of organization intelligence which establishes the basis for controlling the performance of the systems. The prearranged flow of intelligence is necessary for the proper operation of the public fire safety system. The definition of control is not complete without considering some side-effect terminology.

The "control sensitivity" of a system refers to the degree of variation from the norm which occurs before an adjusting response is invoked.[23]

In other words, control is not automatic by definition. At the organization level under discussion, the Fire Coordinator or his delegated representative must evaluate deviations relative to a criteria base. Coupled with sensitivity is the concept of "Control Stability." "Control Stability" concerns the ability of the public fire safety system to maintain a predictable level of performance patterned over time. The essential point here is the ability of the system to correct an undesired level of performance and maintain the correction without further deviations from the norm. If the administrative action does not correct the problem, the system has some degree of control instability.

There is also the concern for rapidity of response in control. This refers to the speed or time element with which the fire safety system can correct variations from stated objectives. In other words, can the system be corrected the next day or does the undesired condition require the relocation of a fire station which may be five years in the future?

Control Elements Within the Administrative Level

Johnson, Kast and Rosenzweig identify four basic elements in every control system. These elements are considered to always occur in the same sequence and have the same relationship to each other. They are:[24]

1. A defined controlled characteristic or condition.

2. A sensor device or method for measuring the characteristic or condition. (Human or automated.)

3. A control unit or equipment which will compare measured data with planned performance and direct a correcting mechanism in response to a stated need.

4. An activating person, unit or mechanism which is capable of bringing about a change in the operating system.

Illustration IV-1 depicts the relationships that should exist among the four elements of the control network. For clarity of understanding, each point will be accompanied by direct but simplified example.

The first element is the characteristic or condition of the operating system which is to be measured. This element may be the output of one or more of the subsystem functions. Let us consider the monthly administrative report from the Fire Prevention System as processed by the Deputy Fire Coordinator for Operations

---

[21]William H. Newman and Charles E. Summer, Jr., *The Process of Management*, Englewood Cliffs, N. J. Prentice-Hall, Inc., 1961, p. 561.

[22]*Ibid.*, p. 561.   [23]*Ibid.*, p. 562.

[24]*Op. Cit.*, Johnson, Kast and Rosenzweig, p. 73.

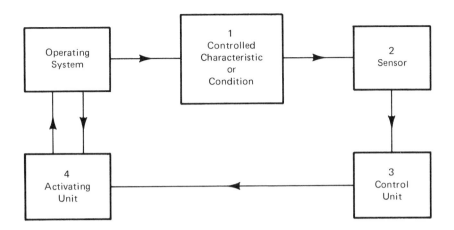

ILLUSTRATION IV-1 THE ELEMENTS OF A CONTROL SYSTEM

Systems. An administrative level objective might be to have all high-life-hazard structures surveyed once per month. The monthly report is designed to depict the target frequency and the accomplishment levels. This is a measurable characteristic or condition.

The second element of control, known as the sensor element involves the measurement of performance. The system or subsystem should be engineered (systems engineering function) to provide a sensory device or method for measuring the controlled item as a characteristic or condition. In our administrative report example condition, the Executive Secretary might be the sensor who checks the incoming report against the established criteria. Here is a human sensor function in a simplified system in contrast to a more sophisticated electronic sensor that might be built into a more complex subsystem. If the target survey schedule is achieved the objective is being met. If the sensor determines that the schedule is not being maintained there is some degree of deficiency.

The third element, designated the control unit, includes the determination of the need for correction and the release of corrective information. Allowable deviation from the plan is usual and is to be expected. If a significant deviation is recognized by the Executive Secretary in the example, the Fire Coordinator is alerted. He in turn might issue a directive to correct the frequency level of the high life risk category of surveys under the Fire Prevention Subsystems. More likely and appropriately the

Fire Coordinator would simply inquire as to the reason for the deviations.

The Fire Coordinator might also view the situation in the following alternate terms. When there is a significant difference between output and the plan, the situation can be considered as "out of control." If the surveys under discussion are only meeting fifty per cent of the target requirement there is a real problem. This could mean that the objective of the subsystem (fire prevention) is not feasible in terms of the capabilities of the manpower resources. In such a case the Fire Coordinator might direct the Operations Committee to study the situation and report back to the Master Planning Committee. Please remember that the example is inserted as a simplified projection of the control system. In actual practice the example given would probably be corrected or administratively altered at a lower management level.

The fourth element of control is the implementation of corrective action. The kind of device or method utilized to direct a corrective action takes a wide variety of forms. In the stated example, it might be alternately determined upon investigation that the problem lies in scheduling the surveys. Members of the survey team spend so much time traveling from one place to another that they simply lose a great deal of time that could be spent on the surveys. A reassignment procedure might substantially correct the situation. This would be the corrective element in the control network.

107

The fourth control element represents a fundamental part of the systems organization. The control network has been advanced as part of the administrative level subsystem. It should be equally emphasized that control occurs at each functional component and at each of the remaining subsystems. However, the responsibility for overall control rests firmly with the administrator — the Fire Coordinator.

This control subsection can be appropriately summarized with a quote by Richard G. Canning:[25]

> The objective of the system is to perform a specified function, while the objective of control is to maintain the output which will satisfy the system requirements. The objective of control in systems design, therefore, is to determine the relevant characteristics which, when controlled, maintain the function of the system within allowable variations.

Communications

Communications play an integral role in implementing the administrative functions of planning, organizing, and controlling. While this specific discussion of communications takes place at the administrative level, communications is an essential element of every function in the organization. Communications represents the key component which allows organizations to function as a responsive system through some degree of feedback control. It involves information flow, a vital element in administrative decision-making.

Terminology Associated with Communications

It appears helpful to examine the terminology surrounding the communication process. The purpose is not to develop a composite definition. Rather, the intent is to place the various terms in a proper systems perspective and to provide a basis for: (1) administrative level communications, (2) management level communications, and (3) the integrated information network to be presented in Chapter VIII — The Integrated Model. Wilbur Schramm states:[26]

> Communication comes from the Latin *communis*, common. When we communicate we are trying to establish a "commonness" with someone. That is, we are trying to share information, an idea, or an attitude . . . The essence of communication is getting the receiver and the sender "tuned" together for a particular message.

Equally important is the concept that communication is intercourse by words, letters, or similar means, and it involves interchange of thoughts or opinions. The term may be expanded to present the concept of communication systems, for example, the telephone, the television and the telegraph system in fire alarm headquarters. Therefore, communication implies information; the terms being considered are part of the same family.

Information in its broadest sense has been defined as "that which is communicated."[27] Another common definition of information is a "patterned relationship between events."[28] Information adds to knowledge or intelligence. In a systems context, information is evaluated in terms of its pertinence for decision-making. Facts, numbers, and data are processed to provide meaningful information. For example, miscellaneous inventory data on fire equipment provide information when arrayed according to box alarm assignments. Real-time graphic displays of fire equipment responding to alarms and in service provide even more meaningful information.

Information can be conveyed in many ways, both formally and informally. Periodic reports with a standardized format provide formal feedback on the operating system. The fire station "grapevine" illustrates how informal interpersonal relationships provide channels of communication.

Information can be considered to be the substance of communications systems. It is important to realize that information comes in various forms — electronic impulses, written or spoken words, informal or formal reports. Also, information is the basic ingredient for decision-making.

There is a distinction in the literature between information and information theory. Information theory, or the mathematical theory of communications, has been described as a powerful tool for studying organizational systems. Its implications are no less important for the Public Fire Safety Systems Organization. The foundations for information theory are generally attributed to Claude Shannon and Warren Weaver.[29]

By involving certain basic assumptions (ignoring semantics or meaning) Shannon proposed a simplified set of mathematical relationships which are considered primarily useful in

[25]Richard G. Canning, "Controlling a Business Process," in Byron K. Kedgerwood, ed., *Control Engineering Manual*. New York: McGraw-Hill Book Company, 1957, p. 14.

[26]Wilbur Schramm, *The Process and Effects of Mass Communications*, University of Illinois Press, Urbana, Illinois, 1954, p. 3.

[27]*Op. Cit.*, Johnson, Kast and Rosenzweig, p. 93.

[28]*Ibid.*, p. 93.

[29]Claude Shannon and Warren Weaver, *The Mathematical Theory of Communications*. Urbana: University of Illinois Press, 1949.

the technical aspects of information transmission. These relationships hold promise for the fire alarm communications process within the public fire safety system.

Harry H. Goode and Robert E. Machol wrote in the text *Systems Engineering* that:[30]

> Information theory is used as a tool in determining the rate at which information can be transmitted under certain specified circumstances. Some of the factors affecting transmission might be the nature of the signal source, whether the signal is discrete or continuous; the nature of the channel and, in particular, its capacity for transmitting information; the nature of noise, if any, which disturbs the transmission; and the fidelity criterion by which the adequacy of the transmission is judged.

Robert C. Hopkins divides information theory into three principal areas: communication systems, mathematical theory (a branch of probability theory and statistics), and various considerations of entropy and uncertainty applied to physical and biological systems.[31] He further states:[32]

> The one thing information theory does not pertain to is "information." The sense in which the term is used in the theory is quite arbitrary in that it has almost no relation to the term as popularly understood.

For purposes of this book, the concept of communication systems or information flow must be broader than that represented by information theory in its technical sense. Therefore, an attempt is consciously made to avoid the terminology utilized in information theory.

The Administrator and Communications

The literature on organizations and the theory of organizations indicates that communication is receiving more and more attention in an organizational context. Administrators have long been concerned with "getting the message across" to subordinates, that is, communication down through the organization. Administrators are often concerned with the lack of effectiveness in the communication process and yet they may not be entirely familiar with the problems involved. In other situations, administrators are concerned with upward communications, that is, soliciting the attitudes and feeling of the lower echelons and encouraging opinion transmission upward through the hierarchical structure. Furthermore, administrators are interested in seeing that the management levels communicate their message requirements outward — horizontally — to other functions on the same relative organizational plane.

The administrator must understand that the organization structure is definitely tied to communications systems. Deutsch explains the organization-communication complex in the following manner:[33]

> Communication and control are the decisive processes in organizations. Communication is what makes organizations cohere; control is what regulates their behavior. If we can map the pathways by which communication is communicated between different parts of an organization and by which it is applied to the behavior of the organization in relation to the outside world, we will have gone far toward understanding that organization ... Generally speaking, the communications approach suggests lines of attack in the study of organizations. First, instead of concentrating on the ostensible purpose of the organization, it will concentrate on two questions: how are the formal and informal communications channels of the organization connected, and how are they maintained?

The concept of organizing and communicating for decision-making is an important concern to the Fire Coordinator. Granting that organization structure and communications systems are inextricably intertwined, there appears to be a problem, identified by the systems theory people, of which comes first. For many organizations, especially in the military complex, communications systems have been designed to follow organizational lines without recognition of the fact that this may not provide for optimal flows of information for decision-making.[34]

Pfiffner and Sherwood respond to the relationship between the organization, decision-making and communication systems as follows.[35]

> The relationship between the communications system and decision-making is extremely important. If decision-making and communication processes are not identical, they are so interdependent they become inseparable in practice. As a result all studies of communication inevitably involve decision-making.

Pfiffner and Sherwood also indicate that under the total systems view, the integration of subsystems into the whole complex is key to organization viability. The decision-making system of any organization includes information, objectives, strategies, alternatives, probabilities, and consequences. The function of

[30]Harry H. Goode and Robert E. Machol, *Systems Engineering*. New York: McGraw-Hill Book Company, 1957, p. 428.

[31]Robert C. Hopkins, "Possible Applications of Information Theory to Management Control." *IRE Transactions on Engineering Management*. March, 1961, p. 41.

[32]*Ibid.*, p. 42.

[33]Karl W. Deutsch, "On Communications Models in the Social Sciences," *Public Opinion Quarterly*, Fall 1952, pp. 367–368.

[34]*Op. Cit.*, Johnson, Kast and Rosenzweig, p. 102.

[35]John M. Pfiffner and Frank Sherwood, *Administrative Organization*, Engelwood Cliffs, Prentice-Hall, Inc., p. 308.

the organization is to facilitate the flow of information and the making of appropriate decisions. Under this viewpoint, the communication system appears paramount, with organization structured around it as a frame of reference. In turn, the communication system is considered primarily as a supplier of information for decisions. More and more attention has been devoted to organizations as decision-making units.

The above connection between decisions and communications is both stressed and summarized by John Dorsey as follows:[36]

> Decisions may be conceived of as a communication process, or a series of interrelated communication events. A decision occurs upon the receipt of some kind of communication, it consists of a complicated process of combining communications from various sources, and it results in the transmission of further communications.

The communication process is obviously important to administration. If administration were thought of primarily as essentially a communication process, including a network of communication systems linking the functional elements of the organization, then administration can be viewed as a communication process. Also according to Dorsey:[37]

> Structurally, administration can be viewed as a configuration of communication patterns relating individuals and collectives of varying sizes, shapes, and degree of cohesion and stability. Dynamically, administration appears as a patterned swirl and flow of communications, many of them channeled through transactional "circuits" between persons and persons, persons and groups, and groups and other groups.

For the purpose of this book, the concepts of communication patterns and flows are vitally important. The linking arrangement and specificity of the flow is considered to be so important that the final chapter, The Integrated System: Perspective and Summary, is essentially a communications base model. The flow patterns relate communications to the organization, and the flow concepts relate to the decision-making process. Thus the several concepts presented — communications, organization, and decision-making — are inexorably interwoven.

Information-Decision Subsystems

It has been established that the concept of information flow is central to the development of communications within a systems concept. The administrative level in the organization is charged with the establishment and maintenance of the information flow patterns. Therefore, the key elements to the information-decision system rest with the administrative level in the Public Fire Safety Systems.

Since the system described by definition requires interrelationships among parts to constitute a composite whole, a system of information flow would necessarily provide information throughout various subsystems and would entail some feedback mechanism in order to represent a looped system.

A simplified but very responsive system is depicted in Figure IV-2.[37a] The skeletal model of the statewide information system has been somewhat compressed to show the basic flow of information necessary for established objective accomplishment. This demonstrates where the administrator must consider internal capabilities in light of the environmental information in the process of establishing goals and objectives. In other words, what does the public accept as an acceptable risk?

Premises with regard to urban, state and federal government relations, the systems political environment, the competition for a share of the resources, the public response to fire occurrence, the demand for public safety emergency services; all reflect and evolve over a period of time to form a frame of reference for administrative level planning.

Under the information flow scheme, plans for repetitive and nonrepetitive activities are transmitted to the operations system and to storage (Central Processing Unit) as a function of the control system for later comparison with output from components of the operating system.

Feedback up to the administrative level is obtained on the output performance of the system in terms of potential factors discussed in Chapter I such as loss ratios, survey frequency, engineering analysis and performance cost data. The operations system is monitored at the administrative level in order to maintain objective control and deviation sensing provides feedback at the earliest possible time for correcting imbalance within the Operations Subsystem.

Special stress must be placed on the realization that information flow is an integral part of the control system because it provides the means of comparing results with formulated

[36] John T. Dorsey, Jr. "A Communications Model for Administration," *Administrative Science Quarterly*, December 1957, p. 309.

[37] *Ibid.*, p. 310.

[37a] Hickey, H. E., "A Minimum Statistical Data Base for Statewide Public Fire Department Management Information Systems," (Topical Report FPP TR 5) Silver Spring: The Johns Hopkins University/Applied Physics Laboratory, 1972.

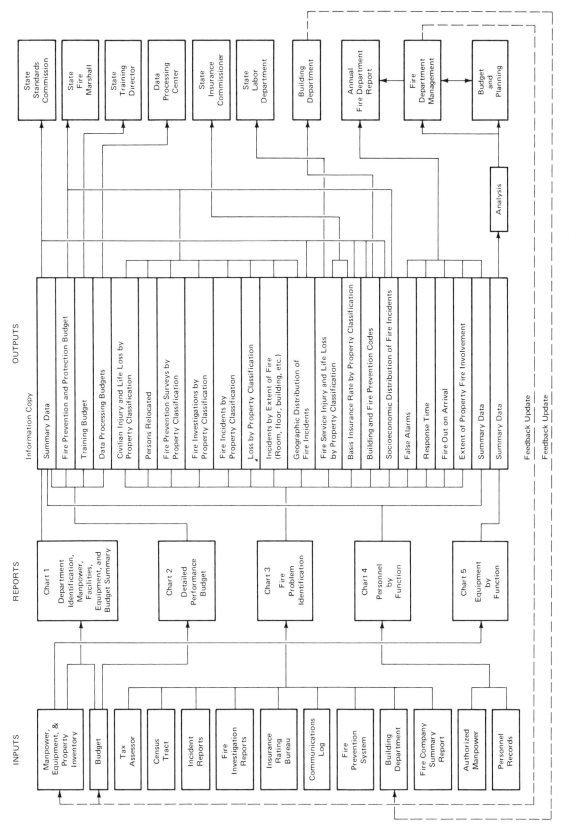

INPUTS REPORTS OUTPUTS

FIGURE IV-2: FLOW OF INFORMATION WITHIN A STATE ORGANIZATION FRAMEWORK

plans. Feedback data coming from the suppression systems (primarily from incident reports), the fire prevention system (survey reports) and the fire protection systems (engineering analysis and feasibility studies) are collected and analyzed. Again, the analysis consists in processing data, developing information, and comparing the results with plans.

The administrator may delegate that decisions can be made at the Deputy and Division Coordinating levels for routine adjustments in the system through established procedures and instructions. This means that the control system has a multi-level connotation. Sensor units can be built into several of the functional categories. Within each element of the control system there is a flow of information to implement changes to the overall program based on feedback from the functional categories depicted under the operations system. Thus procedures are changed, manuals are updated, files are updated and the administration is apprised of change simultaneously with routine decision-making and adjustment to the operating system.

Summary and exception reports are generated by the control level subsystem and become the essential ingredient for the administrative control in terms of adaptation or innovation of goals and objectives. The subsequent planning activity of the Master Planning Committee should reflect such feedback. The intent is to impose a constantly correcting system. In other words, over time, the Public Fire Safety Systems Organization will learn through the process of planning, implementation and feedback. Approaches involving decision-making and the propensity to select certain ends (acceptable risk levels as one possibility) and means of accomplishing ends (the balance between fire prevention, fire protection, and fire suppression) change as organizational values systems evolve. The external environment is probably the biggest factor in this involvement.

It is essential to note that the simplified depiction of information flow (Figure IV-2) represents necessary arrangement regardless of the organization implementation level.

The term information-decision system is used to emphasize the fact that information developed should be requested relative to the decisions to be made throughout the organization. The point being made is that an information-decision system is utilized and therefore should be designed as a communication process relating the necessary inputs to the stored information and the desired analysis outputs. It is likely that decisions at one of the defined Public Fire Safety Organization Systems levels represent an output from one communication process and information flow for a subsequent decision at the same level of service, a lower level of service, or a higher level of service. The overall information flow must be regarded as a system with many independent elements and subsystems.

The administrative level information-decision system should be considered in conjunction with the fundamental administrative functions: coordinating, planning, controlling, communicating, directing and resource allocation. Of special interest at this point is the notion that the traditional report structure would be replaced by a communication-information-decision system. If the Public Fire Safety Systems Organization is to implement a communication-information-decision system in conjunction with planning, coordination and control; then, the key to success appears to lie in the integrated model of information flow. The importance of this statement cannot be over-emphasized in relation to the Fire Coordinator's role in the systems context.

The following attributes of information flow described by D. Ronald Daniel should be followed in structuring the administrative level communication-information-decision systems:[38]

1. *Coverage* — good planning information is not compartmentalized by functions. Indeed, it seeks to transcend the divisions that exist in a company and to provide the basis on which integrated plans can be made. In contrast, control information hews closely to organizational lines so that it can be used to measure performance and help in holding specific management level persons more accountable.

2. *Length of time* — planning information covers a fairly long period of time — months and years rather than days and weeks— and deals with trends. Thus, although it should be regularly prepared, it is not developed as frequently as control information.

3. *Degree of detail* — excessive detail is the quicksand of intelligent planning. Unlike control, where precision and minute care do have a place, planning (and particularly long-range planning) focuses on the major outlines of the situation ahead.

4. *Orientation* — planning information should provide insights into the future. Control information shows past results and the reasons for them.

The above points emphasize the differences between information appropriate for planning purposes and information appropriate for control purposes. The points also indicate the importance of carefully designing information decision systems. Blind adherence to organiza-

[38]D. Ronald Daniel, "Management Information Crisis," *Harvard Business Review*, September-October 1961, pp. 112–113.

tional patterns for the flow of information often will hamper the development of an optimal system. Also, the Fire Coordinator must identify key decision points and the concepts of information flow must be kept paramount when redesigning or adjusting the overall system of information flow. This could occur under the proposed Public Fire Safety System when it is deemed necessary to change from one organization level system to another level.

In summary, the communication-information-decision complex at the administrative level requires development to the extent which will provide the proper flow of information among the action points (functional points) in the organization complex. The proposed Public Fire Safety Systems Organization has been structured around such a defined pattern of information flow. The final chapter in this book is structured to support this contention.

Both the formal and the potentially informal communications channels have been recognized in developing the Public Fire Safety Systems Organization structure by placing a committee structure in the framework at three different levels. The Fire Coordinator must constantly analyze the informal communication patterns once the organization is activated. This analysis must be in detail because the communication-information-decision system may follow "natural" patterns within each subsystem, even though these "natural" patterns are not recognizable on the formal organization chart. Future planning and control will be easier to facilitate once the overall communication-information-decision system has been established.

The Administrator and Resource Allocations

Under a traditional form of line and staff organization, an administrator is concerned with specific features of the budget, the staffing of the organization with competent dedicated individuals, plus the procuring and distribution of equipment and facilities. The Fire Coordinator is no less concerned with these elements under a Public Fire Safety Systems approach. However, the emphasis and understanding associated with each resource element take on a new dimension under a systems framework. The elements combine to establish a unit of concern; the functional unit is designated by the title resource allocation. Resources must be obtained from the larger Urban System and allocated to the internal system to achieve objectives. The resource allocation process essentially involves budgets, manpower, equipment and facilities. The administrative level of the organization should spend a great deal of time dealing with resource allocations.

The intent of the immediate discussion is to cover the Fire Coordinator's specific relationship to the resource allocation process under a systems approach to organization. The detail aspects of managing resource allocations are covered specifically in Chapter V.

Probably the principal concern of the Fire Coordinator should be to establish a financial plan that will yield resources to carry out a service plan of action. Until recently, the theoretical writings on financial administration possessed more of an economic flavor than an administration outlook. According to Lieutenant Colonel John B. Sperry, "this was primarily attributable to the relatively longer development of formal economic theory vis-à-vis management theory."[39] The accent now being placed on the development of management science has fostered an increasingly close relationship between total administration (in this literature case synonymous with management) and financial administration. The outgrowth of this perceived relationship is to broaden the perspective of the organization administrator. No longer is the administrator concerned solely with the details of budgeting, accounting and auditing. As Colonel Sperry states:[40]

Rather, he has come to place these activities within the broader framework of organizational resource utilization and their overall contribution to the accomplishment of organizational objectives.

Only by taking a wider perspective of financial matters can the Fire Coordinator generate the type of monetary data required to advance organizational goals within an uncertain environment of increased competition for the dollar, exploding technology, and the turbulent social and political conditions to be found in the urban environment.

The main purpose of the Public Fire Safety Organization financial plan is to prescribe the fiscal direction for the Fire Coordinator. The elements of the financial function in relation to organization administration level has been set forth by the Financial Executive's Institute as depicted by the following title and point outline.[41]

[39]Lieutenant Colonel John Sperry in Fred Brown, ed., *Management: Concepts and Practices*. Washington: Industrial College of the Armed Forces, 1967, p. 127.

[40]*Ibid.*, p. 127.

[41]Financial Executive Research Foundation, "Developments in Financial Organization (A Special Supplement)," *Financial Executive*, September 1965, pp. 19–20.

1. To maintain an integrated control plan of operations. [Cost standards, budgets, forecasts, financing, and investment.]

2. To measure and evaluate performance against predetermined standards. [Accounting systems, financial reports, and statistical records that lead to cost-benefit analysis.]

3. To establish and administer tax policies and procedures where appropriate. [This is appropriate for the public fire safety system since much of fire protection is supported by a special fire tax.]

4. To supervise or coordinate the preparation of financial reports to the respective governmental agencies.

5. To interpret the impact of external economic and social forces upon organization objectives. [This is an attempt to answer the question of what the public demands in the way of services or what risk is to be assumed.]

6. To safeguard organization assets and to measure effectiveness of organization policies and procedures. [The internal control and internal audit systems.]

7. To participate in the determination of organizational objectives as they relate to financial obligations.

The financial plan must provide the Fire Coordinator with a quantitative basis on which to make decisions for the resolution of organizational problems. The quantitative phases of activity involving the financial plan bring to focus the related subject areas of economics, administrative theory, statistical analysis (cost-benefit analysis) accounting and electronic data processing. This might be termed the integrated approach to financial planning with a growing emphasis on performance appraisal in relation to functional costing.

Efficiency and effectiveness of organizational performance are key concerns of the Fire Coordinator. The systems approach incorporating such techniques as performance budgeting, cost-utility analysis, and Program Performance Budgeting Systems provide new tools for responding to performance evaluations. Prior to giving an overview of these special concerns under the financial plan, it appears appropriate to insert a few words about the budget as a tool of the administrator and as an instrument of the overall financial plan. The view is broad; the details come in Chapter V.

Wayne Keller and William L. Ferrara state that,[42]

... a budget is a quantitative plan of action and an aid to coordination and control. Budgets basically are forecasting statements which express in monetary terms "administrator's" future plans. Budgets ... represent a systematic tool for establishing standards of performance providing motivation, gauging results, and generally aiding management in the attainment of its objectives. For effective use, however, budgets must not

be regarded as absolute requirements of performance whereby unfavorable deviations are criticized and faorable variances applauded.

Thus, after it is developed as a plan of action, a budget should not be used to evaluate actual performance under actual conditions in comparison with budgeted performance under expected conditions. The proper comparison is between actual performance under actual conditions and budgeted performance under actual conditions.

From other literature examples, the budget is often described as a plan set forth in financial terms.[43] That is, organizational activity is translated into expected results with dollars as the common denominator. Several writers stress the positive planning aspect of budgetary control rather than the strictly control phase. Yet, the connotation of restriction and constraint is widespread both at the local government and national government levels.

The administrative procedures of budgetary control can be applied to a wide variety of situations. Newman, Summer and Warren express several basic elements that are involved in financial budgeting.[44]

1. *Expressing in dollars the results of plans anticipated in a future period.* These dollar figures are typically set up in the same way as the accounts in a company's accounting system. The budget shows how the accounts should look if present plans are carried out.

2. *Coordinating these estimates into a well-balanced program.* The figures of organization divisions ... must be matched to be sure that they are mutually consistent; financial feasibility of all plans added together must be assured; and the combined results must be examined in terms of overall objectives. Some adjustments will probably be necessary to obtain a balanced program.

3. *Comparing actual results with the program estimates that emerge from step two.* Any significant differences point to the need for corrective action. In short, the budget becomes a standard for appraising operating results.

For the present discussion it suffices to say that the budget with its attendant control, as described above, nearly parallels the administration process. It involves planning, coordinating, and controlling.

The symbol PPB stands out in all the recent literature dealing with financial administration. The "planning-programming-budgeting" philosophy was developed by the Department of Defense in an attempt to give more of the planning connotation to the federal government budgeting process.[45] However, there is no reason why PPB has to be restricted to the federal government. Its implications are so

---

[42]Wayne Keller and William L. Ferrara. *Management Accounting for Profit Control*, 2nd Ed., New York: McGraw-Hill Book Co., 1966, p. 389.

[43]William H. Newman, Charles E. Summer, and E. Kirby Warren. *The Process of Management.* Englewood Cliffs: Prentice-Hall, 1967, pp. 697–698.

[44]*Ibid.*, p. 698.

[45]Colm Gerhard, *Integration of National Planning Budgeting.* Washington: National Planning Association, 1968.

sympathetic to the systems approach that it appears only natural to extend this concept to any systems oriented form of organization.

PPB as it is currently conceptualized, can be viewed as both a set of goals or objectives and as a system for achieving these goals. It seeks to accomplish the following ends.[46]

1. PPB calls for careful identification and examination of goals and objectives in each major area of government activity.

2. PPB is to analyze the output of a given program in terms of its objectives. It forces programs to have specific measurable objectives.

3. PPB is the measurement of total costs, not for just one year but for at least several years ahead. It seeks to provide the decision maker with all the relevant costs that his decision would entail.

4. PPB is the formulation of objectives and programs extending beyond the single year of the annual budget submission. Major changes in objectives, operating practices, and budget allocations must be accomplished in light of long range goals.

5. The PPB system is the analysis of alternatives to find the most effective means of reaching basic program objectives, and to achieve these objectives for the least cost.

6. The goal of PPB is to establish analytic procedures as a systematic part of budget review. Further, PPB seeks to subject policies and programs to analysis and to integrate the decisions into the budgetary process.

The administrative aims of PPB may be summarized as: requirements for the specification of objectives; the evaluation of program output as it relates to objectives; the measurement of total systems costs; multi-year program planning; the evaluation of alternative program designs; and the integration of policy and program decisions with the budgetary process.

The financial plan and the allocation of resources are intertwined. The following premises are associated with the administrative resource allocation component of the systems organization. The systems design concept is especially structured to develop integrated arrangements of facilities, manpower, and information flow in order to accomplish given objectives. It should be recognized that the system by itself is the most important resource in the organizational framework. This is one reason why the function of Systems Engineering is placed under the broad component of Resource Allocation in the Public Fire Systems Organization.

Implementation is implicit in the connotation of the total Public Fire Safety System design; otherwise the whole system construction process would be an empty exercise. Therefore, the interface between the Fire Coordinator and the Systems Engineer (systems designer) is

critical, and mutual understanding is essential in order to maximize returns from the systems design efforts.

Also important is the realization that the system requires tailoring to the needs of the organization framework and the framework must be adapted for systems compatibility as levels of service change. The need and the circumstances promoting a change in the level of service are usually translated in terms of resource requirement which in turn means the allocation of resources. The Fire Coordinator should play a large and active role in the systems design effort in order to ensure the development of a useful system.

Returning to the area of resource allocations, it should be noted that functional areas of manpower, facility and equipment resources are established to provide the operational system with the elements necessary to accomplish the organizational mission. The process includes the acquisition of new facilities (fire stations), the provision of equipment for these facilities, manpower recruitment and assignment to activate facilities or the reallocation of men and/or equipment and/or facilities as the system service requirements change. Since the manpower aspect of the fire safety system will probably represent close to ninety per cent of the financial resource requirement, it may be understood the financial plan is tied directly to the resource and allocation plan. The Resource Allocation functions naturally fit together. The complete implementation features of resource allocations will be reviewed in Chapter V.

The Administrator and the Intra-Organizations

The Fire Coordinator is viewed as a multiple organization role player. Obviously he is deeply committed to the interpublic fire safety organization. The perceived role of the Fire Coordinator in relation to the internal organization has been the subject of earlier portions of this chapter. He is or should be deeply committed to an interface relationship with other functional units in the urban environment; with civic groups; with county and/or state level safety functions and with applicable federal programs. While the organization chart supports a Public Relation Coordinator (Under Facilitating Systems) the Fire Coordinator retains the spotlight as the real public relation spokesman. He is the top man, he speaks for the organization, his image and influence can not be delegated with the same impact. His charisma or lack of personal impact is a factor

[46]Charles L. Schultze, *The Politics and Economics of Public Spending*, Washington: The Brookings Institution, 1969, p. 19.

in the relationship of the Public Fire Safety Organization to all other organizations. Certainly a major problem with some Fire Chiefs in the current structure of fire department organizations is that they do not fully appreciate or project themselves into this extra intra-organizational role. The purpose of the following subsection is to demonstrate the need for administrative external involvement, the nature of this involvement, the impact of involvement on the public fire safety organization, and the integration effect of outside forces to support the functional elements of the perceived Public Fire Safety Organization structure.

Public Fire Safety does not work in a vacuum. Its involvement in the safety of the community touches every facet of the urban scape. The question to be answered is: Just how does public fire safety act and react in a total environment?

The Public Fire Safety movement should be responsive to the wishes of the community. Such wishes are neither uniform nor static. One community may want one type of service (i.e., the contrast between paid and volunteer; strictly a suppression force or a public service force) while another city demands and pressures for a different service or performance level. In the too frequent case the community does not react at all — there is a general lack of concern towards the whole subject of fire safety.

Regardless of the demand or lack of demand related to fire safety, the Mayor or his organizational equal probably has a genuine feeling for the pulse of the community. The Mayor then becomes a key individual in setting organization goals, of developing performance standards and appraising organizational output. In the Public Fire Safety situation this development might better be termed "putout" because a major visible criterion of performance is just how well the city fire department puts out fires. The Fire Coordinator must respond to the Mayor. Where the Public Fire Safety System is organized on a sector or regional base, the Fire Coordinator must respond to several Mayors, City Managers, County Administrators or their equal. The individual sensitivity associated with such a coordinating task is very complex and demanding.

Without the Mayor's support the systems approach to public fire safety will never be initiated; therefore, the Fire Coordinator must be responsive to the Mayor or his equal. Mayors usually respond favorably to functions and service that perform well, are a pride to the community, receive favorable reactions from the citizens, and create a minimum of administrative problems. One current problem that detracts from responding to the needs of the Mayor is the lack of objective criteria on which the Mayor and the citizens can adequately judge public fire safety performance. One should not forget that every citizen tends to evaluate the fire service relative to his contact with the service.

Probably the greatest achievement that the Public Fire Safety Coordinator can foster is to demonstrate quantitatively and qualitatively the capabilities or lack of capabilities of the organization. The Fire Coordinator should be able to project probable losses within the jurisdictional area, the foundation for these projections and the necessary resources to change such projections. This is an operational evaluation, as opposed to an appearance evaluation that the fire department is "good" because a new pumper was purchased at a cost of $50,000.

The Mayor needs to be educated and probably the best possible teacher is the Fire Coordinator. The better educated the Mayor, the fewer problems between the central administration and the fire safety administration.

In addition to the top Urban Administrator, the Fire Coordinator is required to respond with and to other administrative level personnel. One such person might be the City Attorney. Public Fire Safety is created as a legal government function. As such, it must operate within the constraints of the applicable law. For example, the law might require modification in several states to accommodate the type of organizational levels projected in this paper. The responsible legal authority would act as a key determinant to the success or failure of the required legal action to implement change.

Most of the operational functions of fire prevention and fire protection are structured on the basis of fire prevention codes and/or building codes. The enforcement of the code is a legal activity. The rights, the obligations, the methods of enforcement of code provisions must be developed with the jurisdictional community function. If the city attorney is not willing to prosecute or if there is selective prosecution, the Fire Coordinator has real problems. An arson case can be won or lost by the expertise and perseverance of the prosecution. Legal services relative to the Public Fire Safety Organization are very important.

There is usually a separate personnel division within the administrative structure of the larger urban context. The nature, scope and activity of this personnel group can have a significant effect on the internal public fire safety manpower resource function. The urban personnel group is usually the authority in matters of civil service, pay scales, insurance and other fringe benefits, and the employees' retirement programs. This division of local government can get involved in the scheduling of vacations and the investigation of sick leave. Depending on the size of the organizations serviced, the personnel division may handle all the duties and activities perceived under the manpower resources function. This does not necessarily present an organizational conflict between urban government and the public fire safety system. It simply means that a higher level of administrative coordination will be required between the Public Fire Safety System and the larger urban system. The Fire Coordinator would be deeply involved in following through on the implementation and control of internal and external system arrangements.

Several other urban functional systems should be examined in relation to the role of the Public Fire Coordinator. One of the important areas for his involvement is with the city or municipal planning function. This may be a planning group, a planning commission or simply an urban advisory group. The specific term associated with the planning effort is not important; the organization relationship is important. Above all, the Fire Coordinator should be aware of the projected patterns of urban growth or renewal. Changes in urban growth patterns can materially affect the public fire safety service level. For example, a new freeway could alter fire apparatus response patterns; a shopping mall could pose access problems for truck companies; a new medical services complex could overtax the manpower available for search, rescue and evacuation; an urban renewal project could reduce a potential conflagration hazard. The list of possible occurrences in the urban environment that might affect public fire safety features appears almost endless.

A direct working relationship with the urban planning group is one of the best formulas for procuring information to structure the long range internal plan. At the same time the Fire Coordinator has the responsibility of informing the planning group of cause-and-effect relationship to public fire safety in a specific manner. It is not a simple case of a proposed plan being bad; the reason for a plan being unacceptable is the important concept. It is perceived that a large number of the present fire

safety problems in the urban environment could have been avoided if the jurisdictional planning groups were aware of the fire protection implications.

There is also a definite relationship between the Fire Coordinator and other urban service functions.

Public water supply represents a service area where a very close cooperative coordination and planning activity should take place. Water supply is considered by many fire safety authorities to be the most important element in instituting public fire safety. Without an adequate and reliable supply of water, the fire suppression operational function is severely limited. Therefore, the Fire Coordinator should be just as interested in the water supply system as the Water Superintendent. While the actual engineering design and analysis features of the water system may be delegated to the Fire Protection Engineer under the Protection subsystem, the Fire Coordinator again retains responsibility for the overall assessment of water system strength and weaknesses relative to public fire safety. He has the extended obligation of translating deficiencies into perceived consequences in the case of fire as specific locations. Water supply planning, maintenance and evaluation represent a distinct activity of public fire safety that requires coordination at the highest level.

The Fire Coordinator is also interested in activities of the highway department. Transit conditions between a facility site and a fire incident may have a bearing on the loss potential. Such transit conditions relate to the type of roads, the condition of roads, the congestion of roads and the access to and from roads. These factors are all concerns of the Fire Coordinator. Above all the fire safety operational subsystem needs to be notified when roads are impassable for one reason or another. Such notification results from prior planning and coordination at the administrative level.

Fire and police have developed some interesting relationships over the past dozen years. Some points on this subject were advanced in Chapter I. Regardless of potential stresses and strains between the two services, when an emergency arises there is usually good cooperation between the two services at a field incident. It appears that cooperation could be improved and could be more consistent with better advanced planning. The specific support role and obligations of firemen and policemen at fires, accidents, natural disasters, civil disturbances and similar emergency situations need to be fully explored and charted at the administrative level. Public fire safety needs the support of the police operations.

Many urban governments support a separate building department. To the building department is entrusted the procedure for evaluating structures and occupancy conditions in relation to what might be termed total building safety. A significant portion of this total safety complex relates directly to fire protection. The degree of fire resistance afforded building components, or the lack of it; building egress and access, interior finishes, plus building fire protection features such as fire alarms, sprinkler systems and standpipes, represent some of the more prominent aspects of fire safety relegated to the building department. Too often this treatment is administered without the knowledge, consultation or input from the public fire department. Yet, the implementation and enforcement of a building code represents a major element in predicting fire safety within the code's jurisdictional area. The Fire Coordinator must see that the Public Fire Safety Systems Organization plays an involvement role with the building department. The closer the cooperation between the two functions the more probable will be the degree of safety afforded occupants of buildings within the urban environment.

The Fire Coordinator should set the stage for implementing a series of checks and balances between the building department, if there is one, and the appropriate level Fire Protection Engineer under the Protection Project subsystem. This coordination should include preliminary and working drawing approvals, on site inspections, and consistent recommendations for corrective action. Such a relationship is only possible if initiated at the respective organization's administrative level.

Moving from a discrete urban environment to a larger frame of reference — the state — the Fire Coordinator is viewed in still another role assignment. Once again, in a broad perspective he must be aware of the services, the technical support, manpower and equipment support, and the financial sharing that can be expected from the state. Long-range planning, coordination and integration are key administrative areas the Fire Coordinator must be concerned with in obtaining a maximum utilization of state supported fire safety capability.

A state's fire safety offerings are often quite dysfunctional. This means identified state level services are found to be administered by several organizational units. Some of the more important community concerns are statewide firemen training programs that are usually under the administration of the state agency for vocational education, a State University or a special office for local government. A State Fire Marshal may retain responsibility of state-owned property, for the investigation of certain fires, for the hazard survey of a certain class of buildings and for the implementation of certain fire incident reports to obtain a statistical data base. Other selected departments in the state government, such as a special labor department, might have certain fire safety responsibilities for industrial establishments. Education departments might have responsibility for school construction and/or the survey of the school plant. Several states have pending legislation to make a department of the state government responsible for the fire safety of nursing homes.

The above examples reflect the need for the Fire Coordinator to "coordinate" the activities of his organization with those of horizontal and vertical governmental units. Certainly one prominent problem of today's Fire Service is duplication of the building survey effort. In other words, several different authorities are inspecting the same building for essentially the same general fire safety purpose. The duplication of effort sometimes results in a conflicting set of recommendations that completely confuses the owner/occupant. The lack of building survey coordination is also the responsibility of the Fire Coordinator.

The Fire Coordinator has a still higher form of government to be concerned with in relation to planning and coordinating processes. The Federal Government is deeply involved with public fire safety. With the establishment of the Fire Research and Safety Act it appears that the Federal role in public fire safety will widen. The specific range of programs and the future involvement of the Federal Government are still quite unclear. From 1971 to 1973 a National Commission on Fire Prevention and Control appointed by President Nixon attempted to define, evaluate and report upon the broad spectrum of fire safety. The 1973 Commission report, *America Burning*, had many recommendations bearing on the development of goals, the organization structure and the future direction of urban fire safety. The Fire Coordinator must keep abreast of these developments and be prepared to relate his organization to the direction outlined by the National Commission.

118

Beyond the scope of governments, there are at least two private organizations that currently have an impact on the broad spectrum of public fire safety. The first of these organizations to be considered is the National Fire Protection Association. NFPA supports many standing committees that prepare fire safety standards. The standards have been adopted by many cities as law or accepted by the courts as prima facie evidence of the most suitable standards available. Probably one of the most pointed examples of the NFPA standards is the Life Safety Code (Standard 101). This document represents the basis for determining adequate egress from selected building and occupant building classifications in time of emergency. Other NFPA standards pertaining specifically to the organization and management of fire safety were cited as references in Chapter II.

The NFPA has been constantly active in the field of fire reporting. Its current effort in this area centers around the UFIRS Program. UFIRS (Uniform Fire Incident Reporting System) is an attempt to design and conduct a feasibility test of instituting a uniform fire reporting system at the local fire fighting level.[47] The UFIRS system, or a comparable system, could give Fire Coordinators a new tool for total systems appraisal.

Chapter I stressed that the insurance industry has played a major role in public fire safety. This role involvement has been established in two categories. First, it has been established, the *Standard Grading Schedule of Cities and Towns* is utilized to evaluate municipal fire defenses. One point relating to the *Grading Schedule* appears clear. Fire Chiefs have overreacted to the criteria contained in the *Grading Schedule*. In other words, the *Grading Schedule* has been utilized to acquire resources of men, equipment and facilities and to disperse these elements in the environment according to insurance-motivated criteria. This administrative approach to public fire safety has not necessarily created an efficient or a particularly effective organization. However, there is one very strong administrative criterion for utilizing the standards of the *Grading Schedule*. There appears to be no better documentation or criterion for a fire administrator to follow. Like many other aspects of the urban environment, if there is going to be criticism of the *Grading Schedule*, then one must be prepared to offer an improved replacement. This book represents an

attempt to move the organized effort of public fire safety towards a more effective and efficient means of accomplishing this objective. It does not advocate divorcing the *Grading Schedule* from administrative consideration. It does recommend that the *Grading Schedule* be placed in the proper perspective as an administrative tool.

A second aspect of the insurance business is related to the property premium assessments for the establishment of levels of insurance protection in the event of loss. The process utilized to determine insurance rates for mercantile, industrial and other special types of properties involves a risk assessment process. This assessment process normally involves a survey of the property and followup surveys at periodic intervals. These surveys rarely are conducted with the Fire Service's knowledge. This uncoordinated procedure is a concrete example of the lack of coordinated effort between public fire safety and outside interests. These surveys usually result in the owner or occupant receiving a host of recommendations to affect some undefined level of fire safety. Depending upon the insurance survey authority, these recommendations can differ widely.

The administrator is involved with many publics, and this brings up another important question. How does the Fire Coordinator work effectively with all of these groups and how does he maintain a coordinated balance between the intra- and the inter-organization? The answer is not a simple one but some important clues lie within the directing function of the Fire Coordinator.

The Administrative Function of Directing

As the principal figure in the Public Fire Safety Systems Organization, the Fire Coordinator has the responsibility for directing the action of many persons. This direction process amounts to informing personnel what is expected of them, when it is expected, how it should be achieved, and probably most important, why it should be accomplished, to achieve mutually agreed purposes. In a very modern sense this process might be referred to as soft-sell directing. Informative direction is in contrast to the rigid style of directing which might be considered bullish, very authoritarian and military in aspect.

This book assumes that direction involves cooperation. This is not inconsistent with good discipline and personnel responsiveness — both of which are essential to the Public Fire Safety Systems Organization. Admiral Arleigh Burke

---

[47]Carl Peterson, *"Fire Incident Reporting: What Does It Mean To The Changing Fire Service?" Fire Command!*, October 1971.

wrote that[48] "a well-disciplined organization is one whose members work with enthusiasm, willingness, and a zest as individuals and as a group to fulfill the mission of the organization with expectation of success." Based upon Admiral Burke's words, direction can be viewed as moving men towards objectives; moving men with a sense of esprit-de-corps; moving men with a sense of accomplishment; and moving men with respect for their leader.

Don Favreau indicates that leadership and direction are synonymous.[49] He uses the following definition of leadership: "Leadership is the ability to get something done, by someone else, because he wants to do it." Thus, there is merit in viewing the terms directing and leadership as a single entity. There is a considerable amount of literature on the subject of leadership. The purpose of this chapter is to reveal enough of the desired characteristics of a leader to demonstrate a developing image of the Fire Coordinator as the principal director, the principal leader, and the principal administrator of the public fire safety system.

Favreau has also revealed some succinct guideposts for looking at administrative leadership. He notes that the Department of the Army has developed a list of leadership principles that appear to have guided the conduct and action of its leaders through both war and peace. These principles are listed as follows:[50]

1. Be technically and tactically proficient.

2. Know yourself and seek self-improvement.

3. Know your men and look out for their welfare.

4. Keep your men informed.

5. Set the example.

6. Be sure that the task is understood, supervised and accomplished.

7. Train your men as a team.

8. Make sound and timely decisions.

9. Develop a sense of responsibility in your subordinates.

10. Employ your command in accordance with its capabilities.

11. Seek responsibility and take responsibility for your actions.

There also appears to be some significant traits associated with leadership. These might include:[51]

1. Confidence

2. Enthusiasm

3. Effective human communications

4. Knowledge

5. Vision

These points can be supplemented with an additional set of personal characteristics that are considered important for effectiveness as a leader.

Integrity	Initiative
Courage	Responsibility
Honesty	High Principles
Pride	Unselfishness
Determination	Bearing
Faith	Dependability
Forcefulness	Loyalty
Judgment	Reliability
Tact	Self-Discipline
Decisiveness	Desire to know
Endurance	

A lot is required of a man that seeks to be an administrative leader. Then, in addition to the administrative leadership, the traditional Fire Service has attempted to make the leader a suppression tactical officer. The demand, the load, the requirements in their pure sense are almost incomprehensible. These almost super-human requirements represent one basic reason why this book attempts to separate the executive administrative function from the operational service system. If the public seriously desires an efficient and effective fire safety organization, the Fire Coordinator cannot serve simultaneously in two capacities. If he attempts to fill both roles, one will suffer from neglect, or inattention. This message is not to convey that the experienced and educated fire suppression officer cannot move, by demonstrating leadership and competency qualities to the top administrative post of Fire Coordinator. However, it must be remembered, the Fire Coordinator is the principal administrative officer and not a fire ground commander. The responsible fire suppression officer is the system fire chief, which admittedly is a departure from the traditional fire department. This organizational concept is a necessary departure if public fire safety is to be administratively effective and efficient. If this concept is not implemented fire departments will continue to function on the present

[48] Admiral Arleigh Burke in Donald Favreau, *Fire Service Management*. New York: The Reuben H. Donnelley Corporation, 1969, p. 27.

[49] *Ibid.*, p. 26.

[50] U.S. Army, *Leadership Principles*, Field Manual 22–100. Washington. Department of the Army, June 1961, p. 28.

[51] *Ibid.*, p. 29.

level of momentum without any significant opportunity to improve in efficiency and effectiveness.

Administrative Information

Much has been said in this chapter about the administrative function applied to a perceived organizational framework entitled: "A Public Fire Safety Organization: A Systems Approach." A special concentration of effort has been placed on the communications aspects of the administrative function in relation to decision-making and integration of all the functional components into a total systems framework. Information as such has received an introductory and functional review. Before looking at the management requirements associated with functional specialties it is necessary to establish exactly what information the Fire Coordinator must know to guide the organizational development in accordance with a mission plan.

The Fire Coordinator requires information to accomplish at least two objectives. First, the Fire Coordinator requires information about his internal organization and the several outside systems organizations in order to make intelligent and rational decisions about the organization complex. Such decisions are formulated on a short-range effect basis and a longer range effect basis. Short-range decisions are intended to accommodate daily situations or at the longest — weekly situations. In contrast, long-range effect decisions are formulated for handling perceived problems or executing performance after the lapse of several months or possibly years. The relevant point in this contrast is that the information requirements for short-range decisions and long-range decisions differ considerably. In this sense decision-making information is nearly synonymous with planning information or at least planning and execution are very closely integrated.

Second, the Fire Coordinator has need for information to answer problem situations. There is a constant stream of questions that must be answered at the administrative level. The response to the Mayor or the public may have to be immediate and adequate. Such a requirement is created when a catastrophe takes place, such as a serious fire with loss of life. The ranking fire official is immediately requested to give a cause, why did the incident happen? Was there a violation of the law? Would a different action on the part of the fire department have changed the outcome? Less immediate questions, but certainly significant to incident analysis, might include: How many men were on duty? What pieces of equipment were out of service? A fire or emergency situation often provokes responses that may become difficult to substantiate and support. Routine questions often cause embarrassment and a lack of confidence in the fire department, because the fire official should know the answers but he does not have the details and the needed data.

The remaining chapters will advance specific details concerning the requirements and the potential sources of information at each functional level. Selected information generated at defined functional points will pass to the Fire Coordinator. The objective of this chapter is to trace broadly some of the pertinent classes and details of information that the Fire Coordinator needs at his disposal in order to respond properly to immediate problems and to formulate the process for both immediate decisions and long-range decisions. Since problems and decisions are most often initiated as questions, this type of format is utilized to conceptualize the administrative information requirements. For purposes of clarity the questions are divided into somewhat arbitrary areas.

The Resource Questions

What are the resources of the Public Fire Safety Organization? The question may actually be formulated in a more specific manner. It is important to realize, the Fire Coordinator should be completely knowledgeable about his organization. This does not imply that every single item on every piece of apparatus in the organization should be committed to memory but it does imply that he should have this information at his fingertips for ready and immediate reference. The Public Fire Safety Systems Organization is structured to operate at a given level; this level may change by the day or within the day. Regardless of this condition, there should be a given resource of men, equipment and facilities at any designated time known to the coordinator. The Fire Coordinator needs to be informed of any substantial change in the resources, and this information must be kept very current. If the administrator has the occasion to know, the details should be available, should be timely and should be very accurate.

The resource question may also require an answer on a somewhat different time frame. The resource picture should be clearly depicted for the central urban administration at periodic intervals. Usually this means preparing an annual report that includes basic inventory type information. To be really meaningful, the resource projections should state trends over a period of time and the cost factors associated with the resources. In other words, the Fire Coordinator should be in a position to illustrate the systems resources at any given time and to attach a pricing label to the resources.

The Problem Questions

What Is the Community or Jurisdictional Fire Problem?

Such a broad-base question is difficult to respond to in a definitive manner. The typical answer has been to cite the annual loss of life and total damage figures for the aggregate number of fires. Other slightly more revealing quantitative indicators might include: (1) Fires per capita; (2) Loss per capita; (3) Fires per thousand dollars of assessed value; (4) The loss per thousand dollars assessed value; and (5) Average loss per building fires. These indicators are not terribly meaningful and they do not really give an adequate reflection of the urban fire problem. Furthermore, they do not include any reference to other important variables within a given community such as the type of business community, the varied structural conditions, the socioeconomic levels and the attendant problems. Nor do the stated indicators attempt to measure effectiveness of what has been defined as the major project systems components.

The urban fire problem needs to be defined in terms of probability theory and cost-ratio effectiveness. The Fire Coordinator should be able to state in specific terms responses to implied questions like the following:

1. The probability of having a fire by structural classification, occupancy classification, and socioeconomic level.

2. The frequency of fires by structural classification, occupancy classification and socioeconomic level.

3. The frequency of incidents by nonstructural type:
   a. Natural cover fuel fires;
   b. Transportation fires;
   c. Miscellaneous fires;
   d. Rescue assistance;
   e. Service calls.

4. The frequency of alarms by classification type:
   a. Reception of alarms: telephone, box fire alarm, central station, patrol, internal detection system.

   b. The alarm outcome: false alarms, needless alarms, equipment malfunctions, fire extinguished upon arrival, events requiring an alarm.

5. The frequency of alarms according to time sets:
   a. Frequency of events by hour of the day, day of the week, and week of the year.
   b. Cross correlate the frequency data to the severity analysis to establish patterned relationships.

6. The relationship of alarms and events to homogeneous units within the jurisdictional area. This would entail a frequency distribution based upon classification sets composed of:
   a. socioeconomic levels;
   b. occupancy classifications;
   c. geographical districts.

7. The frequency of defined severity levels for building classifications, occupancy classifications, and socioeconomic levels. The defined severity levels could be equated to established modular level parameters.

8. The frequency and severity of events need to be transformed into the probability of severity for the same classification structure advanced under point seven. This technique would translate the events into statements of risk that anyone could understand.

9. The frequency by established incident cause:
   a. Utilizing the NFPA 901 reporting system, establish the causal pattern for previously identified categories.

10. The formulation of cost-ratios through equating losses to established modular levels in order to predict the cost of a potential fire.

11. The fire problem involves related costs in addition to the direct loss problem. In addition to the direct cost attributable to the fire the following factors should be considered:
    a. The cost of providing the fire safety organization.
    b. The cost of providing private protection.
    c. The cost of insurance (over and above loss payments) for the jurisdiction area.

d. The pro-rata costs of other community services related to the public fire safety effort such as:
   (1) Water supply;
   (2) Building department;
   (3) Legal time;
   (4) Personnel and accounting time;
   (5) Police.

An informed reader of the public fire safety problem could now start to expand this initial problem information list. The above points are offered as an informational means to an end requirement and not as the end-point of information requirements. Also, the above points have been generally restricted to defining the urban fire safety problem. The value of these factors to the public fire safety organization must also be demonstrated.

The Fire Safety Organization Questions

How Efficient and Effective is the Public Fire Safety Organization?

Several tools and techniques have been employed to present the efficiency and effectiveness of public fire departments. Most of these evaluation techniques have missed their objective. Probably the most referenced crterion has been the A.I.A. grading number for the jurisdiction in question. The inadequacy of this approach was reviewed in Chapter I. The Fire Coordinator, the urban administrator and the public at large need and deserve a set of viable factors on which to evaluate responses to the question.

One possible measure of the fire safety service system suppression component effectiveness relates to the differential in damage that occurs to a piece of property after the fire department arrives and starts its operation. A contrasting situation should serve to illustrate this point. A fire unit responds to an alarm for a dwelling fire. Upon arrival at the scene the officer in charge observes fire issuing from a kitchen window. Hand lines are ordered advanced, and an attack and knockdown operation takes place under carefully coordinated conditions. The fire is suppressed, a rapid overhaul is made in the room of origin. A salvage cleanup is made. The rooms are deodorized for smoke odors as necessary and the dwelling is left in as near normal a condition as possible. The fire did not appreciably advance after attack was made. The total operation can be considered efficient from the viewpoint of holding fire related damage to a minimum through the utili-zation of the right amount of manpower effort. Manpower not committed to the fire suppression operation are immediately released for other potential duty.

An alternate situation results in a different conclusion. Again fire units respond to an alarm for a dwelling fire. Upon arrival at the scene the officer in charge observes fire issuing from the kitchen window. He immediately calls the fire alarm dispatcher on the radio and states that the building is involved in fire and for all responding engine companies to lay supply lines and attack the fire. The ensuing response results in a multiplicity of activity that is highly uncoordinated. The initial attack team has the fire driven back in their face as a second hose team advances through the dining room to the kitchen. The smoke thickens, so all the windows are knocked out for ventilation. By this time enough firemen have entered the building to physically hamper the fire suppression effort. Once the fire is out, the crews pick up and return to quarters.

The Fire Coordinator should be concerned about the tactical and operational problems. In response to these efficiency and effectiveness questions, the Fire Coordinator should be in a position to demonstrate with case studies incorporating cost analysis, the effectiveness and efficiency of the fire department. At the same time he should also be in a position to demonstrate that the fire suppression forces cannot save something that has been destroyed before the fire suppression crews go to work.

The Fire Coordinator should be in a position to respond to related effectiveness questions about the basic activities of the fire department. Some of the more pertinent questions might include:

1. How many structural fires can be handled by the first due fire company?

2. How many structural fires require extra alarms?

3. What is the percentage of manpower commitment by duty assignment at a specified type of fire (i.e., time devoted to: rescue, ventilation, extinguishment, salvage, overhaul, equipment operation, or just standby)?

4. What is the correlation of fire unit time involvement in relation to the probability of severity?

5. What is the correlation between response time and the probability of severity?

6. How much money would it cost to change the severity probability by some defined magnitude?

Again the list is utilized to simulate related questions that should receive factual answers. The information system must be structured to provide answers to the above and related questions.

This subsection has been developed to illustrate not only the range of potential problems that the Fire Coordinator might be faced with but equally important the information needs of the Public Fire Safety System administrative level to adequately respond to the urban administrator and the public being served. The generation of specific data to develop the necessary information and the flow patterns for the perceived information requirement will be discussed in the remaining chapters.

Profile of the Fire Coordinator

It appears appropriate to conclude this chapter with a profile of the Fire Coordinator in the context of the Public Fire Safety Systems Organization. A Fire Coordinator under a Public Fire Safety System and a present-day fire chief are more dissimilar than similar. The Fire Coordinator does not directly fight fires; he does not directly command personnel at fires; however, he is scientifically knowledgeable about urban fire problems. Above all, the Fire Coordinator is an administrator. His main responsibility is to coordinate men, materials, and equipment to prevent fire occurrence, protect private and public property in case of fire, and to suppress fires in the most efficient and effective manner allowable under the constraints of allocated resources. The Fire Coordinator also attempts to serve the public demand with related emergency services such as hazard control, property damage prevention, rescue, first aid, and the emergency transport of disabled persons.

The Fire Coordinator should be devoted to running a business. A legal government function is a public business in the strictest sense. It deserves to be administered by the best techniques of political science, public administration, business administration and engineering technology. The Public Fire Safety Systems Administrator — the Fire Coordinator — requires some specific talents to fill this role. Few men would qualify for the perceived position at the present time. However, it should be made perfectly clear that the door is not being closed to aspiring fire department officers and personnel. On the contrary, the door of challenge is being opened for Fire Service personnel to move up, and outward in a total scheme to achieve public fire safety.

Considerable attention is currently being focused on higher level education for the Fire Service. The perceived Public Fire Safety Systems Organization is going to demand a lot of education talent. The Fire Coordinator must possess the highest degree of educational attainment possible. A man without a recent Baccalaureate Degree would probably experience extreme difficulty in implementing the full extent of the described system. A Master's Degree in Public Administration, Business Administration, Economics or Engineering Administration is considered to be the real prerequisite for the position. Only under these stated discipline areas would one be able to achieve a depth of understanding in the areas of: Systems theory; Operations Research; public finance and monetary policy; the urbanizing process; the interface of science, technology and government; the metropolitan planning process and administrative coordination so essential to a complete understanding of the described organizational potential. The Doctoral Degree with a research emphasis in the field of public fire safety should enhance one's imagination to expand the proposed organization concept to something even more viable.

Administrative level people in the proposed organization would not be required to come up through the ranks of the Fire Service. However, few people should argue that a man who has experience on the fireground as an officer, and acquires the educational prerequisites, would probably bring more depth and insight to the issues to be confronted by the Fire Coordinator. This point of view can be summarized very briefly. Either the Fire Service is going to provide educational opportunities for its internal personnel relative to administrative responsibilities or outside people are going to be solicited for the top administrative posts; or as a third alternative, public fire safety is going to plod on in a fashion that is out of character and sequence with other units of urban government. As urban administrators become more talented, it seems unlikely that they will allow fire departments to be administered by men who cannot adequately respond to the relevant demands and pertinent questions. Public fire safety administrative personnel should also keep in mind that their counterpart in public safety — the police — are educationally outpacing them. While the Fire Service is initiating two-year fire science and management programs, policemen in selected areas of the country are graduating from college with Bachelors' degrees and in a few instances with advanced degrees.

Chapter 4

Bibliographical Entries

Books

Breton, Lee and R. Preston. *Planning Theory*. Englewood Cliffs: Prentice-Hall, 1967.

Brown, Fred, ed. *Management: Concepts and Practices*. Washington: Industrial College of the Armed Forces, 1967.

Burke, Arleigh, in Donald Favreau. *Fire Service Management*. New York: The Reuben H. Donnelley Corporation, 1969.

Corning, Richard. "Controlling a Business Process," in Bryon K. Edgerwood, ed. *Control Engineering Manual*. New York: McGraw-Hill Book Company, 1957.

Goode, Harry and Robert Machol. *Systems Engineering*. New York: McGraw-Hill Book Company, 1957.

Guetzskow, Harold, "The Creative Person in Organization," in Gary Setiner, ed. *The Creative Organization*. Chicago: The University of Chicago Press, 1965.

Johnson, Richard, Fremont Kast and James E. Rosenzweig. *The Theory and Management of Systems*. New York: McGraw-Hill Book Company, 1967.

Kast, Fremont and James Rosenzweig. *Organization and Management — A Systems Approach*. New York: McGraw-Hill Book Company, 1970.

Keller, Wayne and William Ferrara. *Management Accounting for Profit Control*, 2nd Ed. New York: McGraw-Hill Book Company, 1966.

Lepawsky, Albert, ed. *Administration, The Art and Science of Organization and Management*. New York: Knopf Publishers, 1955.

Litterer, Joseph A. *The Analysis of Organization*. New York: John Wiley and Sons, Inc., 1965.

Negro, Felix. *Modern Public Administration*. New York: Harper and Row, 1965.

Newman, William, Charles Summer and E. Kerby Warren. *The Process of Management*. Englewood Cliffs: Prentice-Hall, 1967.

Pfiffner, John M. and Frank Sheppard. *Administrative Organization*. Englewood Cliffs: Prentice-Hall, Inc., 1969.

Schramm, Wilbur. *The Process and Effects of Mass Communications*. Urbana: University of Illinois Press, 1954.

Shannon, Claude and Warren Weaver. *The Mathematical Theory of Communications*. Urbana: University of Illinois Press, 1949.

Publications of the Government, Learned Societies, and Other Organizations

Charlesworth, James, ed. *Theory and Practice of Public Administration: Scope, Objectives and Methods* (Monograph 8AAPS and ASAA) Philadelphia: The American Academy of Political and Social Science, 1966.

Department of the Air Force. *The Management Process*. Air Force Manual 25-1. Washington: Superintendent of Documents, 1954.

Gerhard, Colm, *Integration of National Planning — Budgeting*. Washington: National Planning Association, 1968.

Gulick, Luther and Urwick, Lyndall, eds. *Papers on the Science of Administration*. New York: Institute of Public Administration, 1957.

Hopkins, Robert. *Possible Applications of Information Theory of Management Control*. IRE Transactions on Engineering Management, March 1961.

Schultze, Charles L. *The Politics and Economics of Public Spending*. Washington: The Brookings Institution, p. 19.

Sperry, John, in Fred Brown, ed. *Management: Concepts and Practices*. Washington: Industrial College of the Armed Forces, 1967.

Periodicals

Daniel, D. Ronald, "Management Information Crisis," *Harvard Business Review*, September–October, 1961, p. 112.

Deutsch, Karl, "On Communications Models in the Social Sciences," *Public Opinion Quarterly*, Fall 1952, p. 367.

Dorsey, John, Jr. "A Communications Model For Administration." *Administrative Science Quarterly*, December 1957, p. 309.

Financial Executive Research Foundation. "Developments in Financial Organization, (A Special Supplement)" *Financial Executive*, September 1965, p. 19.

Kast, Fremont, and James Rosenzweig, "Planning: Framework for an Integrated Decision System," *University of Washington Business Review*, April, 1960, p. 39.

Peterson, Carl, "Fire Incident Reporting — What Does It Mean to the Changing Fire Service," *Fire Command!*, October, 1971.

Sayre, Wallace, "Premises of Public Administration, Past and Emerging," *Public Administration Review*, XVIII, No. 2, Spring 1958.

Chapter V
The Management of Resource Allocations

Overview on the Management Level

The management functions within the Public Fire Safety Systems Organization are perceived to be distinct from the administrative functions. It has been established that this separateness can be viewed in relation to policy formulation, complex organization coordination and decision-making. Frederic Hooper reinforces this book's contention about the management process by stating:[1]

> By management . . . we mean management as distinct from the framing of policy; this is "management" covers the complex operations below the administrative level down to and including the lower supervisory levels.

Mr. Hooper's management intent represents the subject matter for the next three chapters. The management level discussion will revolve around those individuals and functions that either support the major project subsystems or that are directly involved in the major project subsystems.

Stress should be made on certain features of the management process within the total organizational complex. First, the functional directors and coordinators do not make total organizational decisions. Their primary role is advisement. Each works through the Fire Coordinator to establish policy direction and guidance in dealing with persons and agencies outside of the system. Each functional head, with the exception of the service system, is responsible for planning, coordinating and communicating within the functional category. Deputy Coordinators, Division Coordinators and the System Fire Chief have a different set of policy guidelines to function by; each policy area will be reviewed in proper sequence.

[1]Frederic Hooper, *Management Survey.* Baltimore: Penguin Books, Inc., 1960, p. 11.

Introduction

The concept of resource allocations within the framework of the proposed Public Fire Safety Systems Organization was introduced in Chapter IV on Administration. The concern of this chapter is to detail the manner in which resources are to be procured and allocated within the organization subsystems. The objective of the allocation process is to examine specific activities and duties associated with the management of each depicted function in relation to the total system. It is a further objective of this material to illustrate the interaction of functions not only within the resource allocation group areas but as related to the total Public Fire Safety Systems Organization.

A committee has responsibility for planning implementation, the general conduct of business, and activities delegated to the resource allocation group. The committee as defined in Chapter II includes:

Chairman: Deputy Fire Coordinator
         Resource Allocations

Secretary: Executive Secretary

Membership: Director — Performance Budgeting Systems
        Director — Manpower Resources
        Director — Equipment and Facility Resources
        Director — Systems Engineering
        Deputy Fire Coordinator — Operation Support System

Ex-officio Membership:
    Director — Research and Development
    Division Fire Coordinator — Facilitating Systems
    Division Fire Coordinator — Major Project Systems

The Deputy Coordinator for Resource Allocations serves as chairman of the committee to maintain an awareness perception and continuity of the resource allocation group functions. The basic responsibility of the Resource Allocation Committee is to structure an economic balance within the organization. In other words, the committee examines the demands generated from the several element subsystems, costs each project out, and relates change in demand to the projected resources. Conclusions from this deliberation would be passed to the Master Planning Committee with supporting recommendations. Since such a request will most frequently originate under the operations systems, close coordination is needed between the two Deputy Fire Coordinators. Once the Fire Coordinator and the Master Planning Committee take action on the request package, it would go back to the Resource Allocation Committee for implementation.

An example of the resource process might be as follows. If the training facility needs an expansion program, the detail requirements including supporting documentation would pass from the Operations Committee to the Resource Allocation Committee. The costs, the benefits and the time frame would be worked out by the committee. The training facility improvement project would then be forwarded to the Fire Coordinator to review and place on the agenda docket for the Master Planning Committee. The Resource Allocation Committee may work out a bonding program that would allow for starting the project in the next fiscal year. However, the Master Planning Committee may feel that the total economic picture requires holding the project back for two years with the idea of exploring Federal matching funds. However, they also see the urgency to move forward so the package is returned to the Deputy Coordinator for Resource Allocation with directions to proceed to engage an architect to draw up preliminary plans and to investigate the long-range possibility for Federal funds. This directive would also probably place a maximum dollar expenditure for initiating the project.

The specified functional areas under the responsibility of the Division Coordinator for Resource Allocations are concerned with organization support activities. The specific scope of each function is reviewed under the following area headings. The concept of flexibility needs to be emphasized at this point. Four separate functional areas are depicted on the organization chart. However, it has already been noted in Chapter IV that the larger urban government might assume the responsibility for at least a portion of some functions. Under the condition of higher government functional involvement it would be quite feasible to combine two or more functions under one director.

The Performance Budgeting Subsystems

The performance budgeting function represents the financial arm of the total Public Fire Safety System. The Performance Budgeting System is much more than a simple accounting division within the proposed organization structure. It is deeply involved in the patterned financial relationships between the subsystems relative to the financial resources and the financial expenditures. Above all, as the title would imply, the Performance Budgeting is concerned with budget preparation.

Melvin Anshien talks about an organizational budget as an instrument for management activity and administrative analysis. He makes the observation that, "the budget is related to the complete administrative range from analysis through planning to management and control."[2] Anshien further states that in its end form, the budget should summarize five points. They are:[3]

1. The problems to which the analysis has been applied.
2. The analytic concepts and techniques brought to bear on these subjects.
3. The information relevant to their solution.
4. The proposed (ultimately, the determined) decisions.
5. The administrative structure through which performance of the approved budget will be executed, controlled, and appraised.

The primary operational utility of a budget is to serve as an instrument for aggregating and displaying annually the expenditure proposals of the organizational administrator as a basis for appropriate resource decision-making at some higher level.

A budget presentation contains an estimate of organizational income developed from forecasts of the general level of economic activity and existing or proposed taxes. A budget's more significant content in a managerial sense is its statement of estimated expenditures in terms of dollar amount and program objectives to be achieved. It should also be recognized

[2]Melvin Anshien, in David Novick, *Program Budgeting*, Harvard University Press, 1965, p. 3.

[3]*Ibid.*, p. 3.

that a corollary purpose of a budget is to serve as the control medium through which spending decisions are administratively implemented and financially accountable.

The fundamental problem to be resolved through the budget process is the familiar one of distributing scarce resources (as measured in terms of real money) among a variety of competing claims within the organization. The budget system should be concerned with a design that will aid decisions on the allocation of money and other well defined inputs (i.e., mutual aid support) to attain objectives that are also well defined. David Novick states that a budget design involves three related operations:[4]

> First, it is necessary to determine the most efficient way to attain given objectives. Second, it is necessary to determine the optimal set of concurrent objectives. Third, it is necessary to determine the optimal size of the total budget.

Novick also makes the following pertinent observations about a budget:[5]

> A good budget system supports and informs judgment in making determinations. It does this by providing information that is relevant to the required decisions. Relevancy may be defined by the following criteria: (1) Aggregation of information in totals that illuminate meaningful decision alternatives and aid rational comparisons among them; (2) With respect to each alternative objective, identification and summation of all pertinent input requirements, both current and future; (3) organization of information in detail that facilitates efficiency measures of inputs in relation to outputs, means in relation to ends, investment in relation to return. (Such efficiency measures are often referred to as cost-effectiveness or cost-utility analysis.)

How the budget information is organized for decision-making can illuminate or obscure its significance for meaningful analysis. The budgeting system in the proposed Public Fire Safety Systems Organization would attempt to respond to the following typical questions.[6]

1. What is the present budget commitment for each of the subsystem support functions and the three major project subsystems?

2. What incremental changes in positive contributions to defined problems might be attributed to the requests for added budget commitments? For example: A request is made for three new fire protection technician positions under the prevention system. How would the efforts of these people contribute to the frequency of building surveys and/or fire investigations in quantitative terms?

3. What significant minimum or threshold budget levels would underwrite useful activities in problem areas not currently provided for by ongoing programs? For example: How much would it cost to initiate a fire investigation course for unit fire officers in the training subsystem?

4. What feasible increased rates of program activity can be identified relative to functional allocations? For example: How could routine inservice inspections be increased by a reallocation of a portion of the program budget for fire prevention to the service units?

5. Can operationally meaningful differentiations be made between the effectiveness of various approaches to the fire suppression operation? For example: Would one or more "floating squad companies" effectively reduce the average modular loss levels in potential fires? If so, can such a differentiation be related to system service support in the costs in the immediate future or on a long-range basis?

It is this exploratory mechanism that becomes the work activity of the Performance Budgeting System personnel. Questions like those above may look unreasonable to some; unanswerable to others; but they appear to be the type of questions that need complete examination in the area of Public Fire Safety.

An important point to be remembered is that the proper questions need to be raised for each functional element of the organization in relation to budget requests. It is also necessary that each question be implicitly answered in any budget decision relating to defined problem areas. The significant budget issue is whether the answer rests on intuition and guess, or on a budget system that presents relevant information so organized as to contribute to rational analysis, planning and decision-making. Even a partially quantified and qualified descriptive response would raise the value of the budget process over the presently utilized line item budget.

Before moving further into this discussion it appears appropriate to develop some special definition of terms. In review, the budget is a quantitative plan of action and a major aid to coordination and control. The budget is basically a financial forecasting statement which expresses in monetary terms the administration's future plans.[7] The program budget in contrast to the line budget specifically lays out

---

[4]David Novick, *Program Budgeting*, Cambridge: Harvard University Press, 1965, p. 5.

[5]*Ibid.*, p. 5.

[6]Note: The statements and questions are modified to fit the context of the Public Fire Safety Organization from Novick's book, *Program Budgeting*.

[7]Fred Brown, *Management: Concepts and Practice*, Washington: Industrial College of the Armed Forces, 1967, p. 147.

a quantitative plan according to the major (and in some cases minor) functional programs of the organization. A Performance Program Budget goes one step further to illustrate the financial plan in accordance with prescribed objectives for each program function. A Performance Program Budget should state how the objective accomplishment changes with the potential allocation of resource money. There is a specific consideration more inherent in the Performance Program Budget than is implied by this simple definition.

The Performance Program Budget represents a framework that may be described as building a bridge between concepts of political responsiveness (i.e., What is public fire protection for — to prevent unwanted fires or to simply suppress unwanted fire or to achieve some defined balance between the two?) and the administrative function of assigning scarce resources (money) according to the organizational objectives. The organizational objectives and the political responsiveness may or may not be in tune with each other. The main advantage of the Performance Program Budget is that the budget document makes the objectives of both the political sphere and organizational sphere very visible for all to scrutinize. The secondary advantage falls into two parts. The Program Performance Budget promises to be a more effective and efficient organization tool by (1) providing a framework for more clearly defining the alternatives among which choices must be made and (2) creating an information system that will assist in measuring costs in relation to accomplishments. The preparation of a budget as a totally viable document would be the main responsibility of the Director of Performance Budgeting Systems in the organizational context presented.

The previous comments have set forth the basic charge and direction for structuring the Performance Budgeting System. The objective of the management areas of this book are structured to specifically outline the input-processing-output requirements for each functional unit. The following material is devoted to this objective.

A basic element of the systems approach is to produce definable objective output whether this be a budget report or a task activity. Therefore, output is the principal concern of each function. A concept of this book is the premise that the required output dictates the need for both the processing component and the input requirements. If the system action is looked at in the basic form, the input leads to processing which leads to output. This oversimplified action process presents a danger. Systems analysts often use the phrase, "garbage in — garbage out." This phrase simply reveals that if one tries to analyze everything or if the input data is not carefully selected, the output will have little meaning. To avoid this problem a reverse action process is initiated. The output is examined first followed by a determination of the kind of input as required to achieve the desired output.

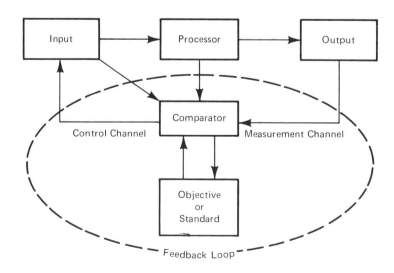

ILLUSTRATION V-1 INPUT-OUTPUT-PROCESSING-FEEDBACK-INFORMATION LOOP

The Director of the Performance Budget System is charged with preparing an annual budget to be delivered to the Fire Coordinator on a stipulated date. Based upon the governmental jurisdiction within which the total fire safety system operates, this budget may be for the next fiscal year or it could be a projected budget for one, two or three years in the future. The budget document should depict the organizational mission with the monetary requirement to achieve this mission. Beyond this point the organization chart is examined from an inverted position. In other words, projected objective accomplishments are viewed in terms of the three major project systems: the Protection System; the Prevention System; and the Service System. In reality the remaining functional units starting from the position of Fire Coordinator down to the project level support the three project system areas. Therefore, one possible output structure could be patterned as follows.

Budget Output:

1. The Fire Coordinator's statement of pertinent accomplishments and future objective expectations. The expression of expectation should be equated to identified problems.

2. The requested change in performance level for each project program:
   a. Expectation objectives for the Major Project Systems
      (1) The current level of funding
      (2) The proposed level of funding
         (a) Statement of utilization (i.e., proportions allocated to manpower, equipment, space facilities)

3. The request for a change in performance level for each of the Facilitating Subsystems.
   a. A statement for each system demonstrating the present levels of performance and the problem areas in meeting previous objective expectations.
   b. The future expectations for each organizational function and how the funding program will in turn support the major project systems.
      (1) The current level of funding
      (2) The proposed level of funding
         (a) Statement on the utilization of the proposed funding

4. The total operational system budget request.

5. The request for change in performance requirements for the resource allocation support systems.
   a. A statement for each subsystem demonstrating the present level of support to the other functional units of the organization.
   b. An indication of current problems in providing request support functions (i.e., where does the current resource delivery system or central processing system break down?)
   c. The future expectations for each resource subsystem as it relates to the specific requirements of the administrative level and the operational system
      (1) The current level of funding
      (2) The proposed level of funding
         (a) A statement on the utility of funding

6. The Administrative Level Budget request
   a. The request for a change in administrative support through personal involvement, research and development and staff assistance to the executive secretary.
   b. A statement demonstrating present involvement in relation to the inter-organization and the intra-organization.
   c. A statement of administrative direction and emphasis under the new budget
   d. A statement of the research and development needs to achieve improved objective performance and why this R & D effort is different from that being carried on outside of the organization.
   e. A statement of how a change in budget would allow the administrative level to better support and coordinate the total organization effort.
      (1) The current level of funding
      (2) The proposed level of funding
         (a) A statement on the utility of funding

The budget preparation must keep two points in mind. The best budget is a short budget. The best budget is a succinctly definitive budget. The next step in the budget process relates to the input requirements to achieve the desired output ends. The output statement gives a definitive direction to the input process.

The input requirement process should start with an objective appraisal of each function including the strengths and weaknesses. This portion of the budget evolution might be indicated by the following pattern.

1. A determination from Systems Engineering where the "objective failure structure points exist." In other words, what functional components can be identified as the least contributors to the organizational mission?

2. Examine the "failure structure points" to determine projected needs.

3. Examine the Fire Coordinator's appraisals of each function.

4. Conduct functional area hearings, committee hearings and interview the Fire Coordinator on projected needs.

5. Consult a second time with Systems Engineering and Research and Development concerning modeling of component elements to illustrate alternate paths to achievement.

6. Construct a cost/utility study of all functional components.

7. Review the constructed model studies and cost utility studies with the Fire Coordinator and Executive Secretary.

8. Prepare an initial budget draft.

9. Submit the budget draft to the Resource Allocation Committee for approval.

10. Make necessary changes for compliance with the Resource Allocation Committee.

11. Submit the Resource Allocation Budget to the Fire Coordinator.

12. Make final document changes according to administrative discretion.

13. Print the final budget.

Actually each proposed step can be viewed in terms of an input-processing-output function. A large Level 1 Public Fire Safety System may require sufficient analysis to support computer techniques for examining alternative courses of action. However, most of the processing analysis can probably be accomplished on a multi-stage desk calculator. The basic inputs are the perceived monetary requirements of each functional element to accomplish functional level goals. The processing evaluation would possibly involve a matrix or set analysis of alternate paired relationships. Output values would express cost to benefit ratios.

The Performance Budgeting System might be viewed as a catalyst for the whole organization system. It can be viewed as no less than a major coordinating and communicating activity of the organization. It therefore requires a very special person as director.

The director must possess a real sensitivity for the systems concept. He must be economically astute and be well grounded in the fundamentals of quantitative analysis techniques.

Manpower Resources Subsystems

The manpower resources subsystem is also headed by a director. In a broad sense, the director is concerned with the people who perform all of the organizational functions from the Fire Coordinator to the recruit fireman. Among the more basic responsibilities of the Manpower Director is the selection process, the continual education process and the proper placement process of suitable people into the most appropriate positions. His next major concern is that of continually appraising staff and operational personnel, of providing promotional opportunities consistent with individual motivation and demonstrated capability, of relocating individuals to maintain a balance of involvement and achievement within the system and to reflect changing requirements of the enterprise. An all-inclusive treatment of personnel management is beyond the scope and intent of this book. However, it is the intent of this book to cover the functional aspects of manpower resources in the total systems concept. In the absence of a higher urban government level unit involvement in manpower, it is perceived that the manpower resource function would operate according to the following structural-functional analysis:

1. Upon administrative level authorization for personnel, a functional unit submits a position description and a request to the Director of Manpower Resources (input). This group then recruits, examines and establishes a list of eligible candidates for functional categories (processing). The lists are then sent to the Resource Allocation Committee for final review and recommendation to the Fire Coordinator.

2. The Fire Coordinator completes the selection process.

3. New personnel are appropriately assigned to the functional units for which requests were approved (output).

4. Records are established on all personnel and updated as required. As a minimum this would probably include:

a. Original application
b. Original examination (entrance or promotional)
c. Original appointment
d. Probationary documents
e. Educational documents
f. Medical records
g. In-service training records
h. Activity records (functional and emergency involvement records)
i. Achievement awards
j. Sick leave and vacation records
k. Pay and fringe benefit records
l. Assignment records
m. Special action records (disciplinary action)

5. Assessment of personnel records to detect strength and weakness in the system and to report these findings to the Resource Allocation Committee for appropriate action.

6. The preparation of pay vouchers.

7. The establishment of work schedules.

8. The maintenance of a balanced work force. One of the daily responsibilities of the manpower resource group would be to achieve a manpower balance and coverage in each functional area with special emphasis on the service system. In other words, as each manpower shift changes an instant report is made to the Manpower Resource Director. Transfers or substitutes are immediately dispatched to balance assignment levels. This activity may be by-passed and handled by the Communications Coordinator for volunteer service units. This concept will be fully explored in a subsequent section.

9. The management of special service plans which might include: retirement, health, credit union, and emergency relief plans.

It is expected that most of the system's routine personnel record processing would be accomplished with computer assistance. Once the system is established, each personnel transaction would immediately go on a punch card or paper tape for storage. The data may be sorted and analyzed according to desired outputs such as the payroll within the manpower resource subsystem or as summary personnel reports for other functional units. Some of these specialized outputs might include:

1. Individual records of fire and emergency service involvement could be summarized and transmitted to the training coordinator. These records could demonstrate the existence of area deficiencies and the need for reinforced skill development.

2. Total unit manpower summary records could be transmitted to the Division Coordinator for Major Project System for analysis and assignment balance correction.

3. Total unit manpower summary records could be transmitted to Director, Research and Development, who could make analysis of the manpower required to handle given types of fire situations.

4. Total unit manpower records might also go to manpower resources for determining average, minimum and maximum manpower responses for the current ISO survey report.

5. Individual involvement records might be utilized by the Manpower Resource Committee to automatically schedule a physical examination after so many duty hours of fire suppression activity.

6. Manpower records might be statistically summarized and analyzed for the annual administrative report.

The Director of Manpower Resources or his staff personnel should provide specialized talent(s) in the areas of personnel administration, statistics, psychological testing and possibly human factors engineering.

Equipment and Facility Resources Subsystems

This identified subsystem would work primarily with the materials aspect of the total public fire safety system. The Director would be charged with the responsibility for purchase, allocation, inventory, repair, improvement and replacement of all physical structures, equipment, and supplies. This subsystem then must be highly coordinated to every other functional unit in the system.

The Equipment and Facilities group would initiate action revolving around the preparation of guide and cost specifications for routine requested items. Many items should be available on an "off-the-shelf" basis. Such items would be handled by an interfunctional purchase and billing procedure.

Occasionally purchased items would be procured on the basis of purchase specifications to be developed by this functional group. Upon authorization from the Fire Coordinator, a

Deputy Coordinator or a Division Coordinator, this group would prepare purchase specifications, submit specifications for bid, receive bids, and depending on the authority delegated, would either let the bid or make a recommendation to the Master Planning Council for deliberation and action. Specification writing would be closely coordinated with the Fire Protection Engineering Staff.

This group would act as advisor for cost estimations to the Performance Budgeting Group, to Systems Engineering and to Research and Development.

This function would be responsible for determining repair and improvement frequencies for structures (i.e., painting, remodeling, etc.) and for the general cleaning routine of all structures.

The Equipment and Facility staff in cooperation with the Research and Development Division would analyze equipment failures for determining replacement schedules and for improving performance specifications.

Inventory control would also be a responsibility of this functional unit. The inventory process would involve setting up a mechanism for identifying all items, coding of items and auditing items. Again, most of inventory control could be automated with a simple punch card system of logging, storage, updating, and retrieval printouts. The inventory data requirements could be cross correlated with the repair, improvement and replacement program.

Every major function and subfunction of the total system becomes an input point for the Equipment and Resource Function. Possible input categories would include:

1. Stock item supply orders
2. Specification development and purchase request
3. Item utilization data cards
4. Inventory verification data cards
5. Special improvement requests that are out of phase with the programmed repair and improvement routine
6. Maintenance completion cards
7. Equipment allocation change requests

In addition to the direct supply service to functional units, the output of this function could include several types of control reports that would be submitted to the Resource Allocation Committee for review and action. The administration concepts presented in Chapter IV stressed the fact that the administrator must have at his disposal an updated location inventory of all major components of the system. Such a documentation would largely be the responsibility of the Equipment and Resources Facilities Group.

The Director of the Resource Allocation Function is viewed as a specialist in business management with special expertise in purchasing, specification writing, inventory control, operations research, accounting, and data management.

Systems Engineering

The Systems Engineering function is viewed as vital to the initiation and viable continuance of the total system. Therefore, total organization design, functional design, functional implementation, systems integrated communication channeling plus systems modification would be considered the main activities and responsibilities of this function. The systems engineering activity and process is considered to be so compatible with the computer technology required for the operational system that the central processing unit has been placed under the responsibility of the Director for Systems Engineering.

The term systems engineering as defined by Johnson, Kast and Rosenzweig means: "making useful an array of components designed to accomplish a particular objective according to a plan."[8] The implication for the Public Fire Safety Systems Organization would be to array men, facilities and equipment in patterns to provide an objective service. These authors continue by stating "Systems Engineering further suggests the development of a man-machine integrated system which should function as a task-oriented assemblage."[9] Furthermore, there is also an implication for a continued analysis of the system as well as the creation of the system.

The Systems Engineering function comes closest to implying a design activity. Once the systems approach has been decided upon as a course of organizational action, the Systems Engineering function must be created. Its first activity would involve the initiation of the specifically required functional components for the organization level of service anticipated, the intricate subsystems design, the larger complex of project systems, facilitating systems and resource allocation systems, and finally the composite whole system.

Systems Engineering must be cognizant of the effective characteristics of the systems approach in developing a total integrated design.

[8]Richard A. Johnson, Fremont E. Kast, and James E. Rosenzweig, *The Theory and Management of Systems.* New York: McGraw-Hill Book Company, 1967, p. 339.

[9]*Ibid.*, p. 340.

As a minimum, such characteristics would include:[10]

1. Simplicity — the system does not have to be infinitely complex to be effective. On the contrary, the greater the degree to which the system is understood, the higher the degree of success it will enjoy. There would appear to be a positive correlation between simplicity and reliability. A system becomes complex when the boundaries between systems and/or subsystems are not defined. It is important, therefore, that Systems Engineering make the limits of functional operations very definite.

2. Flexibility — Environmental conditions change and Systems Engineering should be prepared to adjust the system operations accordingly. There appear to be two ways to meet an evolution process in the operation of a subsystems environment: (1) self-sustaining new systems may be carved out of the geographical districts in existing systems. (2) the reverse process could take place; the operating system level could be expanded to include geographical sectors and regions. To be effective and simple the system must be well defined. But to be practical, the organization framework cannot be rigid. The Public Fire Safety System Organization chart should not be viewed as a static framework. Systems Engineering would have the responsibility for seeing that all personnel realize the flexible features built into the functional elements of organization. Finally, Systems Engineering could plan to accept minor variation in the proposed structure without a drastic disruption to the systems concept.

3. Reliability — System reliability is a very important consideration in organization development and maintenance. Reliability refers to the consistency of operations day by day. For example, one subsystem objective would be to respond to emergency incidents with a prescribed manpower and equipment complement. A given organized public fire safety system could vary from a prescribed output level all the way down to zero output. The latter possibility has happened during major strikes. Since the desired performance objectives for the operating system would probably never be fully realized, it can be assumed that the system will operate somewhere between the two extremes mentioned. Systems Engineering would have the responsibility for maintaining the highest degree of reliability in the system by designing into the system a process of careful balance of functional arrangements and operating components. Arrangements for mutual-aid coverage by fire suppression units of adjacent systems is one simple example of establishing service reliability for a system.

4. Economy — A system may be effective without being economical. For example, the work of the proposed fire prevention system and the service system can be singled out to make the point. One of the established areas of responsibility within the prevention system would involve building surveys. The fire prevention system could and often does, conduct all of the building survey work. At the same time personnel assigned to the service system may spend a significant portion of their time on "standby" duty. This is not an economical system even though the target objective of surveys to be completed could be met. Possibly a more economical approach for the system would be to share the work load so that all manpower is productive. Often it is dysfunctional and expensive to develop one functional element of the system with much greater capacity than some other part of the system. Also, Systems Engineering should be aware that building in great redundancy or providing for every contingency usually destroys the operating economy of the system. The Director of Systems Engineering must work very closely with the performance budgeting subsystem, the Equipment and Facility Subsystem and the Manpower Resources Subsystem to determine what a systems organization is operating in the most economical fashion without overdevelopments or underdevelopments. Awareness of what is going on in the system is key to Systems Engineering effectiveness.

5. Acceptability — Any system, no matter how well designed, is worthless unless accepted by the people who operate it. If the people working within a system do not believe it will work — it will break down. If individuals do not perceive how the system will benefit them, if they develop an opposition to the system, if they

[10]*Ibid.*, p. 34.

135

are pressured into becoming a part of the system without true consent, or simply think that the system is poorly developed, the system will not work. One of two events might take place if these conditions prevailed. First, the system might be altered to operate as the employees perceive it should operate regardless of the organizational chart, or second, the system will be used ineffectively and will ultimately break down. The actual occurrence of these possible situations might create a performance condition that would be less responsive than the "presystem era." The realization of this potential problem focuses on the reason why it is so imperative for the Systems Engineering design to be excellent; why it will be so important for the Director of Systems Engineering to work with all functional components of the total system so the individual roles, responsibilities and opportunities would be fully understood. Some systems design people feel that the key to organization acceptance lies in the decentralization of responsibility which tends to foster involvement in the organizational process at an earlier time in the career development pattern.

It should be obvious from the preceding discussion that a great deal of the success or failure of the Public Fire Safety Systems Organization will depend upon the Director of Systems Engineering. Therefore, the individual selected for this position must possess some unusual abilities. The academic degree could come from several areas including engineering, business administration, industrial education, economics or public administration. What appears to be most important is a recognizable talent for working with people and obtaining accomplishments in accordance with organization objectives. In addition to this, an individual should be well versed in advanced organization theory, systems theory, technology of administration, operations research, quantitative analysis and advanced computer programming. This is a large but necessary academic demand. Undoubtedly the Director of Systems Engineering should demonstrate his ability from previous experience in similar undertakings.

The Director of Systems Engineering might be thought of as a major sensor in a multientry feedback loop for the entire system. He is constantly sampling output from every function in the system. Actually each subsystems output documents would serve as the input for the Systems Engineering group. Recommendations are the output function of this group and are forwarded to the Resource Allocation Committee. Such recommendations might suggest alterations to maintain the system in a state of simplicity, flexibility, reliability, economy and acceptability.

The Central Processing Unit within the systems organization may be defined as "the computer computational system that contains the arithmetic, logic and control units necessary for the interpretation and execution of programmed instructions to produce results of a desired kind on a device external to the processing mechanism."[11] Some concepts concerning the utility of the Central Processing Unit need to be developed in a compatible framework to this definition.

First, the Systems Engineering group would be responsible for all computer programming, computer data processing, computer time-sharing priorities and output formating. Other functional units such as Communications, Research and Development, and Performance Budgeting may also write special computer programs but it remains the responsibility of Systems Engineering to insure program-system-computer compatibility.

Second, the Central Processing Unit would be supported by a staff of data process handlers and computer programmers. This group of people would be under the responsibility of the Director of Systems Engineering.

Third, the Central Processing Unit should coordinate activities with the Equipment and Facilities Resources to provide designated functional units with remote input devices, remote printers, cathode-ray-tube viewers, and other display equipment.

Fourth, the central processing would be responsible for the storage and handling of all computerized data.

Chapter III established that the man-computer complex is essential to the large systems organizational structure. The computer, the prime element of the Central Processing Unit is considered to be the nerve center for the whole organization. The system could be made to work, just as fire departments do operate today without computer assistance, but not in the efficient and effective manner perceived for the Public Fire Safety System. The Central Processing Unit is considered essential to the organization mission.

[11]Robert R. Arnold, Harold C. Hill, and Aylmer V. Nichols, *Introduction to Data Processing*. New York: John Wiley & Sons, Inc., p. 310.

Chapter 5

Bibliographical Entries

Books

Anshien, Melvin, in David Novick. *Program Budgeting.* Cambridge: Harvard University Press, 1965.

Arnold, Robert, Harold Hill, and Aylmer V. Nichols. *Introduction to Data Processing.* New York: John Wiley and Sons, Inc.

Brown, Fred. *Management: Concepts and Practices.* Washington: Industrial College of the Armed Forces, 1967.

Hooper, Frederic. *Management Survey.* Baltimore: Penguin Books, Inc., 1960.

Johnson, Richard A., Fremont E. Kast, and James Rosenzweig. *The Theory and Management of Systems.* New York: McGraw-Hill Book Co., 1967, p. 339.

Novick, David. *Program Budgeting.* Cambridge: Harvard University Press, 1965, p. 5.

The Operations Systems

Introduction to the Operations Systems (Chapters VI and VII)

Most of the discussion to this point has revolved around support considerations to the direct service areas of the Public Fire Safety System. The Public Fire Safety System originates and remains active to provide a defined public service; this is the mission. The service rendering functions under the total system are referenced as the Operations System which is composed of several specialized but interrelated project subsystems. Part of the subsystem is designed to supply a support function to three major project subsystems. The Major Project Subsystem consisting of the Protection Subsystem, the Prevention Subsystem and the Service Subsystem work directly with the public to carry out assigned tasks and activities. The Operations Support Subsystems (i.e., Communication, Training, Public Relations, and Maintenance) may also work with the public but normally through a more indirect approach.

The following two chapters attempt to explain the functional elements assigned to the Operational Subsystems.

Chapter VI deals with the Facilitating Support Subsystems. Facilitating Systems in the context of this book means the provision of dependent support functions to the project subsystems. For example, a fire suppression unit would be dependent upon the communications system to receive a fire alarm call, determine the nature and location of the emergency and dispatch the proper prearranged unit assignment. The facilitating subsystem functions operate to serve all functional elements with special emphasis on the Major Project Systems.

Chapter VII deals with the three Major Project Subsystems. The inclusive functions are more readily understood because of their comparability to the existing type of public fire protection organization. Under the systems concept employed the three interrelated projects areas are designed to achieve a desired degree of fire safety and emergency service to a jurisdictional area.

The combined functions to be depicted in Chapters VI and VII would be coordinated through an operations committee. The committee headed by a Deputy Fire Coordinator for Operations Systems receives progress reports, statistical reports, problem identifications, memoranda, plus resource requests from both the facilitating systems and the Major Project Systems. The Operations Committee has the opportunity to view all of the input information from the identified functional areas in a total objective context. On the basis of their deliberation, the committee would recommend the approval or disapproval of resource changes to the Master Planning Council. The Operations Committee would authorize procedural changes for the operational subsystems. This concept is considered a part of the decentralized decision-making process. The same committee would conduct hearings on grievance cases and discipline matters that might be appealed from the Division Coordinator level. A committee opinion is sent back to the appropriate Division Coordinator for final action.

Additional responsibilities of the Operations Committee would be the implementation of new programs approved by the Master Planning Council and the realignment of the Operations System to accommodate a new level of organization. In other words, a change from a type three project system to a type two project system would be effected by this Committee.

Probably the main concern of the Operations Committee would be to be constantly "tuned in" on the functional subsystems to anticipate problems and to properly handle potential situations before they disrupt the balance of the system.

The Deputy Fire Coordinator for Operations Systems is a kingpin in the total organization. In this capacity he must possess certain talents. Academically, a degree in Public Administration, Business Administration, Fire Protection Engineering, or Civil Engineering would appear to be an appropriate background. The academic foundation should include courses in statistical inference, data processing systems, and systems analysis and/or operations research; additional courses relevant to the management process would be helpful.

An individual chosen for this position should also possess certain basic experience qualifications. A minimum of five years in one of the project system areas would appear desirable or experience as a Facilitating Systems Division Coordinator for a period of two years.

Chapter VI

The Management of Facilitating Subsystems

The management process for the facilitating subsystems of communications, training, maintenance and public relations is structured under the direction of a Division Fire Coordinator. The facilitating subsystems are presented as a major bicomponent of the total Operations System. The facilitating subsystem's unitary function has already been described as producing a service activity for the major project systems. The horizontal coordination and communication requirements are considered to outweigh the vertical requirements. This can be supported on the basis of the service level to be performed.

The Division Coordinator must not only thoroughly understand his own functional relationship but probably more important he needs to understand all facets of the Major Project subsystems with special emphasis on the Service Systems. In this capacity, the Division Fire Coordinator should possess a degree in Fire Protection Engineering, Engineering Technology, Electrical Engineering or possibly Industrial Education (with mechanical and electrical minors). Experience should preferably come from the Major Project System Division initially. Being the coordinator for one of the facilitating subsystems would be a logical stepping stone in promotion.

The following subsection will review the basic considerations associated with each of the subsystems functions. Special attention will be given to the general scope of activity for each function, the input-processing-output activity of each function and the basic integration concept (coordination-communication-control) aspects of the function. The total concept of functional coordination is left to be explored in Chapter VIII.

The Communications Subsystem

The Central Processing Unit described in Chapter V was depicted as a nerve center to the organization. The Communications Systems is also a nerve center to the organization. There is no conflict in these two statements. The interdependence of the communication function with the central processing unit is an essential ingredient of the systems concept.

In most cities of the United States, the business of the fire alarm office — consisting of the receipt, processing and transmission of fire alarms can be considered as largely a manual operation. Several cities, including New York and Los Angeles, are currently developing very sophisticated real-time communications systems that are highly oriented towards automating most or all of the processes.[1] A unique characteristic of the fire alarm communications subsystem is that the entire sequence of events in the alarm process can be handled manually; this is the case in most American communities. Now it is being recognized that public fire alarm systems can combine automation with manual operations in a variety of ways, including a high state of automation.[2] The degree of fire alarm activity should be a determining factor in the interface requirements between a manually operated subsystem and a totally automated subsystem.

Prior to discussing specific activities and process of the fire alarm communications subsystem, it would appear appropriate to present the objectives and projected achievements for this subfunction.

---

[1]Walter H. Carter, "Communications Join Computer Era," *Fire Engineering*, February 1970, p. 57.

[2]*Ibid.*, p.58.

First, fire alarm communications can be considered the link between the external environmental system and the internal service systems. Fire alarm communication is also the direct link between all subsystem nodes of the internal system. The actual number of linkup combinations is almost infinite. Chapter VIII will illustrate a number of the possible linking arrangements under a highly automated system.

Under emergency conditions, the linking activity or the processing of requirements to produce a desired action should take a minimal amount of time. For example, a woman detects a fire in her kitchen; she calls the fire department by phone to request help; the communications dispatcher collects all of the necessary information possible from the woman; he looks up the dispatch assignment for the location given; he dispatches the proper equipment; he listens for the units to acknowledge being dispatched; and then he is alert for a status report from the first fire units on the scene. The procedure can be developed in a logical pattern and would not be considered too complicated in most emergency cases.

The process can be complicated when combinations of the following occur: (1) several calls for assistance are received simultaneously or in very rapid succession; (2) an alarm of fire requires extra alarms involving numerous radio transmissions; (3) several fires and/or emergency situations are in process at the same time. Activity in a communications headquarters becomes hectic under these potential conditions slowing the dispatch process time from a few seconds to minutes.

Time appears to be an important variable in emergency situations. Some of the literature in fire protection theorizes that alarm sequence time along with other time patterns has a direct bearing on the severity of the fire.[3] Until more quantitative data can identify the relative importance of time patterns that enter into the variable situation, the alarm function should support an objective of keeping the dispatch process time to a maximum of thirty seconds.

The dispatch time objective stated above simply means that the entire sequence of events from the point of alarm receipt to the dispatching of equipment would be less than thirty seconds. If no interrupting factors such as additional calls, and/or radio messages occur, a manual operation could be effective. However, when message transmission becomes heavy and

concentrated signal priorities emerge, the time span for task completion lengthens. There must be a move to an automated system when the potential for this condition becomes evident.

A second objective reflects on what is termed communications command and control. One of the most significant problems in effective and efficient fire suppression is achieving a coordinated and controlled condition at the emergency scene. So many actors are playing so many simultaneous roles that the big picture can become a jumble of detail to the ranking fire officer. Under the systems concept of organization presented, it is apparent that the communications function would be the most logical unit to provide the necessary information for achieving optimal understanding and performance in emergency operations involving command, control and communications tasks.

To accomplish objectives one and two it would appear necessary to incorporate a number of special features into the design of the communications function. The choice between a manual process and an automated process is a matter of examining time intervals and expected complexity of operations. For example, three units on a fire scene can probably be well coordinated with a simple tactical display and resource kit. However, an event involving thirty units with a complement of around two hundred men can turn into a complex, uncoordinated process, a situation where communications becomes difficult at best. Equally important is the realization that a single fire officer or a small group of fire officers are severely taxed to comprehend and recall all of the rapidly occurring events in a manner that would support proper decision-making. It should be obvious that fire officers need automated assistance in complex situations. The communications function should have the responsibility of maintaining a chronological and real-time appraisal of all functional and unit activities. Such a requirement would demand a minimum interlocking framework of the following components.

1. Instant communications capability between units and Control Central; between individual units; between the coordinating field unit and Control Central; and between the coordinating field unit, and individual emergency units.

   a. Accomplishment by: Radio and remote terminal telecommunications.

2. Back-up or reserve communication capability between Control Central and field units.

[3]Frederick Salzberg, *Fire Department Operations Analysis*, Office of Civil Defense Contract DAHC20-70-C-0208. Chicago: Illinois Institute of Technology, 1970, p. 7.

a. Accomplishment by: Fire alarm, telegraph, portable telephone, commercial telephone, messenger service.

3. Message handling capability. Message transmission is of little value without action on the part of the receiver.
   a. Manpower must be available to handle voice communications and either process manually the directions, or input the information into the CPU for processing to produce an output format.
   b. The second possibility is that both Command Central and the field command unit would have the capability to directly make input to the CPU with the alternate command unit being utilized as a sensor to achieve a desired output. For example, a request for an additional alarm assignment could go directly to a preprogrammed alarm matrix in the CPU. The computer could search, select and dispatch the requested assignment.

4. Recording, transcription, and playback features for all voice transmissions.
   a. This could be accomplished at Command Central with a tape deck, a log and a digital time dubber.

5. Real-time unit status capability. There is a need to know where every unit is at all times and the availability or commitment of each unit.
   a. Visual display boards using lights or magnetic symbols manually inserted, positioned and deleted as the status changes could achieve this goal.
   b. As an alternate means, the human element could be bypassed to a certain degree, the equipment status could be flashed on a cathode ray tube synchronized to the CPU and updated by either Command Central or the field command unit.

6. Real-time status of water supply for mobile pumping units. This type of information can only be obtained by a rather complex differential pressure analysis of the relationship between consumer consumption and fire-flow demand.
   a. Computer analysis is the only feasible way of establishing a real-time reflection of water supply demand availability for mobile pumping requirements. The location of hydrants, primary, secondary and feeder supply lines

would be programmed into the CPU, along with a Hardy Cross network analysis technique. The CPU would analyze, on the basis of current profile pressures, the available water supply at designated points on the pipe grid and compute the volume-pressure relationship. The output format could consist of either a printout of the results through a remote teleprinter or a display of flow curves directly on a cathode ray tube.

7. Depict with both diagrams and narrative special features of the building or area under consideration. Many details are associated with each emergency problem. The proper knowledge of these details can increase the efficiency and effectiveness of the confinement, control and suppression operation. Some of the more significant details that should be immediately available to fire suppression officers include the following items. It should be pointed out that several techniques could be utilized for the rapid retrieval of the indicated information. A great deal of the information could be contained in computer storage and recalled along with the alarm transmission. The responding fire officer could have this information in his hands before leaving the service facility.
   a. Photo isometric views of the front and rear of the building or site area.
   b. Layout views of each floor with details such as: fire protection equipment, stairways and elevators, utilities, and special hazards.
   c. A plot plan of the immediate area with exposure outlines.
   d. Area water supply volume pressure graphs and maps of the grid arrangement.
   e. Owner-occupant information including the proper person to contact in the event of emergency.

8. The provision for special information upon request. This class of information might include the proper identification of potentially hazardous materials found in a building or at the scene of an accident. A quick query to a preprogrammed source data bank in the CPU could provide essential information almost instantaneously.

The third objective relates to nonemergency communications services between the public and the Public Fire Safety Systems Organization and between functions within the system itself. This communication level amounts to an answering and routing service. The importance of this function is not to be underestimated. The efficiency with which such communication links are made between the public and the communications center and the center with each of the functions could bear on the effectiveness of the total system.

The normal mechanical communications links between the public and the organization would include the telephone and the telegraph box alarm system. Radios, telephones, telegraph systems and voice systems are utilized for internal communication. A paging service might also complement the basic elements of the system.

The communications function serves to act as a connector between identified units and as a coordinator and sensor function for the operations systems. Therefore, the Communications Coordinator should not only be technically proficient in electronics, communications systems, and computer hardware, he must also be sensitive to a systems communication concept for complex organizations. The academic discipline most complementing this requirement would probably be Electrical Engineering.

The Training Subsystem

Men and women must be proficient to perform assigned duties and activities in an efficient, effective and safe manner. The Public Fire Safety Education Training Coordinator has the responsibility of increasing the skill levels within the personnel to desired performance levels. He has the further responsibility of providing programs for career development according to the individual's capabilities and motivation. This second area may require a coordinated effort between establishing activities within the organization system and programs external to the system. The latter case might involve establishing fire science programs in local community colleges and/or the provision of a sabbatical-leave plan for selected individuals to enroll in programs leading to a bachelor's or advanced degree.

Fire department training has been very strongly analogous to skill development and skill reinforcement in the handling of equipment for basic operational procedures. The systems concept applied to organizations does not eliminate this need. However, to carry out the type of systems implementation envisioned in this book will require the introduction of personnel training programs and educational programs beyond the scope and capability of many present-day fire departments.

The training systems under the proposed organization would be responsible for structuring the following developmental program areas:

1. New recruit training for the service system
   a. Emphasis on the individual as an element of the total system
      (1) The expectations of the organization for each individual
      (2) Identification of the individual's expectation of the organization
      (3) The functional elements of the organization in relation to the individual
      (4) The individual and his societal relationship of service through the organization
   b. Basic knowledge development for emergency services
      (1) Rescue practices and emergency medical care
      (2) Predicting fire behavior in structures
      (3) Predicting fire behavior of natural cover fuels
      (4) Predicting fire behavior with hazardous chemicals and materials of transport
   c. The suppression function
      (1) The special objectives of the service system
      (2) The command-control-communications procedures
      (3) The man-task-assignment complex
   d. Functional task development
      (1) Lecture-demonstration from each of the organizational functional units
      (2) Promotional motivation
   e. Service System Task Development
      (1) Fire suppression equipment and application
      (2) Personal proficiency with specific equipment
      (3) Simulation exposure to real-world emergency events

(4) Support assignment to actual incidents

(5) Critique of incidents

(6) Advanced simulation

f. Work study program with operational units

  (1) Briefings and seminar type discussions with the responsible area Fire Chief

    (a) Emphasis and case-study analysis

2. Service System Continual Training and Education Program

a. Program to upgrade service level performance

  (1) The provision for real and simulated experiences to compensate for lack of routine experience (i.e., program tailored to analyze the activity of each man in terms of his experience hours in various defined tasks of emergency service. The program should maintain and upgrade performance levels in all task-related areas).

b. Programmed courses supporting a promotional effort for higher levels in the service systems

c. Programmed courses leading to promotional opportunities in other functional areas of the system

d. Seminar discussions for programmed course participants

3. System Personnel Orientation

a. The development and implementation of a program to properly guide new individuals into the systems organization concept

  (1) This program would be designed for all personnel not assigned to the service system

b. The development and implementation of a program to properly guide system personnel who are transferring from one functional area to another.

4. External Organization Training

a. The development and implementation of a program to educate and train industrial personnel, self-protection personnel, and other governmental unit personnel in appropriate protection suppression areas. (Note: Such a program is to be carefully coordinated with the objectives and internal efforts of all three major project systems: Fire Protection, Fire Prevention and Fire Suppression.

5. Educational Coordination and Guidance

a. The Education and Training Coordinator should also serve as a guidance counselor to college-level programs to academically lay the prerequisite foundations for administrative and management personnel in the defined functional areas.

  (1) Community college programs for: Service Systems Fire Officers, Fire Chiefs and Prevention Technicians,

  (2) Core programs leading to Bachelors' degrees in Fire Protection Engineering, Public Administration, Urban Affairs, Business Administration, and Economics.

b. Develop a career guidance program for advising all system personnel on career and educational opportunities.

The Education and Training Coordinator could probably best serve the system if he possesses a minimum of a Bachelor's Degree in Adult Education, Industrial Education, or Guidance Education. Several years of fire suppression service should supplement the formal education requirement. But above all, the Education and Training Coordinator should have a broad and an imaginative vision of his role in providing the opportunity for each individual in the organization to achieve all he is motivated and capable of becoming. The Coordinator will be instrumental in cultivating the organizational spirit for individual achievement and competitiveness necessary to build a complement personnel.

The Maintenance Subsystem

The Maintenance Subsystem would be structured around two broad activities and many subtasks. This functional element would be charged with the primary responsibility of providing reliable emergency equipment. A second or support element of the function would deal with the activities of routine cleaning, maintenance, repair and improvement for all Public Fire Safety facilities. The two requirements mean that the maintenance function must be supported by a journeyman-level staff.

The maintenance function must be flexible enough to handle emergency repairs while providing for a preplanned preventive maintenance program. The emphasis of activity would be placed on the reliability of the emergency vehicle fleet. The total program would be structured around the concept of preventive maintenance.

The objective of vehicle reliability can best be achieved through the anticipation of failure and the establishment of countermeasures to reduce the probability of failure to the lowest levels economically possible. The Maintenance Coordinator should work very closely with the Research and Development Function to determine failure modes through technological assessment. Based upon this constant analysis program, procedural guidelines should be established for routine facility checks on equipment and periodic overhauls at a centralized maintenance facility. From an economic perspective, the central maintenance activity might actually be shared with two or more separate Public Fire Safety Systems located in relative proximity to each other. The specialized maintenance facilities required for fire equipment could be very expensive. The feasibility of shared services should not be overlooked. One should remember that the hallmark of the systems approach is design flexibility.

The emergency maintenance service should at least provide for the following features:

1. The availability of an emergency maintenance crew at all times to handle equipment malfunctions or complete equipment failures. This emergency service should include the provision for a crane, spare parts, and the specialty tools required to repair fire equipment.

2. A fuel tanker for supporting large-scale operations.

3. An automatic response to defined severity level incidents with the crane and tanker.

4. The provision for reserve equipment that could easily take the place of equipment out of service.

The routine maintenance service for equipment should include provisions for the following activities on mobile equipment:

1. Programmed frequency maintenance for: lubrication, part replacement, safety requirements, performance capability.

2. Major engine and drive line component overhaul or complete replacement.

3. Body repair and alteration to accept new equipment.

In addition to the basic provisions for emergency and routine maintenance service on mobile equipment, the maintenance shops should have the capability of serving other functional areas for special equipment requirements. This might include building specialized pieces of equipment for study and evaluation purposes. An example might be special-purpose hydraulic test equipment. A second example might be to produce specialized demonstration equipment for the fire prevention program. Almost every function in the organization has special requirements from time to time that could be carried out by the maintenance subsystem.[4]

A second area of responsibility relates to building maintenance, repair and improvement. Today, a stationhouse fireman is often assigned several housekeeping duties. Professionalism is not enhanced by improving one's capability as a janitor. Stations manned by paid personnel should receive the support of a cleaning staff for the window washing and floor scrubbing requirements. If the organization is geared to effective and efficient operations relative to the outlined objective, it is perceived that the full-time manpower would not have the time or opportunity to handle the housekeeping chores. In other words, the maintenance function should provide a full-time staff of persons that would handle the basic cleaning, maintenance, repair and improvement of all structural facilities. Again this service might be shared with other municipal service areas.

Stations manned solely by volunteers may present an alternate situation. It is assumed that at least some volunteers donate their services in order to maintain an economic balance within the community. They render a service to keep public costs down. Therefore, in keeping with an economy objective, some volunteer may consider routine cleanup assignments within the responsibility of volunteer membership. There may also be a middle ground where certain identified weekly or monthly tasks are contracted out or provided for by other municipal groups, while daily routine tasks are carried out by rotating membership assignment.

One concept concerning cleanup, maintenance and repair appears clear. Each task area needs to be carefully planned in accordance with a frequency of accomplishment schedule.

[4]David B. Gratz, "Silver Spring's Maintenance," *Firemen*, March 1969, p. 19.

The task frequency periods need to reflect intervals that optimize the performance of equipment and facilities in relation to both reliability and cost expenditures. It would appear that very little research has been done in the area utility/failure analysis on specific pieces of fire protection equipment. The research function in cooperation with the maintenance function should carefully examine the area of failure analysis.

The maintenance coordinator should possess some special attributes. First, depending on the level of service to be provided, the Maintenance Coordinator should present a strong technical and experience background in equipment repair. For a level-one system it might be desirable for the Coordinator to hold a degree in Mechanical Engineering. Scheduling and flexible arrangements for accommodating emergency situations would be an important responsibility of the Coordinator. Therefore, courses in Business Administration dealing with Management Science, Production Management, Cost Accounting, and Data Processing would appear essential to achieve the performance requirements demanded of this position for a level-one system implementation.

The Public Relations Subsystem

The image of the Public Fire Safety is crucial to the accomplishment of the organization mission. There are several indicators to show that the public image of existing fire departments is not conducive to productive public sector-private sector relationships. The *Wingspread Conference* report stated, "There is a serious lack of communication between the Public and the Fire Service."[5] This report concludes that a significant proportion of the citizens in any given community judge their jurisdictional fire department by one or two contacts they make with individual members of the Fire Service. In other words, the fireman on the block may have a bearing on the attitude of citizens towards the local fire company or fire department. This concept was echoed by Chief Engineer Raymond Hill, Los Angeles Fire Department, when he testified before The National Commission on Fire Prevention and Control in Washington, D. C., on February 16, 1972.[6] Chief Hill appears to feel that many of the problems associated with false

alarms, street bonfires, the burning of vacant buildings and possibly some cases of direct arson are the results of a negative attitude on the part of young people towards the fire department. Chief Hill also appears to feel that much can be done to improve communications, cooperation and coordination between the public and the Fire Service at the community level as defined by the area surrounding a particular fire station. His department is concentrating on developing a rapport between the Fire Service and the area school children. The actual implementation of a local community action program by the respective fire companies appears to be reducing the number of false alarms in the Los Angeles metropolitan area.

Chief William E. Clark states that the public's image of the Fire Service starts at each individual fire company's door. He asserts:[7]

> Most citizens never get inside fire stations, but everyone sees the outside of them. What they see helps form their opinions of the department. If the house presents a clean, neat appearance, they get one impression. If it is dirty or disorderly looking, they get another. And firemen lounging in the doorway don't improve the picture. Some firemen would rather take a pay cut than give up the bench in front of quarters. They know they are hurting their image, but the temptation is too great — except in winter.

The mission accomplishment of public fire safety is directly dependent on public support, public concern, public involvement in the problem issues and public reaction to events. The public can only come forward in relation to their perception of fire safety developed from direct contacts with firemen, observation of fire companies in operation, or informal contacts such as presented in the mass media. Public fire safety must be constantly sensitive to the image it presents to the public on an individual basis and on community basis. The establishment of good public relations cannot be left to chance. A Public Fire Safety Systems Organization must provide for a concrete program of Public Relations. The Public Relations subsystem function has been established under the facilitating subsystem category because of the intended support activity.

The Public Relations function in an organization revolves around the concept of coordination, communications, control and the specific element of awareness.

[5]*Wingspread Conference on Fire Service Administration, Education and Research.* "Statements of National Significance to the Fire Problem in the United States," Racine: The Johnson Foundation, 1966, p. 7.

[6]The author's recount of Chief Hill's statement before The National Commission.

[7]William E. Clark, "Fire Company Management," *Fire Engineering,* July 1970, p. 92.

Note: Chief William Clark was serving as Director, Department of Fire Protection, Prince George's County, Maryland, when the referenced article was written.

Public Relations should establish a good rapport with each internal functional component of the organization, in addition to external functions such as the press, civic organizations, individuals and special interest groups. To accomplish this objective the Public Relations Coordinator or his staff must be aware of all activities within the organization on a current status basis. From the unit working under emergency conditions to the Fire Coordinator who issues a new directive, information must flow to the Public Relations subfunction.

With the proper communication channels open, the Public Relations Coordinator can proceed to coordinate press releases, the appearance of Public Fire Safety representatives at public activities, on the scene information at serious emergency situations and the dissemination of requested information from interested parties. In this sense the coordination activity also becomes a control activity. The public at large and other service functions can be properly and consistently informed about the activities of public fire safety without conflict statements or duplication of effort.

In addition to the board and obvious role of public relations outlined above, efforts should be made to cultivate a desire by each member of the public fire safety team to project a worthy image before the public. The International City Manager's Association Training Manual, *Municipal Public Relations*, outlines a series of points and questions concerning each and every organization employee's relation to the public. The public relations function should attempt to stimulate an action program concerning these points with all personnel.[8] The following points are not a direct quotation.

1. The interest shown in the citizen's problems: Do public fire safety personnel give the citizen their complete attention? Do personnel ask questions to clarify the citizen's needs and desires?

2. The quality of information given: Are public fire safety communications to the public complete and accurate — clear and concise?

3. The manner of speech: Do public fire safety personnel utilize grammar correctly? Do personnel pronounce and enunciate properly? Are words of personnel meaningful and appropriate to the situation — is anything really said of value?

4. The personnel attitude: Does each representative of the public fire safety organization express himself/herself in a cordial and friendly manner? Are personnel polite?

5. The personal appearance: Are the members of the public fire safety organization groomed and dressed in tasteful and appropriate manner? This item may require a broad interpretation based upon the current mode of dress and fashion. Also somewhat controversial is the notion that facial expressions should convey a helpful attitude.

The intent of each of the above items is probably more important than the actual wording of the item itself. The important point is simply that the mannerisms of an individual, including his habits and appearance, have an effect on the public. More attention needs to be focused on this concept. The public relations functions draws attention to the responsibility for achieving a desired relationship between the public and the private sector of the community.

The Public Relations Coordinator must be a man of many talents. First, he must possess a pleasing personality coupled with an intuitive judgment for dealing harmoniously with people. Second, he must have an intimate knowledge of every facet of the organization. Such a knowledge is indispensable for responding adequately to the demands for information about the organization. The individual serving in this capacity must have a solid working relationship with the press and prominent civic organizations. Academically, the Public Relations Coordinator might have formal training in Business Administration with emphasis on public relations, Journalism, Speech and Dramatic Arts or even Sociology. The person, rather than the degree, is of utmost importance for this position. Enthusiasm, drive, initiative and the desire to work with people are considered prerequisites to successful accomplishment.

---

[8]International City Manager's Association, *Municipal Public Relations*. Chicago: International City Manager's Association, 1967, p. 17.

Chapter 6

Bibliographical Entries

Books

International City Manager's Association, *Municipal Public Relations*, Chicago, International City Manager's Association, 1967, p. 17.

Publications of the Government, Learned Societies, and Other Organizations

Salzberg, Frederick. *Fire Department Operations Analysis*, Office of Civil Defense Contract DAH-C20-70c-0208, Chicago, Illinois Institute of Technology, 1970, p. 7.

Wingspread Conference on Fire Service Administration, Education and Research, "Statements of National Significance to the Fire Problem in the U.S.". Racine: The Johnson Foundation, 1966, p. 7.

Periodicals

Carter, Walter H., "Communications Join Computer Era," *Fire Engineering*, February 1970, p. 57.

Clark, William E. "Fire Company Management," *Fire Engineering*, July 1970, p. 92.

Gratz, David B. "Silver Spring's Maintenance," *Firemen*, March 1969, p. 19.

Chapter VII

The Management of Major Project Subsystems

The objectives of the Public Fire Safety System are achieved or fall short of expectation through the implementation of defined Major Project Subsystems. The concern of this chapter is to present the unique considerations of each project element as it interrelates with other subsystems to form a viable mechanism for instituting a desired level of public fire safety. The Major Project functions of Fire Protection, Fire Prevention and Service must be systematically coordinated. Therefore, it is logical that the maintenance of organization direction for the identified subsystems be established under the guidance of a Division Coordinator for Major Project Systems.

The Division Fire Coordinator for Major Project Systems would have special responsibility for fusing together the duties and activities of the Fire Protection Subsystems, the Fire Prevention Subsystem and Direct Service Subsystem into a common effort to achieve a desired level of fire safety within the jurisdictional areas. It is apparent that the Coordinator's role can best be fulfilled by concentrating on the sensing of each function, making sure that efforts of each function are communicated to other subsystems and immediately ascertain "why" when an emergency event reaches a severity condition beyond the maximum target loss levels established. Frequent field contact with respective units, fire ground observations, the examination of selected reports (i.e., incident reports, severity reports, survey reports, and engineering specifications) would keep the Division Fire Coordinator finely tuned to the project system areas and their accomplishments.

The specific role of the Division Fire Coordinator — Major Project Systems — in relation to fire suppression operations under the proposed systems organization needs to be made explicitly clear. A subsequent section will establish the premise that the systems Fire Chief retains command and responsibility for all fire suppression operations. Contrary to the schematic arrangement on the organization chart, the Deputy Coordinator is under the direction of the Fire Chief at the scene of an emergency. The Division Coordinator would serve in the Field Command, Control and Communications Unit to supervise other functional personnel (i.e., Protection Engineer, Prevention Technician, Training Coordinator) in supplying support to the Fire Chief. The concept of the system Fire Chief retaining responsibility for fire suppression and emergency services is considered essential to the spirit of melding existing fire department organizations into the systems concept in an acceptable and workable relationship. The Division Fire Coordinator — Major Project Systems — would advise the Fire Chief but he would have neither the authority to make decisions for the System Fire Chief nor to overrule a decision made by the System Fire Chief. However, the Fire Chief stands accountable for his decision after the event has been completed. This point does not depart from existing fire department operation. The objective of the organization structure is to provide coordinative support to the service function.

The relationship of the unit fire officer, the facility Fire Chief, the Sector Fire Chief, the Regional Fire Chief and the System Fire Chief is actually a practical insertion to what might otherwise be described as a normative theory of organization construction. Earlier drafts of this book utilized the individual coordinator concept for the suppression subsystem. The abolishment of the title of fire chief and the traditional fire department chain of command was debated in three graduate public administration seminars and before a selected group of fire chiefs. The basic feeling of these groups was as follows.

The title and power associated with the term Fire Chief has been cultivated by many years of fire department evolution. The title and the position of Fire Chief is a very much sought after prize by the personnel in many fire departments. This appears to be especially true as it concerns volunteer and part paid type fire departments. The spirit of motivation and competition has moved men to seek the position of Fire Chief. To void the title of Fire Chief in the proposed Public Fire Safety Systems Organization would meet with a cool reception if not outright hostility in the real world. If the systems concept is to be introduced and accepted in the urban environment, then nothing is to be gained from alienations. Besides, the title is not critical to the systems conceptual framework. The term coordinator was simply suggested to underscore the primary objective activity of certain key individuals in the organization. Performance is the important criterion. The retention of the term Fire Chief and the role of the Fire Chief in a systems framework makes the total organization proposal more palatable to the traditional fire department organization. Furthermore, the accommodation of this point illustrates the flexibility of the systems concept.

It is now possible to return to the role of the Division Fire Coordinator for Major Project Systems. This position would require a man that possesses a broad understanding of each identified project system including objectives, requisite duties, associative activities, and techniques for appraisal of accomplishments. Therefore, the individual must be technically competent in addition to being managerially competent. A significant portion of the managerial and technical expertise should be obtained by involvement in both areas. Field experience should include a minimum of five years' active fire suppression experience under the system organization level being implemented. The intent is to have the individual demonstrate involved experience rather than simple years of experience. The point may require re-

evaluation but it would seem necessary that an individual have at least an established minimum number of "working fires" on his log (not simply alarms) before being eligible for the Division Coordinator position.

Academically, the Division Fire Coordinator should have a minimum of a bachelor's degree. The actual degree requirements can be quite flexible. Some of the more applicable degrees might include: Fire Protection Engineering, Public Administration, Industrial Education, Business Administration, or Urban Affairs. The point should not be overlooked that one of the nontechnical degree areas (i.e., Public Administration) might well include a two-year foundation program in fire science.

It appears necessary to insert an explanatory note at this point in the book. Actually it is a clarification of an idea initiated in Chapter II. The service subsystem within the framework of the total systems organization would be developed to efficiently and effectively handle community or regional emergencies. The subsystem emphasis is on fire suppression. However, the expected involvement of the service subsystem would be much broader than just fire suppression. The coverage would certainly support a full range of rescue services, semi-emergency services, storm damage relief, and general public assistance. These services need to be rendered whether the emergency event occurs at a main intersection in a city of 500,000 population or at the crossroads in a rural county. What does differ is the probability of the named event happening, the severity of the event, and what is an acceptable loss to those being served in these two extreme conditions. To accommodate a responsiveness to local objectives and local constraints of economic resources, the service system must have a considerable degree of built-in flexibility and adaptability. However, it must be recognized that there are inherent organizational weaknesses in the traditional fire service structure that need to be rectified. The current deficiency simply cannot be accepted if the proposed objectives of the public fire safety system have validity. Specific reference is made to the chain of command at an emergency event. Many Fire Chiefs appear to have the capability, through training and experience, to effectively direct a fire or related emergency that requires the efforts of up to four pieces of equipment and twenty to twenty-five men. However, it also appears that when larger complements of men and equipment are employed to handle an emergency in areas roughly defined as less than 50,000 population, the present system breaks down. Communications, coordination, and control just do not work and every man is doing "his thing." Part of the problem stems from the lack of chief officer experience in handling large-scale events. Traditionally, the Fire Chief of the responsibility community or area continues in command when outside forces are brought in for support. It appears necessary to modify this concept without completely destroying jurisdictional supervision of emergency events. The proposed systems concept presents a framework that should improve command-control-communication capabilities over a range of scaled fire and emergency involvement. The concepts presented under the following Service System Subsection of this book are designed to accomplish this objective.

The Service Subsystem

The basic framework of the Service Subsystem has been presented at several points in the early chapters, beginning with an examination of the fire safety system organization structure in Chapter II. This subsection presentation concentrates on the working components and implementation of the Service Subsystem. Because the objective output of the service subsystem should be established to provide an *immediate* emergency service upon request to citizens in the urban system (the internal system may also experience emergencies), the approach is to start with the emergency service element at initial response levels and move in reverse through an explanation of the subsystem. This approach should demonstrate how the total subsystem multiplies its support function as the severity of the potential or actual situation increases.

A Task Force Concept

The Task Force Concept is an outgrowth of the unusual fire suppression requirements faced by the Los Angeles Fire Department during the civil disturbances in 1968.[1] The concept behind the formulation of a fire-fighting task force appears to have considerable merit for a basic day-to-day incident response. A task force defines a specified complement of men and equipment necessary to optimally perform initial rescue work, attack, confine, control, ex-

tinguish and overhaul a perceived level of fire incident. Therefore, the concept recognizes variable degrees of potential incidents.

The basic reason for implementing a task force unit concept is to provide a balanced-coordinated-flexible-response in selected areas of the service subsystem. The task force structure outlined in this section also possesses the merit of formulating a more tailored response to a given risk or area than the normal box alarm assignment found in most cities. This can be achieved through the selected utilization of basic task force units augmented by special service units and special fire units. The identification of the task force units and the potential task force structural arrangements outlined below is followed by a more complete examination of the implementation process under the systems framework of organization.

The task force unit structure is composed of a number of specified pieces of equipment. The basic task force structure is supported by special units designated as special fire units (SFU), special rescue units (SRU), and special vehicle units (SVU). Several subclasses of equipment may be designated under both the task force and the special unit categories. The following table depicts the task force and special unit service system structure.

Table VII-1

Service System Unit Designations

Task Force Designations

TFU	— The Basic Task Force Unit
TFP	— A Task Force Pumper
TFL	— A Task Force Ladder
TFB	— A Task Force Platform Boom
TFT	— A Task Force Tanker
TFC	— The Task Force Command Unit

Special Fire Units Carry the Following Designations

SPU	— Special Pumper Unit
SAL	— Special Aerial Ladder
SSL	— Special Service Ladder
SPL	— Special Pumper-Ladder
STB	— Special Telescoping Boom
SAB	— Special Articulating Boom
SPB	— Special Platform Boom
SHU	— Special Hose Unit
SFU	— Special Foam Unit
SHF	— Special High-Expansion Foam Unit
SFC	— Special Foam and Dry Chemical Unit
SLW	— Special Light Water Unit
SLC	— Special Light Water Dry Chemical Unit
SFB	— Special Fire Boat
SLU	— Special Lighting Unit
SCU	— Special Compressor Unit
SBU	— Special Brush Unit
SBD	— Special Bulldozer
SAC	— Special Air Crash Unit
SWU	— Special Wrecker Unit

---

[1]Charles W. Bahme, "The Watts Fires and Their Lessons," *Fire Journal*, p. 10.

Special Rescue Units Carry the Following Designations
- AMB — Ambulance
- LRU — Light Rescue Unit
- MRU — Medium Rescue Unit
- HRU — Heavy Rescue Unit
- WRU — Water Rescue Unit
- ARU — Air Rescue Unit

Special Vehicle Units Carry the Following Designations
- SCV — Sector Control Vehicle
- RCV — Regional Control Vehicle
- FTV — Fuel Tender Vehicle
- MSV — Maintenance Service Vehicle
- PUV — Pick-up Vehicle
- SSV — Special Service Vehicle

The service system structure is not limited to the suggested unit descriptions. Specific conditions and problems may require additional support unit designations.

Task Force Unit Descriptions

The task force is conceived of as a homogeneous unit of mutually dependent parts organized to achieve a smoothly coordinated activity at the scene of a structural fire emergency. To achieve this end, each unit in the task force group functions according to a few basic procedural guidelines. Procedures are defined in terms of the unit's hardware (equipment) and manpower capabilities. The following description outlines the basic equipment complement of the basic task force units and manpower assignment. A brief notation is also made concerning the basic operational function perceived for each unit at the fire scene. This explanation is followed by an associative grouping of units into task force levels.

Task Force Unit (TFU)

The basic Task Force Unit (TFU)represents the assigned first due vehicle on all structural fire emergencies. The unit should be designed for rapid acceleration, moderate over the road speed considering localized terrain conditions, and high maneuverability. An enclosed cab should provide a seating arrangement for six persons. Vehicle components should include a 750 gpm pump; a 300- to 500-gallon booster tank; preconnected attack lines to provide a selected capability of booster hose, 1½-inch hose or 2½-inch hose, and a preconnected master stream nozzle (Note: may be incorporated into the required boom); 800 feet of 4-inch or larger supply line; a mounted telescoping boom (up to 50 feet) with an internal waterway, remote controlled nozzle and mounted access ladder; portable ladders should include a 30-foot extension ladder and a short

roof ladder; equipment compartments should be provided to carry a complement of forcible entry tools, rescue tools, ventilation equipment, breathing equipment and salvage equipment for small area involvement fires. This unit is developed to be the basic working unit on all structural type fires. Therefore, the unit should perform the primary attack function at the scene. This unit should be highly successful in combatting, controlling and extinguishing approximately ninety per cent of all structural fires.[2] On larger scale fires the unit is equipped to attack a developing fire with large capacity nozzles either from a street level or from an elevated level. The boom unit should extend the first arriving unit's capability for rescue, access and ventilation. Based upon water supply and structural conditions, the unit may or may not lay its own supply line.

Task Force Ladder (TFL)

The task force unit is supported at the scene by a Task Force Ladder (TFL). The basic feature of this unit is a 100-foot, four-wheel aerial ladder.[3] A rated fire pump would provide a tactical advantage to this unit. A booster pump and a 300-gallon water tank is considered an essential item. Preconnected booster size and 1½-inch size hose should be provided. A ladder pipe should be provided. In addition to a ladder pipe hose line, provision should be made for 500 feet of 4-inch or larger supply line. Equipment compartments should be provided for accommodating breathing equipment, rescue equipment, salvage equipment, ventilation equipment and lighting equipment. A cab, preferably enclosed, should be provided to accommodate six men. This unit would operate at the scene in support of the basic Task Force Unit.

Task Force Platform Boom (TFB)

The specialized Task Force Platform Boom would also support the basic TFU at the scene. The basic component of this unit is a platform boom, either of the articulating or telescoping type with a minimum 75-foot reach. The unit should be equipped with a 1,000 gpm rated pump. Provision should be made for preconnected attack lines in booster, 1½-inch and 2½-inch size. The platform

[2]The author's perception based upon a casual examination of selected fire incident data.

[3]A tiller unit is an acceptable substitute where response and access conditions warrant. A tiller type aerial ladder is included in the conceptual scheme of the task force because of the wide application of this unit within the Fire Service.

should mount a master stream appliance capable of delivering 1,200 gallons per minute. A booster tank should be provided with a capacity of 300 to 500 gallons of water. Equipment compartments should be provided for supplemental breathing equipment, forcible entry, rescue, and salvage operations tools.

Task Force Pumper (TFP)

The suppression units previously described are intended to be positioned at a fire emergency for the best tactical advantage. Except under unusual circumstances, the TFU, TFL and TFB would not be connected directly to a hydrant with suction hose. This implies that additional units must support the basic suppression unit's water delivery. This task becomes the basic objective of the pump units. This point needs to be remembered when evaluating the following description of the vehicle and the manpower complement.

Pumper units in the task force concept lay large supply lines from (or to) the identified suppression units, connect to a water source and pump through the supply lines. Each pumper unit should feature a U.L. rated fire pump, 300 to 500 gallons of water, a preconnected booster and 1½-inch hose line, a 500-foot attack line of 2½-inch hose, and 2,000 feet of 4-inch or larger supply hose in a dual hose bed. Equipment compartments should be provided for breathing equipment, hose appliances and the necessary tools to support the suppression units. Each unit should also be equipped with a rapid water proportioner and fifty gallon holding tank along with fifty gallons of light water and the proper proportioning equipment. A closed operating cab should provide accommodations for four men. (Note only two men would normally respond with each pump unit assigned to an initial task force.)

Task Force Tanker (TFT)

A Task Force Tanker Unit would respond to areas without a piped water system or to areas where the water supply is severely deficient for the potential risk. The tanker capacity should be 1,500 gallons and the unit should incorporate a 500-gallon-per-minute pump capable of operation under motion. The TFT would also carry a complement of 2,000 feet of 4-inch supply hose, one preconnected 1½-inch hose, and one preconnected booster line.

Task Force Command (TFC)

A mobile van equipped as a command, control and communications tactics vehicle forms an important element of the task force group. This unit should at least include multi-channel radio communications, status boards, location and routing information, indexes, preplan information, hazardous element files, resource inventories, tactical location photographs and/or maps, and audiovisual equipment. The unit would respond with the Facility Fire Chief, or the Sector Fire Chief, and an aide.

Supplemental Units

The task force units described may be supplemented with special fire units, special rescue units and other vehicles carrying identifying designations. Special units add a necessary dimension of flexibility to equipment resource requirements necessary to cope with a potential fire or emergency situation. In other words, task force groupings are not limited to those units carrying a task force designation. The key feature of the task force concept is to identify and formulate described units into an organized group that will provide efficiency and effectiveness in handling potential emergency situations.

Task Force Levels

Obviously all fires and emergency situations do not pose the same threat to life and property. Yet certain prescribed minimum responses of men and equipment by type and complement, should be established upon the potential severity of the incident. Matching resources to potential severity must be made on the basis of subjective judgment pending the establishment of probability estimates for specific areas. In introducing the task force concept under the systems approach, it is very important to project an understanding for the potential capability of the task force groupings.

The perceived formulation of prescribed levels of task force groupings and support service development can be utilized to establish this understanding. The following patterned illustrations must be examined within the total systems framework. Furthermore, only the initial response set of units is considered in the following illustrations of possible levels of service. The necessity for supplemental service will depend upon specific conditions and/or events. The supplemental features simply identify the built-in flexibility of the task force arrangement.

The designated basic task force units are formulated into defined task force levels. Initially three task force levels are advanced for consideration. Again, stress should be placed upon the fact that each prescribed task force level may be augmented by special units to adjust the task force for special problem situations. Each task force level is structured on the premise that a prescribed force of men and equipment is required for functional operations. Illustrated examples of functional operations follow the descriptions.

Task Force Level 1

A Level 1 Task Force is basically organized to cope with structural fires possessing the potential for high life loss and/or high property loss. The composition of the Task Force is as follows:

Quantity of Units	Unit Designation	Manpower
1	Task Force Unit (TFU)	6
1	Task Force Ladder (TFL)	6
1	Task Force Platform Boom (TFB)	6
2	Task Force Pumpers (TFP)	4
1	Task Force Command (TFC)	2
	Total	24

Description

The following conditions are advanced as a basic guide to the requirement for establishing and dispatching a Task Force Level 1 assignment to a reported emergency call.

1. Buildings with occupant levels in excess of 200 persons.
2. Buildings with a height in excess of 75 feet.
3. Special Occupancy Classifications. Hospitals, Nursing Homes, Institutions, Places of Public Assembly. (Note: when in operation, regardless of occupancy load.)
4. Special target hazards
   a. Row structures that pose a potential for large-scale fires.
   b. Large manufacturing plants.
   c. Special industrial hazards like bulk oil storage facilities, large undivided warehouses, and process manufacturers.
   d. Shopping plazas and shopping malls.

The above conditions obviously present some overlap in criteria. The objective of describing specific conditions is to illustrate sets of conditions that present a significant and un-

usual risk potential. In responding to risks with known life hazards, it might be desirable to supplement the task force assignment with a light or medium rescue vehicle or an ambulance. Special industrial hazards may require the addition of a foam unit, a light water unit, or other specialized equipment.

It should be noted that all levels of task force development are based upon manpower complements that are quite projective. These projections have been strongly influenced by Warren Y. Kimball's texts, *Fire Attack 1* and *Fire Attack 2*, plus Lloyd Layman's text, *Attacking and Extinguishing Interior Fires*.[4,5] Once the described Task Force Level becomes operative, the suggested manpower complements will require study and analysis in terms of severity statistics and manpower utilization. Such studies may reveal underdeveloped or overdeveloped resource commitments for defined hazard situations. Then the numbers may be changed to better reflect on optimum performance.

Furthermore, the Task Force Concept does not mean that all of the described units must respond from a single station. For reliability and balance within a specific geographical system, the task force might be dispatched from two or three stations. This multiple station response has special applicability for suburban jurisdictions; and should improve the flexibility for dispatching units. In other words, if a unit assigned to the task force is not available or is deficient in the manpower complement, alternate units can be dispatched to maintain the designated task force level.

Task Force Level 2

A second Task Force level is structured to cope with a potential severity level less than those situations described for Level 1. This estimation simply means that the probability of the fire emergency both to life and structures is significantly reduced from situations described under Level 1. A Task Force Level 2 would also be implemented in those areas serviced by either a public or private water distribution system that provides reasonable fire flow adequacy for an extended period of time. However, this Task Force level would be assigned to respond on structural fire alarms in areas not requiring the perceived strength

[4]Warren Y. Kimball, *Fire Attack 1* and *Fire Attack 2*. Boston: National Fire Protection Association, 1966 and 1968.

[5]Lloyd Layman, *Attacking and Extinguishing Interior Fires*. Boston: National Fire Protection Association, 1952.

developed under the Level 1 category. The composition of the task force would be as follows:

Quantity of Units	Unit Designation	Manpower
1	Task Force Unit (TFU)	6
1	*Task Force Ladder (TFL)	6
1	*Task Force Pumper (TFP)	2
1	*Facility Fire Chief	1
	Total	15

*Special Notation

Several qualifications are attached to the units designated to formulate the second level Task Force. The intention of the above grouping is to cover a rather large variety of risk conditions. Therefore, special flexibility should be accorded the Task Force structure. First, the Task Force Ladder may be substituted for by a Task Force Boom where such a unit would better service the defined risk or set of risks. Second, the Task Force Pumper should have the capability of supplying in excess of 1,000 gpm through supply lines to the TFU and/or the TFL. To meet this requirement some suburban areas may be required to initially supplement the Task Force with a special pumping unit. Third, at this level of deployment, a Facility Fire Chief would most likely be the initial command officer. The task force identification does not specify the vehicle type. Once again the initial step probably would be to include existing chiefs' cars. However, as the system progresses it would appear appropriate to include a Task Force Command Vehicle.

Description

It has already been stated that a Task Force Level 2 would respond to all structural fires not included in Task Force 1 assignments where water system distribution is available. Like other groupings of the Task Force System, the Task Force development needs flexibility. Therefore, the following list of general occupancy classifications is suggestive of the areas where a Task Force Level 2 would respond. A good incident analysis after actual implementation of the system may signify the necessity for additions or deletions from the list.

1. All residential occupancies not classified as apartment dwellings.

2. All one-story mercantile structures that do not form an integral part of a plaza complex.

3. Small churches and government buildings where the life-risk potential is present but reduced from the scope perceived for Level 1.

4. Small low potential industrial complexes not qualifying for a Task Force 1 response.

Task Force Level 3

A third level of Task Force is composed of units to handle buildings risks and associated life hazards in urban fringe areas, small semi-residential areas and rural areas not protected by a water supply distribution system. This Task Force level is considered minimal for basic fire protection. The capability of this task force level is considered to be essentially limited to the control and extinguishment of fires that are contained within the room of origin upon arrival. The capability of this task force level to cope with large scale fires is perceived to be one of limiting the spread of the fire from the building of origin to neighboring exposures. The composition of the task force is as follows:

Quantity of Units	Unit Designation	Manpower
1	Task Force Unit (TFU)	6
1	*Task Force Pumper (TFP)	2
1	*Task Force Tanker (TFT)	2
1	*Facility Fire Chief	1
	Total	11

*Special Notation

Again qualification statements are needed to properly convey the nature and utility of this task force level. First, this task force level works under the constraint of a limited water supply. The basic Task Force Unit and the Task Force Pumper should each carry 500 gallons of water. The Task Force Tanker should carry 1,500 gallons of water. Therefore, the initial attack capability is potentially limited to 2,500 gallons of water. Consideration must be given to the time span for water application in reference to requesting and obtaining supplemental support. In order to recognize the use of existing fire equipment, it appears feasible to consider Task Force Pumpers equipped with 500 gpm pumps. Task Force Tankers should also be equipped to initiate attack procedures where they are responding to essentially rural districts. In rural areas, it is to be expected that the facility fire chief would probably respond in a car or ride on one of the pieces of apparatus. It is important that the vehicle utilized by the facility fire chief be equipped with a command, control and communication tactics case or console containing the necessary maps, photographs, survey data and special hazard information to assist in effecting the most efficient tactical operation possible.

Special Emergency Requirements

Flexibility is built into the Task Force concept through specifying special requirements. These special requirements are developed through extensive preplanning. The requirements for special units on a particular risk problem can be developed as part of the Task Force response. The dispatching process should identify the level of Task Force response along with the supplemental units.

Special alarm assignments need to be established for nonstructural fires. Special units can be grouped together to form a requisite response for such problem areas as natural cover fuel fires, investigations, transportation fires, or standby assignments during hazardous operations. Emergency rescue work is a function of public fire safety that is receiving increased attention and the commitment of Fire Service personnel. It appears logical to establish Rescue Task Forces in the same manner as previously indicated for fire suppression work. In other words, a Rescue Task Force assigned to an automobile accident involving personal injury might include a basic Task Force Unit (TFU), a Light Rescue Unit (LRU), and an Ambulance (AMB). The complexity of the defined rescue missions will require the establishment of other rescue Task Force Levels.

Supplemental Response Requirements

Provision needs to be made in the system for supplementing defined task force levels when an actual alarm size-up indicates additional men and equipment are required. The flexibility of the perceived system would allow the responsible officer to make one of two types of requests for assistance. First, he could request a second complete task force with the established complement of men and equipment. Second, he could request special units by number and designation. The second approach is favored under the systems concept in order to establish the sense of a specific need for a specified problem. A special unit request would also allow the total system to balance manpower supply and demand in a more equitable manner.

The Chain of Command

A special notation on fire department officer titles has already been established in Chapters I and II. There appears to be no substantive reason for changing unit officer titles in the service system. The duties, activities, and functions are the important considerations for classifying unit officers. The following basic factors relate to the officer ranks and the officer responsibility in the service system. No distinction is made at the facility level between volunteer and paid personnel. This book assumes that both volunteer and paid personnel have the same defined requisite level of entry training in fundamental equipment skills and emergency operations techniques. In the real-world practice, it may be some time before service personnel reach such an equity. However, both the public and fire safety personnel should be satisfied with nothing less than prescribed performance levels for *all* personnel of a given position classification. To accept anything less is to compromise prescribed levels of public fire safety. It should be further recognized that paid and volunteer personnel may vary significantly in actual emergency experience. The systems model does recognize difference in levels of responsibility and technical expertise between paid and volunteer personnel in the functional area of in-service inspections.

The necessity for paid personnel or volunteer personnel is left to those being served. The question is simply, what the public wants, what they are willing to pay for, and what level of risk they are willing to assume.

Unit Officer Designations

Captain

Each task force unit is supervised by a Captain. He directs emergency operations until relieved by a Facility Fire Chief or Sector Fire Chief based upon the service system structural arrangement. The TFU Captain would normally have the prime responsibility as the "first due officer" on all Task Force assignments. He has the additional responsibility of coordinating designated in-service inspection assignments in the first due area.

Lieutenant

The responsible fire officer for Task Force Aerial Ladders and Booms is designated as a Lieutenant. This title is also appropriate for the responsible officer on rescue units and other special units as designated in Table VII-1.

Fire Equipment Operator

This terminology is utilized to convey a basic designation for all personnel demonstrating qualifications to drive and operate mobile equipment. Due to the multiplicity of responsibility given to the basic task force unit, special guidance should be given to the selection and training of equipment operators for each type of vehicle. For flexibility and mobility of the system, fire equipment operators should be qualified on more than one type of vehicle.

Unit Personnel Designations

Numerous operational personnel are required at emergencies to carry out the required task assignments. Considering efficiency and effectiveness of operation, it appears promising to designate those classifications of personnel to operate at emergencies. The three classifications and their implication to the service subsystems follow.

Task Force Team Members

The Task Force is conceived as a homogeneous unit that places high regard on unit coordination and the efficiency of operations. To achieve these objectives the task force personnel must be educated and trained to function in a unitary concept. The term "Task Force Team Member" is introduced to signify individuals assigned to task force groups. Emphasis is placed on developing an esprit de corps and a motivational level that fosters a top-level performance. Men assigned to the basic task force unit, to task force pumpers, aerial ladders and booms, are part of the task force team.

Emergency Specialists

The service system utilizes a number of Special Units for specific problem conditions. The personnel assigned to man these units may require special knowledge and skills not demanded of the Task Force Team or of general fire suppression people. For example, personnel assigned to rescue units, light water units and air crash rescue units, require special mental and physical qualifications to expertly function with this equipment. Titles can be developed such as rescue specialists, paramedics, suppression agent specialists, or air crash specialists.

Fire Fighter-Fireman

The title of fireman has not been lost in the proposed shift to a systems concept of Public Fire Safety Organization. Firemen continue to be a vital resource to the service system. These individuals form the manpower base for units requested as supplemental to the basic task force and to fill out manpower requirements for specialized units. Volunteers, while certainly not limited to this level of service certainly possess a potential for rendering a considerable service with the special units mentioned.

Facility Manpower: Paid — Volunteer

One point should be made clear. The nature and action of the Task Force Concept would appear to work at the highest degree of efficiency when the designated units are constantly manned according to the quotas specified. However, the concept should also work very well in areas serviced by active volunteers in combination with a nucleus of paid personnel. While the efficiency of team coordination would probably be compromised with full volunteer manning, the task force package still has merit for volunteer operated facilities. It would further appear that a given task force level should have more dispatching flexibility under a volunteer subsystem arrangement. This simply implies that the task force makeup at any given time should be based upon unit and manpower availability. Such a concept applied to suburban areas further means the implementation of a very comprehensive mutual-aid arrangement. It is important to remember that in order to properly evaluate the prescribed task force levels, the proper units with the assigned manpower should respond to the situation under preestablished conditions. When a deficiency condition exists in manpower or equipment, supplemental units should be dispatched to compensate for the inadequacy.

The inverse condition may also prevail. Some fire departments have current running assignments that call for responding with all available units to a given incident. This practice of overresponse to a given emergency may breed inefficiency of a different order. There is the condition of too much zeal "to be a part of the action" creating coordination problems and "overextinguishment" at the scene of fires. The practice of sending more units than is required should be discouraged.

Service System Officers

Sector Fire Chief

The Sector Fire Chief coordinates and controls operations that involve supplemental resources to the basic Task Force Groups. The Sector Fire Chief position is established in the Level 1 and Level 2 Service Systems Organizations. This means that the position is applicable to total Public Fire Safety Systems protecting 100,000 or more persons. (The dividing line between a Level 1 and a Level 2 system is 250,000 population.) The concept is to bring to the emergency scene a competent officer for the coordination of several emergency units. Based upon the intended function and responsibility of the Sector Fire Chief, it is necessary that this position be occupied around the clock with salaried personnel.

Considering the Task Force concept, a Sector Fire Chief should have responsibility for about five facilities with from ten to fifteen task force or special units. The range of units are not intended as magic numbers and the actual sector should be viewed with flexibility based upon the geographical spread, whether the units are manned by paid, volunteer or a combination of personnel, and the work load. The Sector Fire Chief represents the next level above the facility in the special services chain of command for Level 1 and Level 2 systems.

Regional Fire Chief

The position of Regional Fire Chief is restricted to a Level 1 system; meaning that he serves in protected areas over 250,000 population as an arbitrary criterion. The span of control for this position is approximately ten facilities with approximately twenty to thirty regular units. The same factors mentioned under the span of control concept for the Sector Fire Chief are applicable for this position. It is perceived that the Regional Fire Chief would respond to emergencies requiring the manpower and equipment complement equivalent to three task force groups assigned to one incident. The Regional Chief is also a full-time person in the organization.

The System Fire Chief

The System Fire Chief is the top level fire suppression and emergency control officer. The position requires a full-time person for each designated system, regardless of the implementation level. The System Fire Chief serves to coordinate and control operations for all facilities, where the system has a jurisdiction

with a service area not to exceed 100,000 people. To a degree, the System Fire Chief replaces the function of the Sector Fire Chief for this level system.

Based upon individual experience and resources, a Level 3 System Fire Chief might, through mutual aid system contracts be relieved of overall command at a very large or severe incident by a neighboring jurisdictional Level 2 or Level 1 Fire Chief. The implication of this insertion, in fact the implication of the whole organizational framework, is to bring competence, experience, and the responsibility of a full-time fire officer to severe situations.

The role of the System Fire Chief in either a Level 2 or a Level 1 system follows the same patterned relationship and is fully depicted in the proposed organization chart. A promotional relationship for System Chief officer levels should be established. The system is designed to provide flexibility and opportunity for a man to proceed upward into more challenging positions. A Facility Fire Chief might logically advance to a Level 2 Sector Chief or even possibly to a Level 3 Systems Fire Chief. The Level 2 Sector Fire Chief might logically progress to a Level 1 Sector Fire Chief or Level 2 Systems Fire Chief. Levels 2 and 3 Systems Fire Chiefs might enter larger System 1 Organizations at either the sector or regional Chief's level and move upward to a Systems Level 1 Fire Chief. The lateral and hierarchical opportunities within the framework of either the Operations System or the Facilitating System should be numerous and diversified.

The Public Fire Safety Systems Organization structure has been designed to provide open and recognizable promotional opportunities. A person should only be limited by his perseverance, imagination, and education. The organization road map presented has few dead ends.

Two further reflections need to be made in relation to the service system personnel. One deals with education requirements and the other deals with the organization relationships between paid and volunteer personnel and officers. The educational requirements of officer titles from Facility Fire Chief to System Fire Chief require some explanatory comments.

Education for fire officers has been the subject of many conferences in the past several years. As of this writing, there is no universal or definitely accepted educational criteria for fire officers. However, the International Association of Fire Fighters and the International Fire Service Instructors Association are moving forward with certification standards for all fire-fighting personnel. The conceptual framework of the Public Fire Safety Organization would not be enhanced by a lengthy discussion point by point of the certification areas.[6] However, some general concepts are in order.

The Public Fire Safety objectives outlined in this book encompass the concept of preventing fires to some acceptable public level, and both confining and extinguishing actual ignitions to some defined modular levels, and can be achieved by several combinations of programs and efforts under the major project subsystems. The notion that the loss level in general is a function of response time or a function of fire suppression activity alone is considered to be an oversimplification within the perspective of this book. By the same token, the precise performance levels necessary to achieve desired Public Fire Safety objectives have not been established. More extensive research and study are required in this area.

Two points need to be made relative to this observation. First, one does not want to over-stress the fire suppression or service systems activities within the organizational framework. Second, one does not want to overstress educational requirements for the sake of "degree status." Education requirements and education promotion incentives for service system officers should be based upon defined levels of performance competency for the position duties and activities. Formal education should be used to open doors and groom individuals for promotional opportunities in accordance with the overall systems structure. With a prescribed inservice training program, a Task Force Lieutenant can perform very effectively at an emergency scene. To command and control a single suppression unit does not appear to require a college education — not even an associate degree.

If the above point is realistic, the question becomes one of determining just when does a fire suppression officer (service system officer) benefit from the associate degree programs being offered or the full college degree? The answer lies in how much support does he obtain from the rest of the system. First, support is intended to mean coordinated advice and adequate superior coordination on severe situations. Second, assuming adequate support from the Protection Subsystem, the Prevention

Subsystem, the Training Subsystem, the Communications Subsystem, and the Maintenance Subsystem, it is the premise of this book that all officers up to and including the rank of Facility Chief can do a commendable job with the comprehensive background of a basic and specialized training program. With some slight changes in emphasis relative to the systems organization concepts, many state-wide training programs currently offer the courses that would meet the foundation requirements for the facility group officers.

It would further appear from the current direction and content of two-year Associate Degree Programs in Fire Science, that all paid service system officers with the rank of Sector Fire Chief and above could benefit and become more competent in their coordinating and directing role with this level of education. Since the reality of this conjecture is many years in the future, it would seem illogical to talk about a bachelor's degree program for chief officers in this book. Those individuals earning the four-year degree would undoubtedly have the educational capability to advantageously compete for higher levels in the organization structure.

Chapter II noted that the systems organization framework was flexible enough to accommodate volunteer fire departments and still move towards desired objectives. The total systems structure has been designed with volunteer fire departments very much in mind. Functional elements have been framed to specifically support a basic volunteer level of service.

It is apparent that communities and rural areas under 10,000 population (an approximate figure) can continue to be served adequately and economically with volunteer service supported by a total systems organization approach to fire safety. This premise does not compromise the structured public fire safety objective. On the contrary, a volunteer service fits in perfectly with the concept of effectiveness and efficiency. Communities in the 10,000 population bracket cannot support a fully paid fire service. However, the population deserves the same prevention and protection services prescribed for larger cities. If the fire prevention and fire protection service is reduced from established levels, the community must assume the potential for large loss fires. Furthermore, the task force units manned by adequately trained and dedicated volunteer personnel should be capable of effective fire suppression in the following occupancies: one- and two-family dwellings; commercial establishments

---

[6]International Association of Fire Fighters (AFL-CIO). *Apprenticeship Training Standards*. Washington: U.S. Department of Labor, 1972.

with fire areas under 10,000 square feet; barns and miscellaneous small detached buildings; and small manufacturing process of a nonhazardous nature. Assuming the balanced Task Force concept outlined, volunteer personnel can also be relied upon to protect other occupancies that incorporate fire detection and automatic suppression equipment. Volunteers may adequately serve schools and other places of Public Assembly where Level 1 Task Forces automatically respond with a Sector Chief or System Fire Chief.

A less defined area of volunteer capability lies in population groupings ranging between 10,000 (approximately) and 35,000. In this population range one finds many examples of combination fire departments at the present time. This concept can also fit into the systems approach. A typical objective of combination fire departments is to provide a nucleus of paid personnel during defined times (usually day-time hours) when volunteers are not readily available, and/or to provide competent equipment operators.

For instance, a Task Force Level 2 requires three mobile units and a complement of fifteen men. What this means in terms of combination departments is simply a more carefully worked out real-time resource status communications system. When the initial task force cannot be made up by a single facility, a second and third facility automatically fills out the balance of the response. For example: Community A (in the system) has three paid men on duty and two volunteers in the station when an alarm is received. This personnel complement responds with the Task Force Unit short one man. Three men acknowledge to communications (see Chapter VIII) that they are responding to the fire station. Communications assigns these men to the Task Force Pumper and immediately dispatches a Task Force Ladder from Community B with six men. The minimum complement is rounded out and each unit can be cancelled if it is not needed. By the same measure there is not an overdeveloped response of personnel. Any additional volunteers signaling availability go on-standby (Community A, B and C) with unmanned equipment for a second Task Force response or until the first response returns to service.

Geographical Spread

Obviously, there are many rural areas of the country where communities are spread so far apart as to void this interactive concept.

A higher risk assumption with target hazards will probably prevail in such areas. The alternative is to provide a higher level of internal private protection for such risks.

The service system is designed on the thesis that an alarm for a building fire initiates a minimum of one defined Task Force level consisting of the specified equipment and a complement of men. The essential difference between a volunteer response versus a full-paid response involves the time variable. The time factor could be important; it could also be overstressed in relation to the severity of potential fires. The answer to the time problem must be generated and analyzed from a valid data base. A fully paid department should be relied upon to initiate a response within one minute after the alarm is received. The actual response time could be highly variable. However, under the perceived system, if the requisite units did not respond within three minutes, alternative units would be dispatched. The mechanism for this is explained under the *Integrated System* — Chapter VIII. A Part Paid Service subsystem can be considered to offer a quick response but the requisite manpower may be somewhat slower in gaining full strength. The time factor can be considered part of the risk assumption. If a given community can only financially support a volunteer department, then it assumes some proportionately higher risk for unprotected target hazards than would be assumed under a fully paid or combination department. It is the obligation of the Fire Coordinator to clearly define the risk assumption levels and the differentials that exist between service system capabilities.

Special Units

A significant function under the service subsystem needs to be explored. The broad scope of the service subsystem includes not only the major function of fire suppression, but also rescue and special community service work as demanded and financed by jurisdictional areas. The present Fire Service is currently employing more and more specialized equipment to meet community service demands. Some of the more typical equipment includes:

Ambulances for emergency transport of injured or sick persons.
Rescue Vehicles for serious transportation wrecks, cave-ins and building collapses.
Articulating Booms for elevated rescue work and master stream application.
Brush Trucks for the suppression of natural cover fuel fires.

Special Agent Suppression Vehicles for flammable liquid and flammable gas fires (i.e., foam, light water, dry chemical).

Compressor units for refilling the air tanks on protective breathing equipment.

Helicopters for emergency reconnaisance, rescue work, and spot fire suppression.

Fire Boats for water front and vessel protection.

Other very special units may exist in the Fire Service. It should be recognized that each facility cannot support such an extensive array of special equipment. Yet at some future time, almost every community experiences the demand for special equipment to handle unusual problem situations.

The previously discussed Task Force concept is introduced for the specific purpose of proposing a definable and workable suppression force for structural fires. Other types of events such as forest fires, a train derailment, or bulk storage gasoline tank, also require specific capabilities. The task force groups defined may be deficient in special equipment and/or extinguishing agents to cope with an extended list of hazards. To meet special needs, the total Public Fire Safety System must assess special problem areas, their potential location, and the resources required to cope with such emergencies. After such an assessment is made, special units of the type mentioned can be procured and assigned to selected facilities. Manpower complements required to respond with the special units should be provided in addition to the task force groups or the selective dispatching of special units changes the composition of prescribed task forces. A typical example might occur where a facility operates a Task Force Group 1. Personnel assigned to the Pump Unit (TFP) may also be assigned to the ambulance. If the ambulance is on an emergency rescue call when a fire call is received, a pump unit is immediately dispatched from another facility to make up the pump unit requirement.

Considerable attention has been placed on contrasting combination, and paid personnel and the volunteer roles in the perceived Public Fire Safety System. Volunteers could very well augment paid personnel within the service system by providing manpower for special units. Volunteers could render a tremendous assistance even in the larger Level 1 systems by manning special equipment on multiple task force or supplemental assignments. There is some limited evidence of this in existence today.

Another potentially interesting capability of the systems approach is to train nonemergency resource allocation and facilitating systems people in the use and operation of special unit equipment. Functional personnel could respond with special units on severe situations. For example:

Maintenance personnel could respond with a compressor unit, maintenance service vehicle or fuel tender.

Training personnel could man and operate special agent suppression vehicles such as Light Water, Foam and Dry Chemical units.

Prevention personnel could man heavy rescue vehicles.

Protection Engineers could man special boom equipment and water monitors.

Brush trucks could be manned by staff personnel.

The field command-control and communications unit could be operated by the secretarial staff (women).

The above relationships are only suggestive. The point is simply that when there is a need for special services and resources, the whole system serves as a back-up force. Such a concept fosters maximum utility of all personnel.

The structural-functional presentation of the proposed Public Fire Safety Service System establishes a framework that provides for balancing resources to cope with given sets of emergencies. Because of the coordination and control built into the system, the effectiveness and efficiency of operations should be considerably enhanced over present modes of operation. The actual response patterns for any given emergency category could be developed and redeveloped as statistical inferences warrant change. In instituting such changes, it should remain the responsibility of the Fire Coordinator in cooperation with the Public Relations Coordinator to clearly inform the public of the change in risk assumptions. This point has been made before; it is worth repeating. Unless budget cuts are made, it can generally be assumed that changes in the allocation of resources would be to reduce the incident frequency and/or the loss severity. It is to the obvious advantage of the Public Fire Safety System to make these conditions known to the public at large.

The Prevention Subsystem

A second major project system is designated as the Prevention Subsystems. It is the mission of this subsystem to establish and implement procedures and practices that will contribute to the reduction in frequency probability and severity of fires. It is apparent that these objectives can best be served by fostering public educational programs, building survey programs, fire safety standards programs with permit issuance for specified hazardous activities, and investigation programs to identify and categorize problems. The above areas represent the broad concern of this subsection.

Currently, some fire departments expend a considerable effort in the promotion of fire prevention. Other fire departments only provide a token effort in this area. These opposite levels of involvement are evidenced by the annual submission of fire prevention entry booklets to the National Fire Protection Association. Annual awards reflect unique promotional concepts and continuity of activities throughout the year. It appears difficult to objectively measure tangible results from fire prevention campaigns and education efforts. One tangible measure commonly used is the increase or reduction in per capita loss for a geographical area. Other indicators may include aggregate loss figures over the span of several years. The true relevance of such measures can be strongly questioned. It would seem that many important variables relating to the frequency of fires and the severity of fires are left out of such analysis.

One objective of the Fire Prevention Subsystem should be to concentrate on the reduction in frequency of fire occurrence in selected occupancies. The selected occupancies are identified from incident reports analysis. The nature and implication of an incident reporting system are covered in both Chapters IV and VIII. Therefore, concepts rather than details will be reviewed in this chapter. Frequency of events and probability of events (i.e., the relationship of the actual events to the number of probable events) for any given geographical area needs to be clearly established in order to identify problems. Therefore, a logical activity of the Fire Prevention System is to develop programs that will either continue to reduce incident frequencies or maintain incident frequencies at some established level.

One possible method of achieving frequency reductions is through public education programs. Many techniques have been employed in an attempt to educate the public in fire safety measures. Some of the more prominent approaches have included: fire department open houses, public demonstrations, lectures before civic groups, signs, billboards, and stencil-ing on sidewalks; Junior Fire Marshal and Sparky programs in the school systems. Some unique and promising programs are in evidence such as the one developed by Terry Hayes entitled "Fire Prevention Shreveport Style." The Shreveport presentation revolves around a unique multiview slide show accompanied by modern sound innovations for teenage appeal. While such techniques can do nothing but good, the question remains how much good are they doing and are they presenting the most appropriate messages in relation to localized problems?

It has been difficult to assess properly the impact of such programs. One possible measure of effectiveness is to relate control programs to the reduction in frequency of events by causal factors and in relation to the probability of events. For example, it might be determined that the number of incidents attributable to cooking practices in the kitchen were on the increase. An educational program through home bureaus, home economics classes in the school, parent-teacher groups, etc., might be instituted to educate the public on this identified problem. The measure of effectiveness is simply an analysis of the frequency record. It should be stressed that more than one problem area can be covered by such presentations.

Educational programs are necessary if a serious attempt is to be made in the reduction of fire occurrences and the subsequent reduction of both life and property losses. Such programs can be developed around two themes: (1) general knowledge and procedures for emergencies, (2) specific knowledge for defined problem areas. Live demonstrations, lectures with visual and audio support, and conference type discussions, especially with business groups might be quite effective. The educational program has to be well planned, adequately financed and competently staffed. In many fire departments the above component criterion is not in evidence. One objective of instituting a systems approach to organizing public fire safety is to provide a more viable base of operations on which to establish fire prevention and to coordinate the activities of fire prevention into other elements of the system.

A second major objective of the Prevention Subsystem is to implement a building survey program. Property surveys, commonly referred to as inspections, are conducted for the primary purposes of identifying hazards, seeking out potential causes and obtaining the necessary corrections to alleviate identified problems before they become responsible for

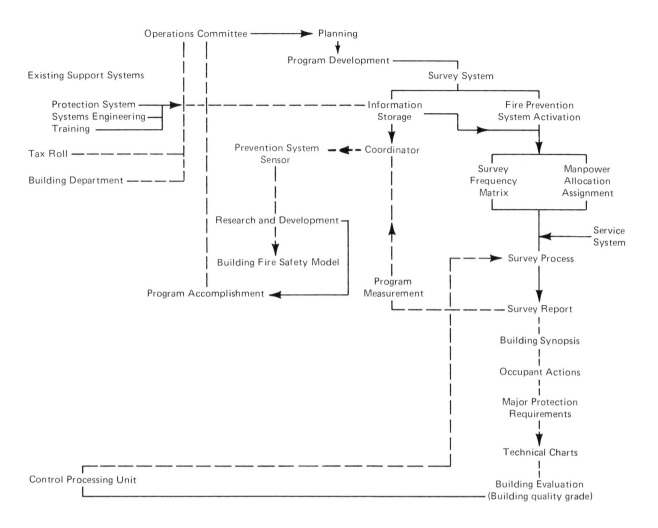

ILLUSTRATION VII-2 MODIFIED DIAGRAM OF A BUILDING PROTECTION AUDIT AND SURVEY
SYSTEM

an incident. The actual conduct of a survey has the secondary benefit of educating personnel associated with a given piece of property on specific fire safety problems and corrective techniques.

The development of a survey program for the Prevention Subsystem follows the pattern established for one of the agencies in the Federal Government.[7]

The Federal Program developed around the fire safety requirements for government owned and leased space is termed "PASS" for Protection Audit and Survey System. PASS was

developed within the framework of a modern management information system. In this context it is essentially a system within a system. Illustration VII-2 is utilized to depict the component elements of the survey system and the interaction flow with the larger system. It is considered that the PASS program developed for the Federal Government, with slight modifications is equally applicable to the property survey requirements for urban public fire safety systems.

Program Development

Survey program development is an essential task of any good organizational framework.

[7]Harry E. Hickey, "Protection Audit and Survey System." Washington: General Services Administration, 1969. (Mimeographed.)

Frequency Period

Modular Conditions	Weekly	Semi-Weekly	Monthly	Bi-Monthly	Semi-Annually	Annually
Sprinklered Property	All (system only)		758, 843, 211			512, 981
One Story Buildings <1,000			758, 211, 311	161, 213, 214	131, 851, 573	512, 599
>1,000 <10,000	931, 932		161, 758, 182	131, 213, 214, 851, 573	512, 581	547
>10,000 <100,000	931, 932	161, 758, 311	131, 213, 214, 215, 851, 573	512, 581	776, 423	
>100,000				796		
Two and Three Story Buildings >1,000 <10,000	931, 932	311	851, 573, 796, 182	461, 453	776, 423	
>10,000 <100,000	931, 932	796, 311	215, 424, 555	461	776, 423	
>100,000						
High Rise Buildings 3 Stories			424			

NOTE: Building Classification Coding According to the National Fire Protection Association "901 System" Coding System for fire reporting.

Key for Selected Common Examples:

131 Church
161 Restaurant
213 Elementary School
214 Junior High School
215 High School

428 Apartment House, over 20 units
512 Food Store
758 Printing Shop
851 Lumberyard
931 Building Under Construction

ILLUSTRATION VII-3   SURVEY FREQUENCY MATRIX FOR PROPERTY CLASSIFICATIONS

Fire Prevention Program development starts with the planning function at the Operations Committee level and is guided by the Prevention System Coordinator. Planning is initiated by establishing the objectives and the parameters of the survey system. After the survey system has been implemented, the planning group serves to audit the results on a periodic interval. On the basis of the audit, a reassessment procedure should be conducted of the total survey system and subsequent modifications should be initiated to keep the total system in balance with the policy formulation.

The Prevention Coordinator is responsible for refining the planning function. The program development group within the Prevention Subsystem would actually structure the details of the survey system. The survey program development would involve, but is not limited to the following procedures:

1. Analyzing other existing and planned automated programs that could serve as an *Input* function to the identified elements of the survey program and to determine what features of the survey program *Output* might serve as meaningful *Input* to other systems.
   a. Input programs might include:
      (1) Water supply analysis from the protection system
      (2) Inservice inspections from the Service Systems
      (3) Aerial mapping
      (4) Sanborn Maps from Urban Planning
      (5) Insurance maps and reports (to the extent available)

2. Providing an organizational structure for the operational elements of the survey portion of the subsystem.
   a. Establishment of the level of Prevention Subsystem Organization (i.e., 1, 2 or 3)
   b. The requirements for staff support assistance
   c. The degree of mission accomplishment that can be carried on by other functions within the framework of all subsystems

3. Establishing the proper control or sensoring elements for reviewing survey reports and conducting an analysis of the reports in relation to providing *output* consistency with established objectives.

a. The normal sensor function should be carried out by the next higher level Prevention Coordinator with certain specific risks reviews by the Prevention System Coordinator.

4. Establishment of the parameters on the scope and content of the program for the evaluation and auditing procedures relative to an assessment of survey program accomplishments.
   a. Establishment of survey report frequency for defined property classifications
   b. Assignment of survey responsibility
   c. Follow-up procedures
   d. Enforcement procedures
   e. Report channels (See Chapter VIII)

Research and Analysis

An essential element of the Survey Program Loop is the research and analysis activity that must be conducted to properly dispose of the problem conditions created by the perpetual survey operation and to analyze the *Output* media of the several functional subsystems involved (i.e., protection, service, systems engineering, training) into meaningful relationships for control of the survey operation. The research and analysis activity is jointly promoted by the Research and Development Subsystem. This research and analysis activity also reviews selected incident reports and severity documents for determining the relationship between causal factors, the modular loss control effectiveness, and a condition correlation reported in previous surveys. Problem identifications as the result of the review of these reports would also be related to the research requirements for the survey criteria.

It is apparent that an adjunct support system may be developed as a subfunction under the research concept that is associated with the Prevention Subsystem. The proposed research could involve a systems model applied to building fire safety. The Building Fire Safety Model would be utilized to study all the events that may be reasonably predicted for a set of defined conditions within a specific type of building under fire propagation. Such a model should certainly consider the type and arrangement of the fuel, the structural components, the fire control mechanisms, and the effects that flaming and products of combustion might have on the life support of the occupants, the property and the assumption of risk. The interrelationship of such variables appears to be highly complex, and the combination probabilities would apparently be incomprehensible without the storage and arithmetic-logic-processing component of a computer (CPU).

Program Accomplishment

The Survey Subsystem is presented as a focal element in the Prevention Subsystem. Every facet of the Survey Loop should be served directly or complemented indirectly by the Program Loop and the Support Loop. The following subsections will enumerate the perceived functional characteristics of the Survey Loop.

Information Storage (CPU)

Information storage includes the substantive guidelines and criteria to be followed in the conduct of a survey, the processing of a survey, and the printing out of the survey results. A portion of this information is considered to be logged in storage books. This information would include the standards and published criteria against which the risk is evaluated for the relative degree of compliance with the established criteria. A second portion of the information storage would constitute such items as a building inventory, a frequency matrix for determining the time interval between surveys, survey assignment codes, survey completion codes, fire protection equipment status conditions and apparent building quality ratings (based upon statistical analysis of the probability of an event and the probability of the outcome). It is anticipated that the building quality grade would be assigned to computer storage. The interrelationship of the Information Storage to the Existing Support Systems will be further referenced under the title, *Existing Support Systems.*

Activating Group

The Activating Group signifies the pool of personnel resources required to accomplish the defined survey process. The activating process includes the functions of establishing a schedule for the conduct of both individual and group surveys and the assignments of manpower to the survey process. The scheduling of surveys should consider the geographical location of the survey process by area codes, the frequency period for the surveys, and the special technical functions to be performed during the survey process. The allocation of manpower should consider resource availability, budgetary controls on travel, and technical competency.

Frequency Matrix

A frequency matrix should be prepared to assist in scheduling the survey work load according to a classification demand cycle established by the planning group. An example of a survey frequency matrix is presented as Illustration VII-3. This matrix depicts the type of surveys to be conducted in relation to the Occupancy Classification (other variables may be introduced) and the frequency period in terms of monthly intervals. The frequency matrix can be simple or complex based upon the scale of operations. The complexity would indicate the necessity for computerizing the allocation assignments.

Manpower Allocations:

In addition to the concepts of manpower requirements advanced under the title *Activating Group*, the survey workload consists of meeting two additional objectives. The immediate objective would be to complete the assigned surveys for a given year within the designated time span. The completion of a proportion of surveys would result in accomplishment levels which could be analyzed as a certain per cent of the total space and as a per cent of the buildings to the total number of buildings in a geographical territory. The second objective involves the need to equate the man-hour commitments necessary to meet the survey requirements. Thus, through the audit phase of the survey program, it should become possible to forecast the manpower requirements necessary to complete the desired survey frequencies.

Some basic assumptions and alternatives have to be inserted into the survey system concept at this point. The actual manpower requirement for the Prevention Subsystem is going to depend to a large extent on the survey manpower commitment from the service system. The manpower commitment from the service system in turn depends on the technical competency of the personnel and whether they are paid or volunteer personnel. Once a prevention survey frequency has been established as consistent with the organizational mission, then the organization is committed to carrying out the surveys according to the frequency schedule. This commitment simply states that a qualified individual in the organization should carry out the prescribed surveys within the allotted time.

It is apparent that a significant amount of the regularly scheduled survey work can be delegated to and completed by the service system personnel. This should be accomplished in the form of in-service surveys. This concept complements the basic prevention effort and the preplanning effort necessary for effective fire suppression operations. Under this delegation of survey responsibility, Fire Prevention Subsystem survey function becomes mainly one of support and technical assistance.

The question of volunteer unit capability for conducting surveys and collecting preplanning information is also important. The answer will necessarily be left to the specific jurisdiction under consideration. Some volunteer groups may possess both the time and the requisite technical talent to conduct surveys. Other volunteer units may consider their role as simply a fire suppression activity. The second condition will require additional personnel for the Fire Prevention Subsystem in order to complete the established survey task. Therefore, a matter of dollars-and-cents efficiency relates to how much of the work load can be delegated to the service subsystem units. Practically, this concept is going to require some reorientated thinking on the part of individuals associated with the present Fire Service. It will not be a new concept for some; it will be a radical concept for others. However, a program of this scope must be implemented if the outlined objectives are to be achieved.

The Survey Process

The prime objective of the survey process should be to determine the existing conditions of designated occupancy space in relation to the established criteria maintained in the computer (or manual) information storage. The actual physical-mental process of conducting surveys is currently perceived to be a human-manual record operation. However, in the next several years it may be possible to significantly reduce the human requirements in the survey process with properly designed computer support. One possible application of computer assistance includes the use of standard survey forms with mark-sensitive sheets to record the survey results.

Instead of writing a narrative type of survey report, the data read from the mark-sensitive survey forms would be processed to record the conditions of finding, a correlary recommendation statement, and in relation to the proposed survey program a fire safety index for the build-

ing would be computed.[8] This premise also focuses on another important consideration of the Survey System. The survey program is designed within a management by exception structure. Therefore, only conditions deviating from the established criteria or performance level are evaluated. The Fire Prevention Subsystem Coordinator may assume if a category is not reported on, such as exit facilities, the survey item complies with the criteria placed in the information storage. This management by exception concept requires a very effective control on the validity and reliability of the Survey Process. A major objective of the survey process is to avoid the duplication of manpower efforts and the recurring documentation of physical conditions. These objectives are accomplished by the development of a procedure for the analysis of buildings on an existing data base formulated through the previous reports of the Building Department (intra-system) and the Protection Subsystem. Continuing with the management by exception concept, each supplemental survey for an identified building would report only on the conditions that are deviant from the previous report. Situations involving conflicting criteria such as those created by new or emerging technology and unusual problems that might be relevant to the entire system would be referred through a program measurement channel to the Fire Prevention Coordinator (Sensor) element for appropriate action.

The Survey Report

A survey report should be the culmination output of the survey process. The complete survey report should provide the Prevention Coordinator with a valid and concise depiction of the current life safety and structural conditions of the building or buildings under consideration. It is acknowledged that there may be a necessity for some direct, informative and definitive statements to supplement the exception conditions already in the survey process. However, many report items such as: the basic building construction features, the building ceiling heights and floor areas, the fixed fire protection equipment, the occupancy load, and technical information on the water supply, could be contained in an updated information storage program through the referenced support functions. It must be stressed that the

---

[8]Harry E. Hickey, "Urban Fire Safety Systems in the Next Decade," paper presented to the 1970 Annual Meeting of the National Fire Protection Association, Toronto, Canada, May 22, 1970.

report function extends beyond compliance with the frequency activity within the prevention system. The survey report becomes the informational input for supporting the service system under actual emergency condition (please refer to Chapter VIII) and as a document to be sent to the owner/occupant of the building(s) surveyed for corrective action.

Building Synopsis

The Building Synopsis should be printed out from the established information storage. Significant changes in a building could be established as addendums to the basic synopsis report. New buildings or modifications of significant conditions in existing buildings should be considered as Input Data through the Protection System to update the information storage.

Occupant Actions

This portion of the survey report identifies the findings and the recommendations that do not require major funding and can be reasonably financed at the building occupant level with normal repair and improvement budgets. Housekeeping and storage deficiency items would usually be included in this category.

Major Protection Requirements

Major protection requirements should involve those recommendations that are beyond the scope of accomplishment by the building lessee. This level of recommendation would go to the building owner for implementation within a given time span. Computer processing restrictions would require that the survey recommendations be prepared in a precise and condensed format by the human evaluator.

Technical Charts

The survey conducted in relation to certain occupancy classifications should require special technical evaluations on the installed fire protection equipment, the water supply, the alarm or detection facilities and the mobile fire apparatus. Some or all of this information should be compiled by the Protection Subsystem. It is also considered desirable to equate the present observed performance with the specified design performance and the previous performance recorded for specified fire protection equipment items and devices. It is perceived that equaling performance levels to established criteria can best be accomplished through the utilization of a series of log charts and graphs.

Building Evaluations

A fundamental objective of the survey program should be to determine the fire safety quality of occupied building space. The concept of a quality measurement in quantifiable terms is important to the measurement of objective performance within the total system. A data set is perceived as a means for initiating such a concept. The data set would include two elements in relations to the categories of building construction, occupancy and socio-economic area. The elements would be: (1) the probability of having a fire in a set condition, (2) the probability of severity in case an event occurs. The following example may clarify the point. The data set might be established for a single family dwelling of wood frame construction in medium-income neighborhood. Based upon the incident data of the previous year, it is calculated that the probability of a similar property set having a fire is .325 with a ninety-five per cent confidence level. If the event does actually occur, the suppression action on previous fires of similar sets reveals that the probability of confining and extinguishing the fire to the room of origin is .821 at the same confidence level. The figures represent one possible way of defining the risk condition as a quantifiable set.

The Sensor Function

The Sensor Function should be one of the most important single *key elements* in the survey system. A sensing unit is placed in the program measurement loop to function primarily as a feedback control on the survey system. As the term would imply, the sensing unit collects, reviews, and analyzes the Survey Subsystem Output. A series of actions should take place if the Output does not agree with the systems objectives and the information storage data. During the initial survey program development under the systems approach, the sensing unit would of necessity be entirely a human activity. In this manner, each output survey should be assigned to one of the appropriate Prevention Coordinator Levels. As the system becomes more refined, certain portions of the sensing procedure may be adaptable to an Electronic Data Processing Subsystem.

It is perceived that the Sensor element should perform the following essential functions relative to the total system:

1. Receive and review all the survey reports.

2. Take one of the following actions on each report:

a. Concur with the finding and recommendation statements.
   (1) Send copy to jurisdictional facilities and CPU
b. Prepare comments on inadequacies, inconsistencies, or obvious lack of information items and return the report to the activating group.
c. Forward the problem areas to Research and Development
d. Forward cost data, statistics relating to building evaluations to the operations committee for period reports (see appropriate channel flow in Chapter VIII)

In relation to the broad aspect of the survey system, the Sensor is perceived as an individual who coordinates the survey activity and acts to adjust and balance the total survey needs and accomplishments.

Existing Local Government Support Systems

It would appear that one or more urban government units might support the survey effort. For example, the tax assessor's office maintains up-to-date accounts of all taxable property, the classification of that property and the assessed valuation. Printouts from this office should be very helpful in determining the survey load and the assignments by jurisdictional areas. This information could actually be utilized in programming a frequency matrix of buildings and their survey assignment schedule.

The Planning Committee could give advanced reports to the Prevention Subsystem for determining future loads and the Building Department could notify the Prevention Subsystem so that "under construction surveys" could commence as soon as ground is broken on a new project.

An Investigation Service

A second type of survey should be initiated after an actual event to determine the causal factor(s), the factors bearing on the loss, the loss severity, special problem identification, and the relationship of the survey process to the loss condition. Possibly the existing concept of fire investigation has concentrated too much attention on investigating thoroughly those incidents where suspicious circumstances are suspected. Many "routine fires" become statistics although no one understands what happened, why it happened and how occurrences of the same phenomena can be prevented in

the future. The investigative function is very much a part of the Prevention Subsystem.

Again, there is the concern over who is going to do the investigative task. A considerable portion of the investigative work can be accomplished by officers of the service system; if these officers are qualified. Persons assigned investigative responsibility should have special expertise in fire investigation methods, procedures and legal implications.

Personnel assigned to the Prevention Subsystem must assume this responsibility when the investigative task cannot be adequately delegated to persons in the service subsystem.

The Prevention Coordinator must possess a considerable breadth of technical knowledge to carry out his responsibilities. This condition holds true regardless of the system level of implementation. Obviously, the Prevention Coordinator associated with a level-one system is going to have greater responsibility and a larger environment of problems to solve than a person in a level-three system.

The minimum perceived level of formal education required for persons in any level of prevention coordinator position should be an Associate Degree in Fire Science or Technology. The course work should include or be supplemented for formal credit courses in psychology, sociology, computer science, law enforcement and local government administrative law. It would seem that one of several bachelor's degrees might complement the Prevention Coordinator's position. These degrees could include Fire Protection Engineering, Civil Engineering, Architectural Engineering, Public Administration, Chemistry, Physics or one of the applied technologies. The level of the position would prescribe the amount of experience that was needed.

In addition to the Prevention position given on the organizational chart, it should be recognized that considerable staff support will be needed. As previously indicated, such support will be highly dependent on how much work can be delegated to the Service Subsystem. In any event the field staff support work by Prevention Specialists should serve as experience for moving up to one of the Prevention Coordinator level positions. The opportunity for both vertical and horizontal movement is similar to that projected for the Service Subsystem Fire Chiefs.

The Protection Subsystems

Few units of local government in the United States have seen the wisdom to employ Fire

Protection Engineers into the public fire safety sector. Local governments that have previously employed fire protection engineers include Seattle, Washington; Alexandria, Virginia; Philadelphia, Pennsylvania; Baltimore County, Maryland; and Montgomery County, Maryland. The Fire Protection Engineer is perceived to offer a vital supporting role to the total public fire safety system. This role is projected through elements and functions of the protection subsystem.

Fire Protection Advisement

Chapter I noted a "Wingspread Conference" statement to the effect that the Insurance Industry influence on public fire safety is waning. Local jurisdictional fire departments have in the past turned to Fire Insurance Rating Bureaus and the parent insurance companies for technical advice. Today, the opportunity to obtain such advice and recommendations on specific matters has been reduced or is non-existent. (This statement is based upon the author's private interview with selected Fire Officers in the States of Maryland, Virginia, New York, Pennsylvania, and New Jersey.) Fire Chiefs in many areas are hard pressed to know where to turn for technical advice on water supply problems, extinguishing system installations, equipment specifications, building codes or hazardous processes. The Public Fire Safety Systems must provide its own technical expertise in the areas mentioned and in other areas to be explored in this section. The technical and engineering arm of the public fire safety organization is structured under the title of Protection Subsystem. The main responsibility of the Protection Subsystem is to provide other functional units within the system and support systems in the larger urban context with scientific advisement.

The Protection Functions

The protection functions are concerned with the design of hardware components, and the evaluation of these components, to detect fires, confine fires, control fires, extinguish fires and fire effects. It follows from this definition that the Protection Subsystem is involved in activities associated with fire alarm systems, all types of fixed fire suppression equipment, structures and building components, and mobile equipment. Some depth of understanding concerning the specific nature of these areas is in order to appreciate the scope and involvement of the fire protection subsystem function.

Specification Development

Good fire protection equipment and devices can only be obtained by starting with good specifications. This simply means that the establishment of good design performance criteria and the writing of specifications to illustrate this performance is essential to achieving desired performance functions with a high degree of reliability. Therefore, it should be the responsibility of the fire protection subsection to prepare design and performance specifications for:
1. All fixed fire protection suppression equipment to be installed within the jurisdiction of the system.
2. All mobile fire suppression equipment.
3. All building fire protection devices such as: fire doors, alarm systems, automatic smoke vents, explosion equipment, panic hardware, boiler controls, and similar protection features.
4. Specifications covering building construction performance and the testing and approval of such performance. Specification preparation should be extended to the development of codes and ordinances to adopt the specifications.

Proposal-Specification-Plan Reviews

There is a need for engineering expertise to review fire protection features in new construction, and in the modernization of existing structures. All plans, proposals and specifications written or prepared outside of the Public Fire Safety Systems should be reviewed for compliance with prescribed fire safety measures. To this extent, considerable coordination must be developed between the Fire Prevention Subsystem criteria for surveys and the criteria utilized for plan reviews. The objective of this function is to move fire protection out of the realm of code compliance to a level of functional design performance engineering based upon the latest technological assessments available. The objective is also to coordinate plan reviews and consultations so that the prospective architect, builder, contractor, and owner do not obtain several and often conflicting recommendations on fire safety features. This also means that at some point in the not too distant future, the Public Fire Safety System should become the authority having jurisdiction with reference to all fire safety matters. The point is a radical departure from most existing practices. However, conflict of similar interests should be eliminated if the prescribed system is going to work and if there is a sincere interest in achieving total public fire safety.

Chapter 7

Bibliographical Entries

Books

Kimball, Warren Y. *Fire Attack 1* and *Fire Attack 2.* Boston: National Fire Protection Association, 1966, 1968.

Layman, Lloyd. *Attacking and Extinguishing Interior Fires.* Boston: National Fire Protection Association, 1952.

Publications of the Government, Learned Societies, and Other Organizations

Hickey, Harry E. *Urban Fire Safety Systems in the Next Decade,* (MP-1-72). Boston: National Fire Protection Association, 1972.

International Association of Fire Fighters (AFL-CIO). *Apprenticeship Training Standards.* Washington: U. S. Department of Labor, 1972.

Periodicals

Bahme, Charles W. "The Watts Fires and Their Lessons," *Fire Journal*, p. 10.

Unpublished Materials

Hickey, Harry E. *Protection Audit and Survey System.* Washington: General Services Administration, 1969, (Mimeographed).

Chapter VIII

The Integrated Public Fire Safety System Organization:

Perspective and Summary

The complete Public Fire Safety System is actually composed of numerous subsystem organization elements. These suborganization elements are established to provide functional capability to the organization framework. Emphasis must be placed on functional activities as support mechanisms for both individual components and the total organization as an integrative structure.

The previous chapters have established a functional identity for a selected group of subsystems within the framework of a total Public Fire Safety System. Perceived objectives have been outlined for each organization component. Now, it is imperative to stress the interface relationships perceived to exist between organization subunits. An appreciation of the interactive nature of the organization should crystallize a conceptual understanding of the total system structure. It should be remembered that one of the fundamental reasons for advancing the application of systems concepts to the organization of public fire safety is to enhance the process of understanding the scope, objectives and methods of instituting sound policies and programs relating to public fire safety.

The basic initiating condition of the public fire safety system is an emergency event. Each event, whether it be a fire, a rescue mission, a service call or a false alarm, stimulates functional components of the organization into action. The event initiator can also produce a chain of reactions within other functional subsystems that are not initially responsive to the emergency alarm.

A sequential digest of the action, activities and results of an event can be utilized to illustrate the independent and dependent functions associated with each subsystem component. The tracing of sequential steps associated with an event should enhance one's understanding of the organization complex.

This chapter is developed around the idea of depicting a generalized framework of association. Elements portrayed in the sequence of respective actions appear to be typical of the process that can be expected during real-world situations. The examples have been generated utilizing a level-one systems organization model. Appropriate modifications will be necessary where a level-two or level-three system organization is employed. Furthermore, the examples cited are not to be considered exhaustive. The conditions presented are regarded as the most significant and repetitive set of conditions common to public fire safety activities. Numerous problems, issues and event-oriented activities could be analyzed in a similar procedure.

An *input-output-feedback* channel analysis is utilized to fully describe the communicative flow process associated with the selected activities. The explanatory statements are keyed to a channel designation diagram. The sequential flow pattern of each diagrammed activity can be identified by reference to the established channel codes. In most examples, it may be readily apparent that the connection channels between the *input* and *output* of the respective functions actually form a loop arrangement. This association typifies the notion that a subsystem function determined to initiate a responsive channel action also is a receiver when the action process has been transmitted. The *input-processing-output-feedback* loop has been established as a hallmark of the systems approach to organization. This concept breeds vitality into the organization. In essence, the Public Fire Safety System can be analyzed relative to its functional capability to produce a channel loop for each intra-subsystem action. This technique is an extension benefit of the systems approach. The channel designation analysis is culminated with Chart VIII-10 (facing p. 192). This chart serves better than any narrative description to impact the complexity of public fire safety to achieve the projected organization mission. However, even the channel network does not fully reveal all of the possible interfunctional input-output loops. Only the channel documentation advanced with the respective sequence charts are summarily imposed on the Channel Designation Analysis Chart. While this chart may appear to defy easy comprehension, it should still be meaningful for the following reasons. First, one must be impressed with the magnitude of interface contact and dependency between functional subsystems of the organization. From the depicted interaction, one must realize that subsystems are not entities that exist by themselves. Therefore, when one proceeds to examine a particular identifiable subsystem, there is a need to place that subsystem within the reference framework of a "whole" organization. Second, it should be realized that the data requirements and transmission channels for the organization scope presented are extensive. It is obvious that an organization of this complexity can easily become a paper mill. The processing link-up between identified functional components and the Central Processing Unit serves to illustrate the potential data processing assistance to be achieved by employing a computerized support subsystem. Third, the channel designation chart is essentially a rearranged organization element chart without the basic connectors. The chart depicts the subsystem categories that are considered essential to mission accomplishment. Service performance is perceived to suffer if some subfunction is deleted. The Channel Designation Analysis Chart should convey an appreciation of what might occur if one or more identified subsystems were simply eliminated. Data communications channels would obviously become open ended. Sensing and feedback on certain functional elements would become nonexistent and the total system would probably operate on some undefined level of efficiency and effectiveness below the desired optimum.

This chapter, the last, also serves to summarize the intent, the accomplishments and the real-world implications of this book. The summary statements begin on page 190. In addition to the routine Bibliography to be found on page 197, Appendix A serves as an important key work reference to the subject matter of this book. The following subsections further serve to identify and describe the channel designations relating to selected activities, tasks, duties and responses associated with the systems concept of organization applied to the mission accomplishment of public fire safety.

Alarm of Incident Sequence

The entire Public Fire Safety System is geared to formulate a desired response in accordance with objective criteria for handling emergency events. The outcome of each event (i.e., incident), in relation to established objectives is highly dependent upon the flow of men, equipment, materials and information to a designated incident scene. The incident alarm sequence pattern is illustrated in Chart VIII-1 to conceptualize one possible approach to *input-processing-output* states associated with an emergency fire situation in the urban system. An arbitrary end-point has been established in the event sequence pattern. A single request for additional assistance has been initiated from the first responding officer. It is important to point out that if additional assistance is needed, a cycle pattern will simply repeat itself until the necessary forces are employed for control and extinguishment.

Channel	Key - Explanatory Statement
A_1	"A" for alarm signifies the event notification from the public sector. The source might be from a telephone, a fire alarm box, central station, citizen report, police patrol, etc. The signal goes directly to the communications subsystem designated receiving point.
A_2	The event variables are established and transmitted to the Central Processing Unit. The essential information would probably include: location, nature of the emergency, the hazard condition and the current weather factor.
A_3	The CPU processes the input data, selects and notifies the proper facilities and units to respond. This task is accomplished through preprogrammed criteria to establish an optimum response in accordance with specified parameters. The program is self-adjusting. This means that the computer can compensate for an unreported

variable such as the specific nature of the hazard which is unknown when a street box is received.

A_4 A sensor feedback channel is built into the alarm system from the CPU to Communications Central. This displays the units that have been dispatched for dispatcher verification. (Also note comparator part with A_5.)

A_5 A sensor feedback channel is also required to access the status of units dispatched (A_3). The units responding to the emergency verify their response by phone, radio, tone, or a combination of techniques. The input is matched with the A_4 feedback channel display. If a match is not made the dispatcher repeats the A_2 transmission and a message update cycle is initiated. Or the dispatcher may override the automated system and dispatch directly.

A_6 An incident data channel is reserved for providing all units with tactical information relative to a specific event. For given buildings, data would be printed out on unit teleprinters or displayed on unit cathode ray tubes (or in combination) relative to construction, occupancy, special hazards, real-time water supply (RT_1), etc. This channel would also serve to update information about the incident without overcrowding the normal voice communication channels.

A_7 A feedback channel is established for the officer in charge or for the arriving first unit to give a status report. This report involves a description of the actual emergency, the commitment or release of units, and the request for additional assistance. This channel then becomes the direct link between the emergency scene and communications central. An assumed request for supplemental assistance is utilized to illustrate the repetitive nature of the cycle effect on the channel links.

$A_2{}^1$ A supplemental request for additional assistance (assumed) is transmitted to the CPU. This may be a preprogrammed supplemental request or communications central may initiate the input for a special response (i.e., a foam truck).

$A_3{}^1$ The CPU processes the supplemental request and notifies the selected units and functions. An incident severity that requires additional assistance would probably initiate the response of special functional units like a Protection Engineer, a Prevention Coordinator, training subsystem staff personnel, the Maintenance Emergency Unit, the Public Relations Coordinator, and the necessary higher chief levels.

$A_4{}^1$ A simple update on the sensor feedback channel.

$A_5{}^1$ A repeat of the sensor assessment feedback channel from the supplemental responding units.

$A_8{}^1$ A special status display channel is initiated. This channel is activated when the first unit acknowledges response to an emergency. The status of responding units, available units and out-of-service units are displayed at communications central and the field command-control-communications unit. The computer constantly updates the status of all functional response units.

Service Response Sequence

A series of response sequence channels are illustrated to establish a pattern for activation of functional units and their respective roles in providing an emergency service. The connectors demonstrate how the system works through the cycle effect of initiating input and processing the requirements to produce a desired output (Chart VIII-1).

Channel	Key - Explanatory Statement
R_1	An initial response channel is designated for each emergency location. The channel implies the opening of a communication link with communications central all along the response path.
R_2	A secondary response channel is initiated upon the demand for supplemental service units and/or functional units within the Public Fire Safety System.
R_3	There is also an outside system response channel. This channel displays the interconnection between the internal fire safety system and the support elements from the external system: water supply, police, highways, building department, public utilities, and mutual-aid service systems from other jurisdictional areas.

Real-Time Sequence

It is obvious that the very nature of an emergency system requires information that is of a very current nature. In other words, the information flowing to an emergency scene must tell a story as it exists right now. For instance, water supply information should indicate the volume and pressure available at the event time, not some time in the past. The real-time channels are inserted on Chart VIII-2 to depict some requirements for real-time data and how each data channel fits into the total information system.

Channel	Key - Explanatory Statement
RT_1	This channel represents the requirement for real-time data on the water system which includes pressure profiles, and volume input data. Sensors on the water system would transmit data pulses to the Central Processing Unit. At the time of a request signal for data analysis and output, the computer

175

CHART VIII-1

CHANNEL DESIGNATIONS: ALARM SEQUENCE & RESPONSE SEQUENCE

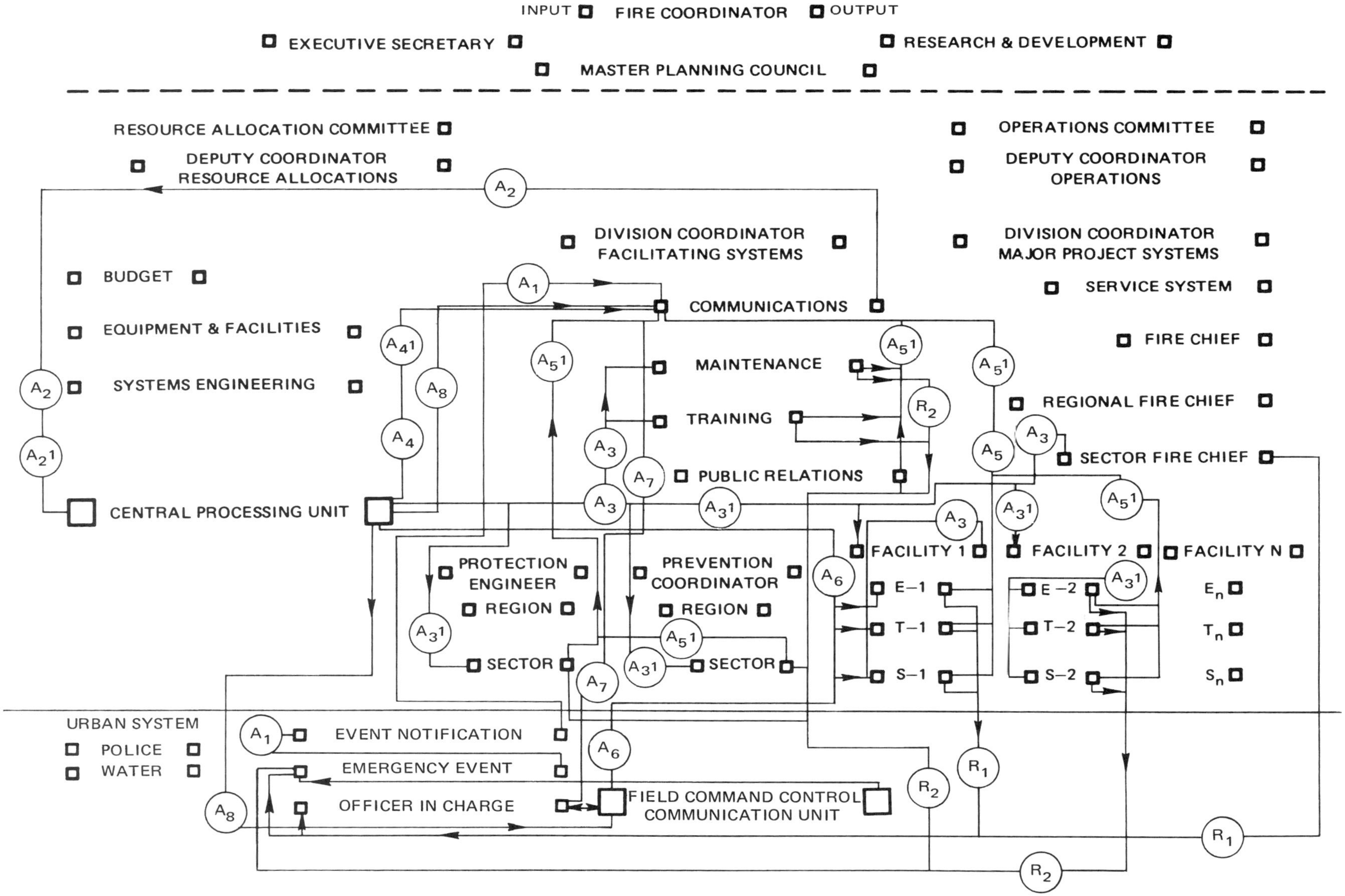
INPUT
FIRE COORDINATOR
OUTPUT
EXECUTIVE SECRETARY
RESEARCH & DEVELOPMENT
MASTER PLANNING COUNCIL
RESOURCE ALLOCATION COMMITTEE
DEPUTY COORDINATOR RESOURCE ALLOCATIONS
OPERATIONS COMMITTEE
DEPUTY COORDINATOR OPERATIONS
DIVISION COORDINATOR FACILITATING SYSTEMS
DIVISION COORDINATOR MAJOR PROJECT SYSTEMS
BUDGET
EQUIPMENT & FACILITIES
SYSTEMS ENGINEERING
COMMUNICATIONS
MAINTENANCE
TRAINING
PUBLIC RELATIONS
SERVICE SYSTEM
FIRE CHIEF
REGIONAL FIRE CHIEF
SECTOR FIRE CHIEF
CENTRAL PROCESSING UNIT
PROTECTION ENGINEER
REGION
SECTOR
PREVENTION COORDINATOR
REGION
SECTOR
FACILITY 1
E–1
T–1
S–1
FACILITY 2
E–2
T–2
S–2
FACILITY N
E_n
T_n
S_n
URBAN SYSTEM
POLICE
WATER
EVENT NOTIFICATION
EMERGENCY EVENT
OFFICER IN CHARGE
FIELD COMMAND CONTROL COMMUNICATION UNIT
A_1
A_2
$A_2 1$
A_3
$A_3 1$
A_4
$A_4 1$
A_5
$A_5 1$
A_6
A_7
A_8
R_1
R_2

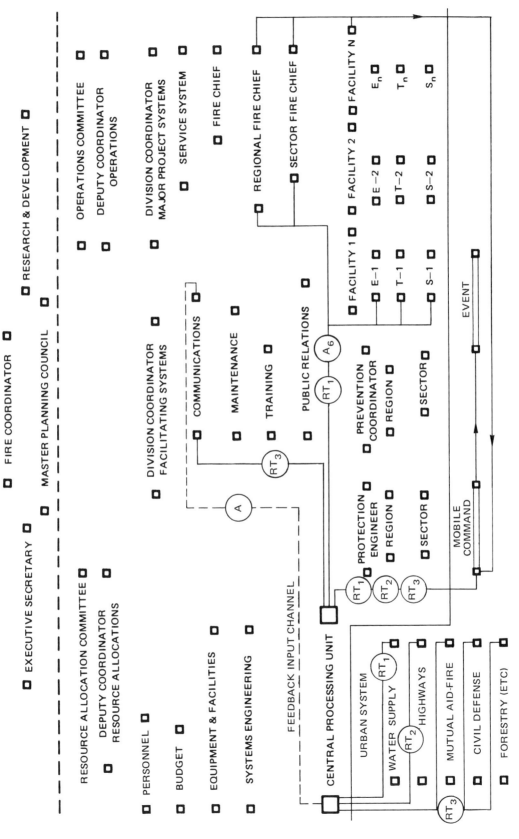

CHART VIII-2

CHANNEL DESIGNATION: REAL TIME SEQUENCE

locks in on the data input, processes the volume-pressure profile data in accordance with a preprogrammed Hardy Cross Analysis Technique and transmits a real-time readout to the first responding unit or the command unit in the form of a log supply curve(s) for area fire hydrants. Output is transmitted over Channel A_6.

RT$_2$ A channel is reserved for receiving real-time data on traffic conditions and road conditions. This information would be sampled and analyzed for expediting fire equipment response over the best time route. The ultimate in sophistication might include a matrix arrangement in the dispatch module that would assign a trip-ticket to each responding unit. This aid would be available through the unit teleprinters or the CRT's. The trip-ticket pattern could also be utilized to coordinate traffic signals over the response route.

RT$_3$ Another valuable real-time aid might include the current status of outside functional units that could be employed in higher level severity situations. This would certainly include the status display of adjacent public fire safety systems, civil defense units, off-duty police and fire personnel (i.e., real-time phone line contact display) forestry units, industrial fire brigades, air crash crews, military units, etc.

Designated Document Channels

A set of selective documents serve as vital instruments for tying the organizational framework together (i.e., forms, reports, orders, studies, memoranda, etc.). Each document is generated within the fire safety system and then transmitted to selected functions within the system. Each channel transmission category is identified by a prefix category letter followed by the letter D for document. This identification has been developed for clarity on the Interaction Flow Charts VIII-3. The following key and reference charts depict the basic elements associated with the document generation, processing, output and selective distribution.

Channel   **Key - Explanatory Statement**

ID$_1$ The basic incident document is generated at the unit level. This document is often referred to as the Company Fire Report. Please refer to Chapter VII for details pertaining to the perceived requirements for the basic unit incident report.
1. ID$_1$ goes to the Facility Chief, who acts as sensor to check for completeness and accuracy.
2. ID$_1$ is next routed to the CPU for coding, card-punching (or taping), sorted and filed.

ID$_2$ A supervisory report is generated at the Sector Fire Chief level.
1. This document is prepared only when the Sector Fire Chief responds to an emergency event.
2. This document also includes a special tactical operations evaluation report.

ID$_3$ A command evaluation report is prepared at the Regional Chief's level.
1. This document is prepared only when the Regional Chief responds to an emergency event.
2. The document is intended to monitor the service system's performance level in relation to the problem presented by the event.

ID$_4$ A Systems summary and evaluation report is prepared by the System Fire Chief.
1. This document is intended to demonstrate the interacting efficiency and effectiveness of the Major Project Subsystems, the Facilitating Subsystems, and the Resources Allocation Support Subsystems. In other words, the Fire Chief's report appraises how the whole system interacts, or maybe fails to interact, to support the emergency service system at a specific event.

ID$_5$ An Investigation Document is prepared by the Prevention System Coordinator.
1. The prevention system prepares a special investigative report if a staff member is requested by the service subsystem to respond to an event or if a member responds automatically based upon a given risk problem or a reported level of severity.
2. One summary document is prepared by the Prevention System for each incident investigated. The investigator submits the report to the next high coordination level. Each successive geographical level serves as a sensor to determine accuracy and completeness of the document. The document is next transmitted to the Central Processing Unit for preparation and processing with the other incident data elements.

ID$_6$ An Engineering Evaluation Document is prepared by the Protection Subsystem Engineer.
1. The Protection Subsystem prepares a special technical report if a staff member is requested by the Service Subsystem, the Prevention Subsystem or if the severity reaches a defined level.
2. One document is prepared by the Protection Subsystem to cover the technical factors relating to the incident under review.
3. The Engineering Evaluation Document is forwarded to the next higher geographical level for review. This process represents the sensor element in the document flow pattern. The document is then forwarded to the Central Proc-

CHART VIII-3
CHANNEL DESIGNATION: INCIDENT DOCUMENTS

(INPUT) ☐ FIRE COORDINATOR ☐ (OUTPUT)

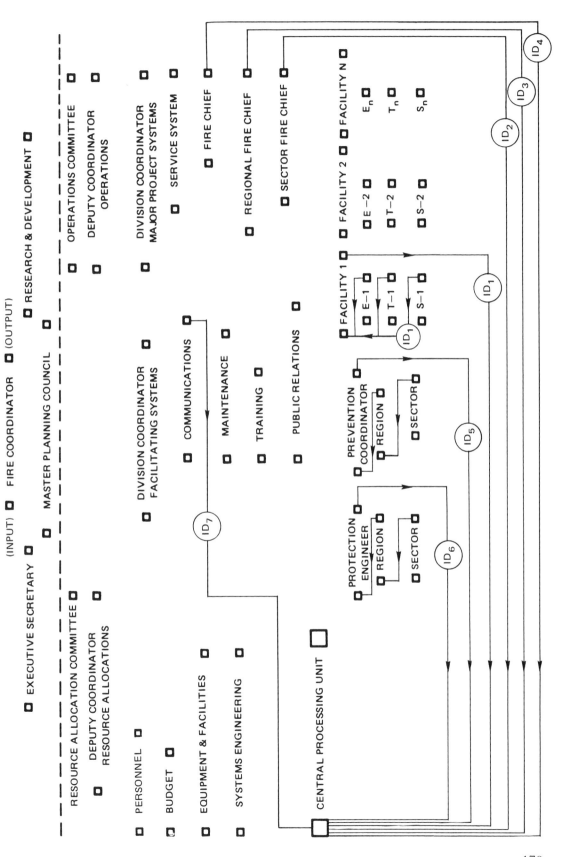

EXECUTIVE SECRETARY ☐

☐ MASTER PLANNING COUNCIL

☐ RESEARCH & DEVELOPMENT

RESOURCE ALLOCATION COMMITTEE ☐
   DEPUTY COORDINATOR
   ☐ RESOURCE ALLOCATIONS

☐ OPERATIONS COMMITTEE
☐ DEPUTY COORDINATOR
   OPERATIONS

PERSONNEL ☐

BUDGET ☐

EQUIPMENT & FACILITIES ☐

SYSTEMS ENGINEERING ☐

DIVISION COORDINATOR ☐
FACILITATING SYSTEMS

DIVISION COORDINATOR ☐
MAJOR PROJECT SYSTEMS

☐ SERVICE SYSTEM

☐ COMMUNICATIONS

☐ MAINTENANCE

☐ TRAINING

☐ PUBLIC RELATIONS

☐ FIRE CHIEF

☐ REGIONAL FIRE CHIEF

☐ SECTOR FIRE CHIEF

CENTRAL PROCESSING UNIT

PROTECTION ☐
ENGINEER
☐ REGION
   ☐ SECTOR

PREVENTION ☐
COORDINATOR
☐ REGION
   ☐ SECTOR

FACILITY 1 ☐
☐ E–1 ☐
☐ T–1 ☐
☐ S–1 ☐

☐ FACILITY 2 ☐ FACILITY N
☐ E–2   E_n ☐
☐ T–2   T_n ☐
☐ S–2   S_n ☐

ID_7

ID_6

ID_5

ID_1

ID_1

ID_1

ID_2

ID_3

ID_4

CHART VIII-4

CHANNEL DESIGNATION: SEVERITY REPORT

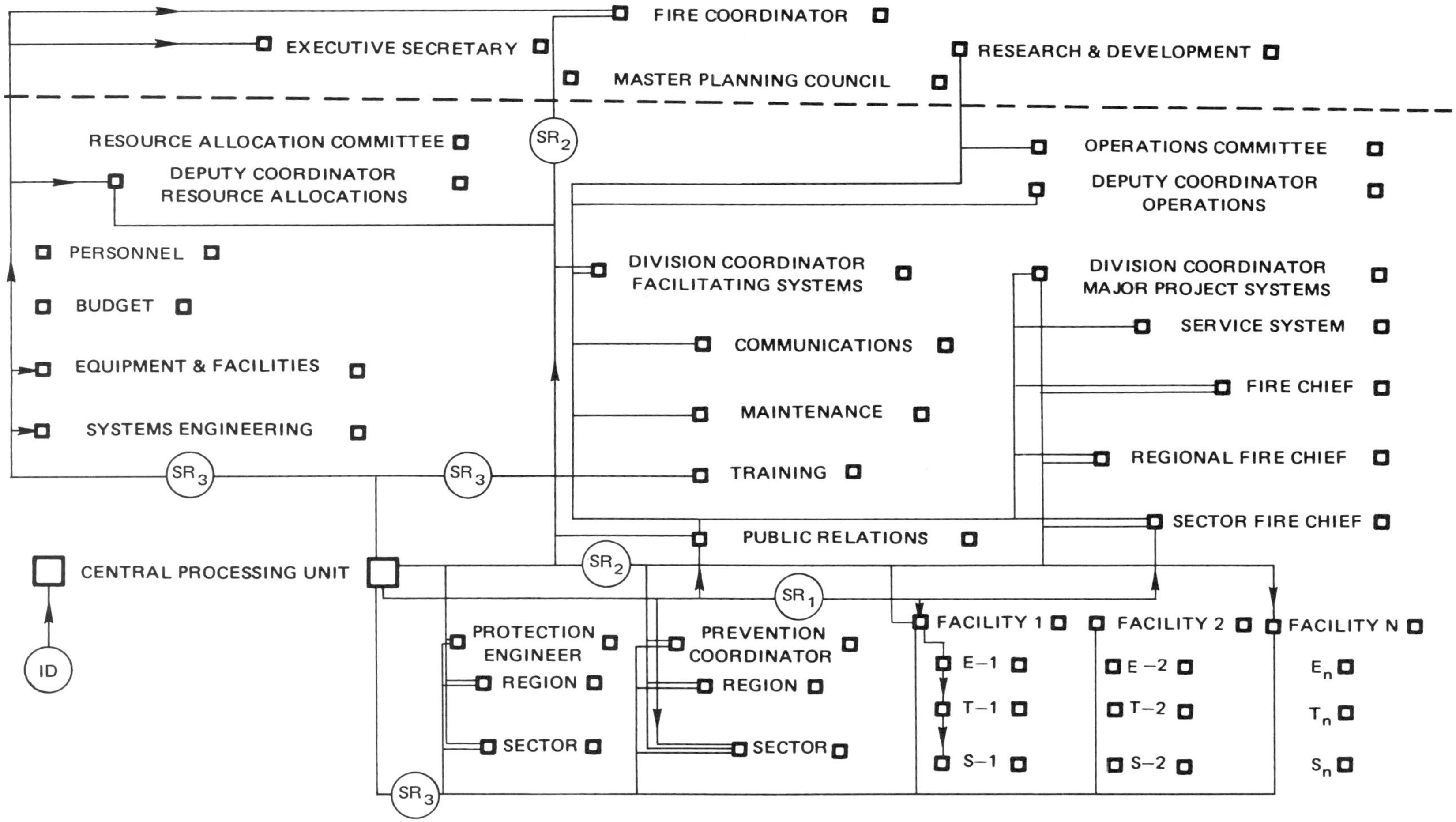

essing Unit for preparation and processing with other elements of the incident data.

4. The Engineering Evaluation Document is intended to focus on technical aspects associated with the incident problem such as: building construction, hazardous processes, water supply adequacy, and the loss relationship to the applicable provisions of the jurisdictional building code and fire prevention code.

ID$_7$ The communications subsystem logs the events related to the incident. This log is introduced as Incident Document Seven.

1. The primary intent of this document is to list chronologically the incident facts from initiation to completion. Time frames are matched to event occurrences. Some of the more prominent examples are as follows:
   a. Alarm time
   b. Dispatch time
   c. Arrival on the scene time
   d. Fire under control time
   e. Fire extinguished time
   f. End of overhaul period
   g. Unit in service time
2. The alarm log is forwarded to the Central Processing Unit for recording and processing as part of the total incident document package.
3. It appears feasible that most of the incident log could be transcribed directly from a time dubbed tape deck.

Severity Report Channels

It may be observed from the foregoing discussion that the Incident Report System is the key to the whole Public Fire Safety System report structure. Specific conditions relating to each event create a cause-and-effect relationship on every functional element in the system. Actually, the raw data from each event are transformed into a series of reports that can be utilized to maintain the system in an objective balance, to measure efficiency and to measure effectiveness. This point will be supported through the flow analysis of the incident data as it is formulated into specific report outputs. The first in the series of these reports is labeled Severity Reports — Channel Code SR$_n$, Chart VIII-4.

The established severity reports are developed around a theme of reporting by exception. In other words, not all functional personnel are concerned with all the finite detail of each incident. A routine unit investigation for the "odor of smoke" hardly requires the attention of all functional coordinators. A shopping plaza fire that destroys five units, severely damages three others, hospitalizes two civilians and five firemen, creates a direct loss of $825,000

and an indirect loss of $1.1 million deserves the attention of all functional coordinators. The report system should be geared to providing identified functional personnel with output reports that provide specific relevance to the concern of their activity. The total event picture is achieved through consolidated reports transmitted to the Operations Committee Level. These points will be expanded on through the evolutionary process of the report system structure.

Channel	Key - Explanatory Statement
SR$_1$	A routine incident report is prepared. This report is designed for minor incidents where the resultant damage is less than ten square feet of involved space and/or less than $100 estimated damage. Also no injuries to civilians or firemen are associated with the event.

1. The Central Processing Unit processes the input data and prints out a simple format that might include: location, occupancy, construction, total loss, causal factor, manpower commitment time, manpower standby time, and the designated units responding to the event.
2. This type of report is transmitted to: the facilities involved, the Sector Fire Chief, the Sector Prevention Coordinator (for follow-through if necessary), and the Public Relation Subsystem.
3. All other data pertaining to the incident is held in storage for the summary reports.

SR$_2$ A special incident report is prepared for Severity Level 2 events. This report is established to depict significant severity; where there is injury to civilians or firemen; where there is modular loss exceeding the room of origin; where the damage level is greater than 100 square feet of involvement but less than 1,000 square feet of involvement; where the loss exceeds $100 but is less than $10,000; or any combination of these factors.

1. The Central Processing Unit processes the input data and prints out a format that would include the suggested items in SR$_1$ plus the time sequences associated with the event (i.e., estimated preburn time, response time, control time, extinguishment time, total service time), number and severity of injuries, total area involved, resource commitment to the incident (manpower and equipment utilized during the event), building loss, content loss, insurance coverage, and occupant displacement manhours.
2. This severity level report is submitted to the respective facilities, all Fire Chief levels, all protection system levels, all prevention system levels, all Division and Deputy Coordinators, the Public Relations Subsystem and the Fire Coordinator.

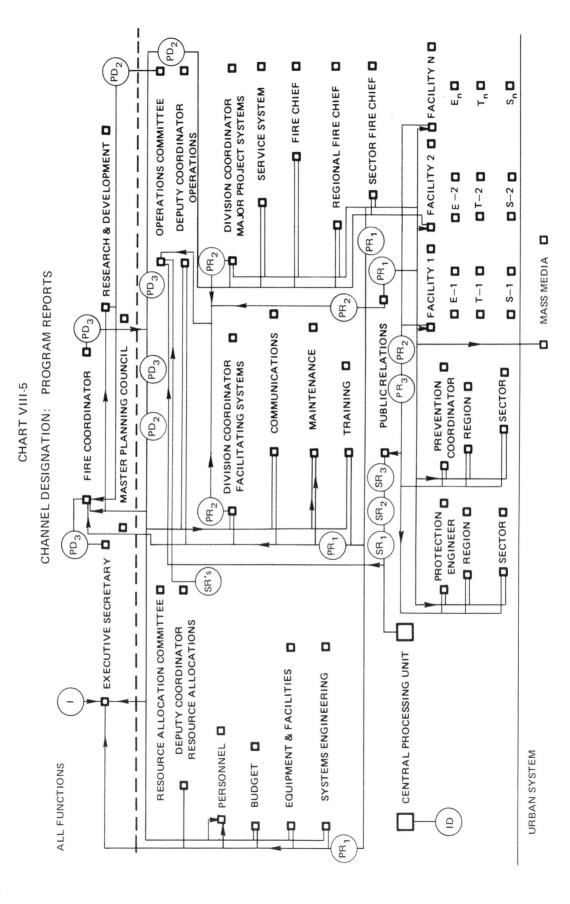

CHART VIII-5

CHANNEL DESIGNATION: PROGRAM REPORTS

182

SR₃   A special incident level report is prepared for Severity Level 3. This level report is to signify a serious event with special loss implications that demand the review of the entire system. The report would be processed and transmitted to include: monetary losses over $10,000; a modular loss involving one floor level or more of nonresidential property; a modular loss involving two separate buildings; an event where a death occurs; or a special occurrence related to the incident (i.e., the closing of a hospital because the incident disrupted utilities).

1. The Central Processing Unit processes the input data and prints out a format that would include the stipulated items for SR₁ and SR₂ plus: a narrative statement rider covering the unusual features of the incident by the ranking service system fire chief. The function or lack of performance of private protection equipment; the degree of involvement, hazard, and/or life risk upon arrival; and the basic tactical operations plan.

2. This top level Severity Report is submitted to all functional levels for review. All SR₃ reports are reviewed by the Operations Committee. All Level 3 severity incidents are critiqued under the appropriate service subsystems prior to the Operations Committee meeting.

Programmed Reports

Up to this point it can be observed that a considerable amount of data has been generated, filed, and processed according to certain established criteria and resubmitted to selected functions within the Public Fire Safety System as a summary for a single event. No summary of combined events has yet been introduced. Currently fire departments employ a number of summary documents including a daily report, a weekly report, a quarterly report, and an annual report.[1] These reports in combination hardly seem justifiable for all functions of the fire safety system. A more selective proposed reporting system is entitled *Program Reports*. This title implies that the reports are prepared in accordance with program objectives for specified functional areas. The reports are not intended as simply an array of aggregate numbers. Rather, each program report category should identify performance conditions in relation to problem identification and program accomplishment. The elements of problem identification and program accomplishment are identified and projected through statistical measures and inferences. The following *Program Reports* are structured with these in mind (see Chart VIII-5).

[1] International Association of Fire Fighters (AFL-CIO). *Apprenticeship Training Standards*. Washington: U.S. Department of Labor, 1972.

PR₁   Program Report 1 is a daily Service System Report prepared by the public relations subsystem and distributed to the mass media, local government units and internal functions. This report identifies the emergency services performed by the Public Fire Safety System, the event location and the event outcome. Emphasis is placed on the role of accomplishment. Subject classifications might include: number of cases where emergency service was rendered. type of service rendered (oxygen assistance, rescue, emergency transport, type and nature of routine services); fire incidents in which confinement is emphasized (i.e., six dwelling alarms were handled with little or no loss [SR₁]); one business fire was confined to the room of origin with moderate damage resulting; one garage fire was confined to the area of a gasoline spill that fire safety personnel found upon arrival at the scene. Damage caused by the spill and ignition was relatively severe (over $10,000). Note: The Severity Reports SR₁₋₃ and the PR₁ serve to keep all functional units of the service subsystem informed on event occurrences and the results of those events. A statistical summary on a frequency of less than once a month probably would not be meaningful. If the Master Planning Council feels that weekly or bi-weekly reports are necessary, the increased frequency can be easily implemented into the system.

PR₂   Program Report 2 is prepared on a monthly basis. This report is intended to present a summary of all functions for the preceding month. Each function would briefly indicate services rendered either directly or indirectly to both the internal Public Fire Safety System and to the external urban system. The report should also state problem areas. For example: The Prevention System was unable to maintain its monthly frequency of assigned surveys due to a 30 per cent increase in suspicious fire investigations. This information coupled with the Service System Severity Report noting that frequency of trash room fires in multifamily apartment buildings is up 34 per cent, begins to identify a potential problem.

Again, the focus of this report should be on frequency, a comparative analysis between the previous month and the previous year, change patterns such as where events are occurring and special summaries relating to the defined levels of severity. This program report should be prepared by the members of the Operations Committee with the Deputy Fire Coordinator for Operations assuming responsibility for the final report.

PR₃   Program Report 3 is designated the administrative report. It is the responsibility of the Fire Coordinator to prepare and issue an annual (fiscal year) report. The specific scope and nature of this report has been developed in Chapter IV. The requi-

CHART VIII-6

CHANNEL DESIGNATION: PERSONNEL DOCUMENTS

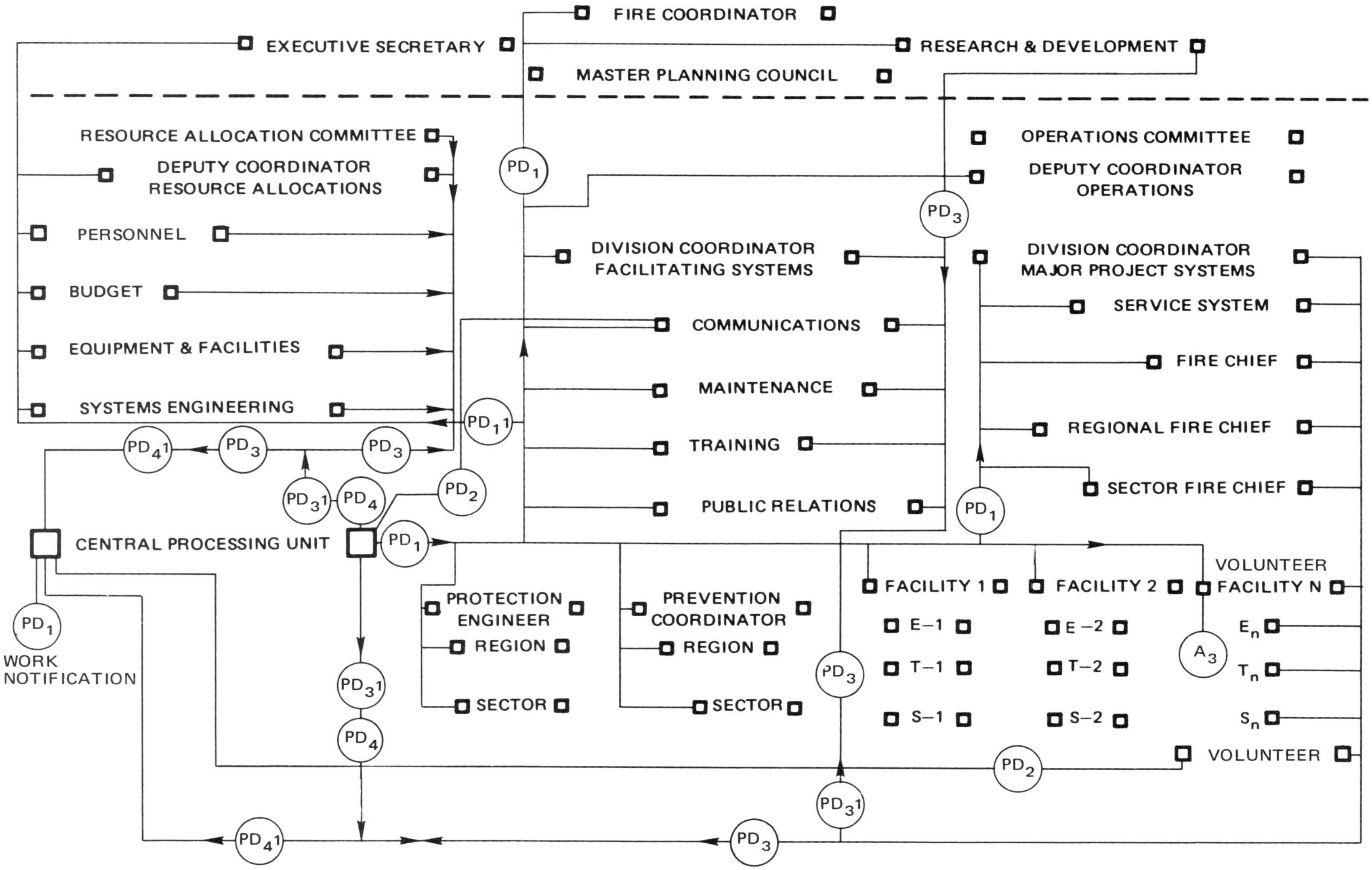

site information for the annual report is generated at all functional levels of the organization. The data and information has to be forwarded to a central point, analyzed and prepared as a smooth flowing document. To achieve this objective, the Executive Secretary is charged with the responsibility for preparing the annual report. However, the report process should be accomplished in close cooperation with the Fire Coordinator, the Master Planning Committee and the Public Relations Coordinator. The Program Report channels are inserted to illustrate how the information flows to the Executive Secretary and how the final report flows back to the internal and external organizational functions.

PR$_3$[1] The Program Report $_3$[1] channel is inserted to signify the completed and published annual report.

Personnel Documents

An organization revolves around people. People make the organization come alive and move toward the goals of the organization, regardless of the systems approach and the automated functions perceived. This premise is especially important when considering the implementation of a systems organization. Such personnel have to be hired, provided for, paid and constantly accounted for in the total system structure. Personnel documents are required to handle the data and information necessary to maintain a viable personnel program. The following documents broadly identify the cycle pattern of information flow necessary to accomplish this task (see Chart VIII-6).

Channel   **Key - Explanatory Statement**

PD$_1$ The first Personnel Document revolves around the primary work status report. In normal business functions this is the time card. In traditional fire department operations, this is the work log. Under the systems approach this document is a data punch card prepared by the CPU unit. As an individual arrives or leaves his duty assignment, an input report is forwarded to the CPU; the nature of an absence is also reported in by the responsible supervisor. As a service system shift starts, an assessment is made of the manpower availability for each facility unit and functional unit. The data input is immediately processed and sent to Manpower Resources. Manpower Resources balances the units by assigning floating personnel. Deficiencies are made up by a mobile floating manpower squad company that can be assigned on a shift basis to any facility. The priority condition is to supply the respective facility units with established manpower re-

quirements. If the extra manpower is not needed for this type of assignment, the floating squad unit may be directed to the Training subsystem, the Communications subsystem, the Maintenance subsystem, or the Prevention subsystem for special detail.

PD$_1$[1] This channel code is utilized to designate the on-duty roster. The duty roster for all functional subsystems is printed and sent to each unit designation. This status process should also improve the daily information flow between functions. When problems or routine business contact are necessary, every member in the organization knows who is immediately available.

PD$_2$ The second Personnel Document represents a very special input to accommodate the use of volunteer personnel for manning service units and as support personnel for the designated functional categories. This concept is utilized to illustrate how the volunteer support approach can function in harmony with the total systems concept. The A$_3$ message channel might select a facility that is manned by volunteer personnel, designated Facility N for this illustration. The A$_3$ channel can be connected to activate sirens, horns, selective call tone receivers, pages or any combination of these devices to alert selected personnel that an emergency event is in progress and preferably some details about the event. Those that are able to respond to the event immediately acknowledge their intent to CPU by simply dialing on a public or private telephone, a phone input number, the individual's social security number, and a code number to indicate that they are (1) responding directly to the scene or (2) responding to the facility and an ETA code. The Central Processing Unit can be programmed to sample this input, evaluate a specified time element (i.e., 1 minute to 5 minutes) and notify the responding officer of the anticipated manpower and estimated arrival times, and/or dispatch additional units if a prescribed manpower and equipment level is not established within a prescribed time frame. An alternate approach might incorporate a perforated identity card similar to a credit card. Upon entering a facility building, the card holder would simply insert the card into a reader that in turn would input the data to the computer. This could be utilized for a real-time status display of volunteer personnel available. Reinserting the card in the card holder would clear the individual from the status display. This technique could also be utilized for an automatic roll call after each event.

PD$_3$ The third Personnel Document channel is designated the personnel action channel. This channel is utilized to depict the numerous personnel actions that take place relative to an individual's work history (hiring data, promotional information, health information, salary information, etc.). Actually, the channel represents all the data

CHART VIII-7

CHANNEL DESIGNATION: FUNCTIONAL SUPPORT DOCUMENT

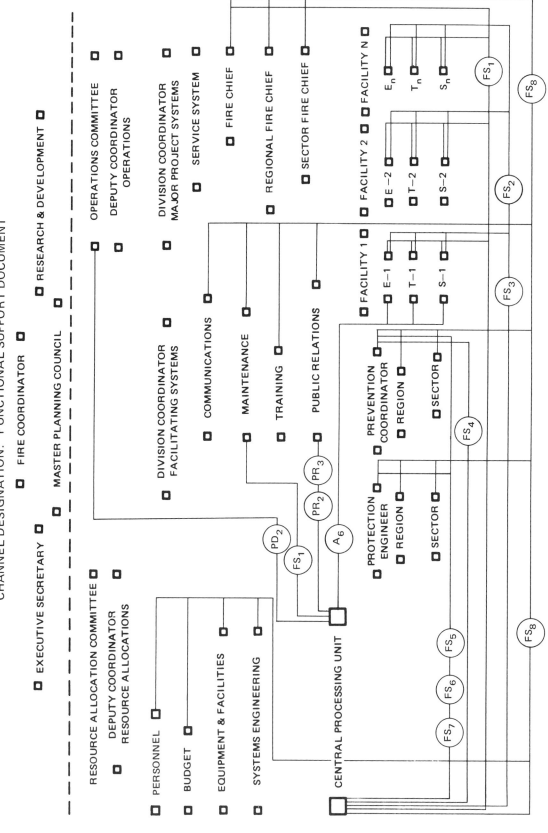

necessary to prepare a personnel log on each individual. Data can be input from any functional level. At some defined time period, an individual "dump" printout is made on each individual for a verification of data. The individual receives the output and becomes a sensor for his own report system. ($PD_3{}^1$).

PD₄   The fourth Personnel Document is designated the pay channel. The regular pay vouchers are prepared, based upon the daily work load, or absentee report. The channel designation represents the personnel accounting program.

PD₄¹   The $PD_4{}^1$ channel is inserted to represent the pay voucher verification report for personnel to review as a sensor mechanism.

Functional Support Document

Each defined function in the Public Fire Safety Systems Organization framework prepares certain prescribed documents in accordance with established responsibilities. For example, survey reports are prepared on a continuous basis by the Fire Prevention Subsystems Survey reports generated at defined function levels contribute to the information flow and requirements of the total systems. The following support documents broadly define the potential data that should be generated at each functional level. The intent of this information section is to illustrate performance levels with each document; not the amalgamation of numbers (see Chart VIII-7).

Channel	Key - Explanatory Statement
FS₁	Functional Support Document One is designated the Equipment Status Check List. This document is prepared daily on all pieces of emergency equipment and other equipment vital to the reliability of the system. Routine repair requirements may be noted. Each individual document is transmitted to the Central Processing Unit for processing and to the maintenance function for sensing and action.
FS₂	Functional Support Document Two is designated the Functional Special Services Document. This item represents a brief completion document to be prepared when a special service is rendered by a functional unit to either another internal function or an external urban system function. For example, an aerial ladder is requested by the City Manager to assist in trimming the annual Christmas tree. The FS document is forwarded to CPU for processing and line printing as an appendix section of the PR_2.
FS₃	Functional Support Document Three is designated Inservice Inspections. Each unit in the service subsystems has the responsibility of conducting an assigned group of inservice inspections. Noted code

exceptions, exceptions to good practice and hazardous situations, are noted on this document. The document is transmitted to CPU for processing and the tactical information is placed in storage for recall under channel A_6. The noted fire safety exceptions are transmitted to the appropriate level prevention Coordinator for action.

FS₄   Functional Support Document Four is designated Prevention Survey. This document is prepared by the Prevention Subsystem for each survey conducted. The completed report is sent to the Central Processing Unit for processing. The completed output record is transmitted back to the next higher level Prevention Coordinator, which acts as the sensor, and then routed to the jurisdictional facility for review and to the territory Sector Chief having responsibility. Tactical information is placed on reserve channel A_6. Protection system exceptions are transmitted to the Protection Subsystem for follow-up action. Irregularities requiring legal action are transmitted to the Division Coordinator — Major Project Systems.

FS₅   Functional Support Document Five is designated Educational Document. This document is primarily intended for the utilization by the Prevention Subsystem but it may be utilized by every function within the total system. Education and training of the public and special interest groups (i.e., industrial fire brigades) appear to be an important aspect of public fire safety responsibility. An educational document is prepared each time a fire safety representative conducts a lecture, a demonstration, or delivers a paper to an urban group. Each respective document is forwarded to the Central Processing Unit for processing. Tabulations of frequencies for similar activities are incorporated into PR_2 and PR_3. Output summary data is immediately transmitted to the Public Relations Subsystem.

FS₆   Functional Support Document Six is designated Plan Reviews. A major responsibility of the Protection Engineering Subsystem is to review fire protection features for new construction, building upgrading, and renovation. Completed reviews, plan and site approvals, disapprovals and recommended actions are forwarded to the Central Processing Unit for processing. The final disposition in each case is reported to the submitter, to the jurisdiction facility, to the jurisdiction sector Fire Chief, and in the case of a rejection, to the Division Coordinator — Major Project Systems. Review summaries are incorporated into PR_1 and PR_3.

FS₇   Functional Support Document Seven is designated Specification Document. A second major function of the Protection Engineering Subsystem is the preparation of equipment and material specifications for the Public Fire Safety System. Changes in specifications should be made known to the entire organization. Therefore, a specification change is

CHART VIII-8

CHANNEL DESIGNATION: MAINTENANCE DOCUMENTATION

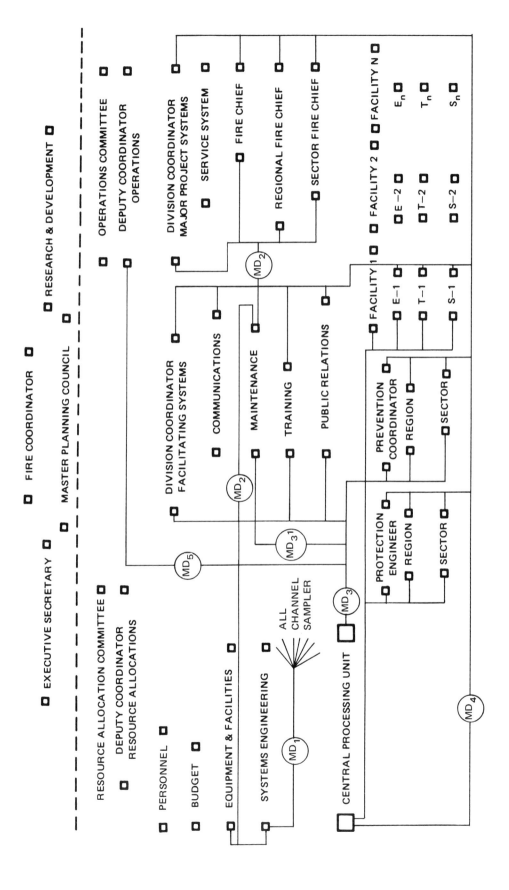

transmitted to the Central Processing Unit for processing and notification to all functions within the Public Fire Safety Organization and to such functions in the urban system that may be affected.

Note: It should be observed from the preceding channel explanation that functional support documents are required for each element depicted in the organizational structure. The support function of each unit has been thoroughly described in the several development chapters. It would appear redundant to continue a functional service document identification. Essentially, a group effect channel, FS_8, is simply illustrated to demonstrate the interlocking effect of information flow created by the several functional service documents.

FS$_8$ Functional Support Document Eight is designated Group Effect Functional Service Document.

Maintenance Documentation

Regular maintenance is the key to a reliable system. This concept ranges all the way from organizational maintenance to small item mechanical maintenance. In the context of the perceived Public Fire Safety System, organization maintenance becomes the responsibility of the top administrator, the Fire Coordinator, the Master Planning Committee, and Systems Engineering. The achievement of the maintenance lies in the viability of all the channel actions within the perceived system. When communication channels close out or the frequency of transmission breaks down, the system needs maintenance. Therefore, it is imperative that Systems Engineering sample the message transmission direction and frequency and report out the findings to the Master Planning Committee and, in turn, to the Fire Coordinator. This is depicted by the Maintenance Document One flow pattern (see Chart VIII-8).

A more visible maintenance effort can be described as routine equipment maintenance. This maintenance concept is more oriented towards the physical equipment aspects associated with each functional area. Actually, it would appear that two equipment maintenance channels exist. First, the Maintenance subsystem determines the frequency for conducting routine maintenance on specified equipment. Procedural guidelines for completing equipment maintenance are distributed to each function (MD_2). Second, programmed notices are sent out from the Central Processing Unit for maintenance completion (MD_3). Items that can be handled at the functional level are transmitted to the respective functions; specialty maintenance is scheduled directly through

the maintenance subsections ($MD_3{}^1$). Finally, a maintenance completion card is transmitted to the Central Processing Unit for each completed task. These cards ($MD_4{}^1$) are processed against the schedule and an exception list is transmitted weekly to the Maintenance Subsystem. Functional elements falling behind in their respective maintenance efforts are reported at the Operations Committee meeting (MD_5).

Channel	Key
MD_1	Systems Engineering Report Channel Check
MD_2	Maintenance Procedural Documents to All Functions
MD_3	Programmed Maintenance Notices
$MD_3{}^1$	Programmed Maintenance Notices to Specialty Areas Within the Maintenance Subsystem Structure
MD_4	Maintenance Completion Card Channel
MD_5	Maintenance Exception Report Channel

Inventory Control

The concept of inventory control is quite similar to that of the Maintenance Subsystem requirements. There is a necessity to supply each functional element with equipment, materials, and supplies. As supplies are depleted, there is the problem of replenishing used items. Therefore, there is a continuing need for inventory control. This can be accomplished with input-output channels between the equipment and facility subsystem and each functional unit. The descriptive inventory would be patterned as follows:

Channel	Key - Explanatory Statement
IC_1	Inventory Allocation Document One is established for each function. The Equipment and Facilities Subsystem evaluates the equipment and resource needs of each function. A functional allocation document is prepared (Resource Allocation Committee Approval Required) and transmitted to all functions.
IC_2	The Second Inventory Control is a Request for Allocations Card. A card is submitted from each function to CPU for processing and printout to Equipment and Facilities for issuance. Note: Prepunched cards are distributed to each function. Requests are initiated by simply inserting a control number.
IC_3	An Inventory Card represents the third control condition. A punch card is prepared for each allocation. There are actually two sets of cards. One is for permanent items (i.e., typewriter) and the second is for disposable items (i.e., paper towels).

CHART VIII-9

CHANNEL DESIGNATION: INVENTORY CONTROL

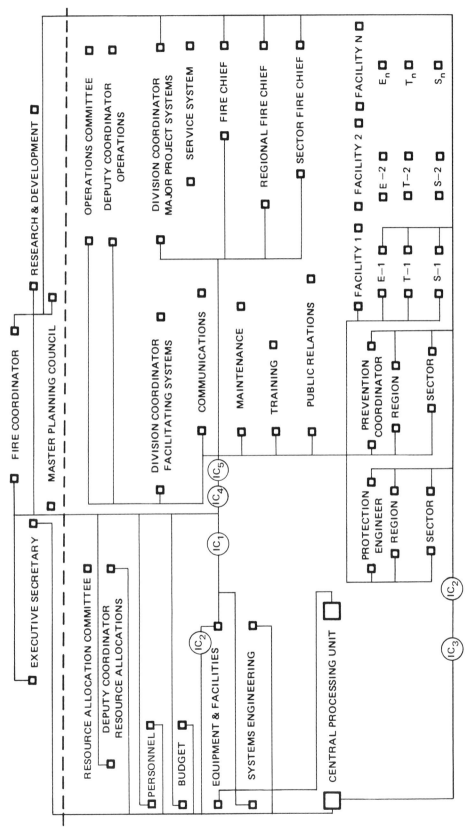

IC_4 A Monthly Inventory List serves as the fourth control condition. A directed printout of allocated disposable items is sent to each unit. The master list is checked against current supply and allocation availability at each facility. An IC_2 is submitted for supply deficiencies.

IC_5 An Annual Inventory Check represents the fifth control condition. An annual printout is made of allocated permanent items to each unit for verification. Missing or nonrepairable items are reported by exception on Channel IC_6.

IC_6 The sixth inventory control is an Inventory Exception Card. This card is transmitted to the Central Processing Unit when an exception to the printout is observed. A monthly summation of exception inventories is forwarded to the Equipment and Facilities Subsystem.

Review Requested

A basic communication, control and coordination technique permeates all channels. Every channel document would carry a suffix code RR with a blank subscript. The purpose of the RR designation is to signify "review requested" by some functional element outside of the normal channel connectors. The subscript is for coding whom the document should be sent to within or outside of the organization structure. One possible example might include a minor fire situation that normally would only require a transmission over the ID_1 channel. Because of a potential disaster that might have occurred or could occur at some future time, the Facility Chief "Requests Review" by the Fire Chief and the Fire Prevention Coordinator. The document would then be routed to these designated functions. This special request is then noted on all transmitted copies.

Summary

The American Fire Service currently has strengths and weaknesses. Certainly an identified strength of the Fire Service is an unquestionable desire on the part of personnel to save lives and property from the ravages of destructive fires. Many firemen, paid and volunteer, can be characterized by their exuberance and *esprit-de-corps* at the time of emergency situations. The dedication and loyalty of most Fire Service personnel is beyond question. The service rendered by a large portion of the American Fire Service personnel is truly above and beyond the call of duty. Yet, the American Fire Service is deeply troubled by a number of problems. Probably one of the most important issues of the time is one's ability to gain a proper perspective of the total fire problem. Few would argue that the total problem is made up of many subproblems.

The "big picture" fire problem in the United States is documented in terms of "excessive and unnecessary deaths and human suffering together with heavy economic waste resulting from avoidable fires."[2] Quantitatively the magnitude of the fire problem is currently expressed in the order of 12,000 fatalities and a property damage figure estimated at $2.75 billions annually. To the monetary figure must be added indirect costs relating to fire protection which raises the estimated fire problem cost to a neighborhood of eight billion dollars annually.[3] There does not appear to be even close estimates of the total hidden and indirect costs associated with the fire problem.

A growing body of literature, most of which has been documented in Chapter I of this book, is beginning to focus on sets of problems relating to organization efforts to cope with the human suffering and loss plus the property loss experienced from unplanned or unwanted fires.

The scope and method of providing adequate organized public fire safety represents a central concern of this book. The ability of urban governments to organize, administer and manage an efficient and effective public fire safety group appears to have a significant bearing on the identification of both the localized and national fire problem picture. This book further contends that on a broad spectrum, current fire department organization frameworks do not provide a viable base for meeting the prescribed ranking objectives of providing:

1. A fire frequency performance level acceptable to the citizens of the jurisdictional area under consideration.
2. A life safety level acceptable to the citizens in the jurisdictional area under consideration.
3. A public fire safety organization capable of confining initiated fires to the modular level acceptable to the property occupants in the jurisdictional area under consideration.
4. A public fire safety organization capable of suppressing initiated fires with the least amount of property damage and occupancy interruption possible.

[2] *The Fire Problem*, The National Fire Protection Association, Boston, 1972, p. 1.

[3] *Ibid.*, p. 1.

5. A public fire safety organization capable of providing selected emergency services relating to life safety and property damage to a defined jurisdictional area.

6. A public fire safety organization capable of meeting the intent of the performance levels established under a favorable ratio of cost to performance effectiveness.

The public fire safety organization is recognized as the key vehicle to providing a mission-oriented program to reduce human suffering and property damage from destructive fires. With some notable exceptions, the nation's Fire Service is not currently organized, administered or managed to achieve systematically the objectives stated. Rather, the present Fire Service can be characterized as an "after-the-fact organization." In other words, the basic objectives of the Fire Service appear in many instances to be oriented around limiting life loss and injury after the alarm has been sounded.

Possibly the number one problem of urban fire protection in the United States is a theory of what constitutes adequate public and private fire protection.

This text only claims to respond to the identified problem with a set of partial testable hypotheses on relating the organizational framework necessary to administer and manage specific programs that could be implemented to measure defined levels of public fire safety. Hopefully, the measurement process will begin to crystallize the magnitude and arrangement of elements necessary to provide defined and accepted levels of public fire safety. When public fire safety organizations possess both the desire and capability to measure performance output quantitatively and qualitatively, urban governments can progress to develop a more valid and reliable theory of what elements should constitute the public obligations and the private obligations for a defined level of urban fire safety.

A summary of this book cannot escape from refocusing on two major factors that appear to be severely hindering the nature of public fire safety to respond to the formulated objectives. First, almost unique to the Fire Service is the dual function of the principal executive, the Fire Chief. One moment the "now fire chief" is administering the affairs of a public business organization. The business of public fire safety is a growing one. One million dollars a year budgets are now common for suburban area fire departments. Even communities in the 10,000 to 20,000 population bracket are supporting public fire departments with six figure budgets. Public fire safety in many, many instances represents a big public enterprise. A thesis of this book is that public fire safety needs to be governed by sound principles of business and public administration. This type of leadership is not coming from the man who tries to wear both the administrator's hat and the fire chief's hat in rapid alteration. The public fire administrator must be divorced from the tactical fire commander.

The economy of scale in providing public fire safety is no small problem. Despite the negative comments advanced about misguided objectives in the current Fire Service, recognition is given to the fact that in many cases a fire chief *could not* embark on fire prevention and fire protection services (as defined in this book) even if his vision moved in this direction because the money for such programs is simply not available. Public fire safety must give serious thought to enlarging the geographical operational base for both direct services and support functions *IF* the objectives of this book are acceptable. The financial obligations and the personnel talent required to carry out the prescribed subsystem functions enumerated in the previous chapters are simply not feasible for heterogeneous groups of less than 100,000 population. This text strongly recommends the County form of government as a reasonable political and geographical base for implementing a mission-oriented public fire safety organization.

Associated with the above concerns and premises is the search for a public fire safety organization framework that can adapt and serve urban areas with defined levels of public fire safety. It would appear that the traditional line and staff type of organization has failed to meet the challenge of providing a responsive public fire safety program as measured by the objectives cited. Part of the perceived reason for this condition rests with the current mode of fire department organization structure. The line and staff arrangements are so compartmentalized in many instances that the identified functional components appear to be "doing their thing" with a minimum of interaction or recognition of interdependency. The organization is fed from the top down. Very little decision-making nourishment comes from the grass roots.

The systems approach to public fire safety organization, as advanced in Chapter II, appears to hold much promise for overcoming or at least recognizing the deficiencies currently associated with the traditional fire department organization structure. The application of a systems organization framework to elements of urban administration has just begun to be conceptualized. As public service systems become more refined and varied, the systems approach will not only help in a rethinking process of basic administrative concepts and principles in their application to a particular phase of development, but also open before public administrators new administration vistas of great value.

Systems concepts applied to organization structure provide a theoretical framework for building an organization. These concepts also provide a sound approach to analyzing the total structure. Equally important is the contention that a systems framework will become more responsive to the environmental factors predicted to shape the future of administration and management.

The literature on Public Administration prepared during the 1960s clearly reveals the need for dynamic, responsive and flexible organization patterns designed to meet objective performance criteria. The factors that are perceived to influence the future of organizations are summarized very pointedly by Warren G. Bennis.[4] Dr. Bennis's precepts have been placed in the context of public fire safety to reveal pointed summary conditions and for demonstrating the urgent necessity to adequately respond to urban change.

1. Local government organization functions will be operating in a turbulent environment which will require their continual adaptation and adjustment to change.
2. Public fire safety organizations will continue to expand their boundaries and domains. They will increase in size and complexity.
3. If public functional organizations continue to follow present practices, activities will become more differentiated causing increased problems of integration and coordination.
4. Public fire safety organizations will continue to have major problems in the accumulation and utilization of scientific and technical knowledge. Intellectual activities will be stressed in response to this problem.
5. Public functional organizations will place greater emphasis upon suggestion and persuasion rather than upon coercion based on authoritarian power as the means for coordinating the activities of the participants and functions within the organization.
6. Participants at all levels of the Public Fire Safety Organization will have a greater influence. Public fire safety organizations of the future will adopt a power equalization rather than a power differentiation organization model.
7. Problems of interface between organizational functions will be greater. New means for effective interorganizational coordination will be developed.
8. Computerized information decision systems will have an increasing impact upon public fire safety organizations.
9. The number of professional public administrators, business managers, fire protection engineers, and fire science technicians will play an increasing role and provide a greater influence on public fire safety organizations. There will also be a corresponding decline in the proportion of sub-professionals holding supervisory positions associated with fire suppression and rescue services.
10. Goals of the public fire safety organization will expand. Emphasis will be placed upon satisfying a number of goals associated with the interface between providing private fire safety and providing public fire safety rather than maximizing the public fire suppression effort.
11. Evaluation of public fire safety organizational performance will undergo many trial and evaluation periods. Many new administrative techniques will be developed for evaluation of performance in all spheres of activity.

The above points not only outline some of the clues to the future of public fire safety organization but they also focus, at least indirectly, on the precept that the present mode of organization structure cannot accommodate these change levels. The systems organizational framework is offered as a technique, a framework, a concept necessary to accommodate the change elements outlined. The broad objective of this book is to illustrate a pattern for adapting public fire safety to a systems-oriented structure. In the adaptive process, care has been taken to focus on basic systems principles that represent a dynamic advancement in management science. The principal concepts are related to organization structure, the adminis-

[4]Warren G. Bennis, "Organizations of the Future," *Personnel Administration*, September-October 1967, p. 6.

tration of the total structural system and the operational management of identified subsystems. The model structure of a public fire safety systems organization makes the following claims:

1. The systems organization development requires that the mission and related objectives be clearly stated in a preferential pattern.

2. The systems organization development further requires that the mission and related objectives be periodically reviewed in terms of performance criteria.

3. The organization objectives are translated in terms of defined levels of service which inversely focus on the risk assumption levels for defined occupancy and property classifications.

4. The systems organization structure clearly identifies the perceived distinction between administrative functions and management functions. However, the interrelationship of administration and management is also developed.

5. The systems organization structure identifies the necessary subsystem components required to support the mission activity. These subsystem components are defined in terms of functional objectives and interface objectives with other identified subsystems within the public fire safety systems and external to the fire safety system.

6. The systems structure depicts an electronic data processing subsystem to support each functional element's data input-output requirements and to integrate all the subsystems with a real-time communications network.

7. The communications network flow patterns attempt to identify the dependency of each identified function to the actual working relationships established for the total organization. The flow network may also be utilized as one tool for evaluating the efficiency and effectiveness of the total system.

8. The systems concept clearly focuses on the specific personnel requirements for each functional activity. Education and experience qualifications for administrative, management, and operational personnel depict levels of professional stature.

Also, the qualification categories clearly define both vertical and horizontal promotional opportunities for all levels of suggested personnel.

Probably the greatest claim advanced for the systems structure of organization is that the basic theory requires a finite description of every function, activity and duty associated with the public fire safety organization. The description process outlines not only the internal functions of each subsystem, but also details the interrelationships and dependency elements between subsystems. The patterned relationships can be utilized for equating the efficiency and effectiveness of the organization complex. These features are not as obvious with the traditional line and staff type of organization structure.

This book has endeavored to illustrate a thesis that one of the significant and growing problems of public fire safety rests with the organization structure of public fire departments. The current mode of fire department organization focuses on functions, activities and duties associated with fire suppression and other selected emergency services. The objective criteria associated with present fire department organizations have produced severe problems in the areas of financial support, manpower utilization, professional development, administrative-operational overlap, volunteer versus paid-personnel friction, public administrator puzzlement over evaluating fire department efficiency and public ignorance of the risk assumption.

The systems approach to the organization of public fire safety hopes to overcome most of the identified problems *or* at least clearly indicate the scope and nature of the problem. To accomplish this task the basic mission and related objectives of public fire safety have been restated. The systems organization design focuses on incident reduction and severity reduction with a clear definition of corresponding levels of risk assumption. Coupled to this mission is the support function of subsystems revolving around fire prevention, fire protection, and service units to perform rescue, fire suppression and related emergency activities. The conceptual framework for the perceived organization has been spelled out in a fashion that should increase a public administrator's ability to equate performance with objective criteria. The systems structure plan outlined in this book would provide public fire safety with a professional administrator working with modern management tools to provide a defined level of public fire safety. Local government administration options have been cited that should place public fire safety on an economy-of-scale financial base to accommodate the administration and management require-ments necessary to achieve an effective and efficient operation.

A conceptual organization framework has been advanced in this book to provide a dynamic method of understanding what constitutes public fire safety and a systematic design for its future development.

•

Chapter 8

Bibliographical Entries

Books

International City Managers' Association. *Municipal Fire Administration.* Chicago: International City Managers' Association, 1967.

International Association of Fire Fighters (AFL-CIO) Apprenticeship Training Standards. Washington: U. S. Department of Labor, 1972.

The Fire Problem, The National Fire Protection Association, Boston, 1972, p. 1.

Periodicals

Bennis, Warren G., "Organizations of the Future," Personnel Administration, September-October 1967, p. 6.

Bibliography

Books

Arnold, Robert, Harold Hill, and Olymer Nichols. *Introduction to Data Processing*. New York: John Wiley and Sons, Inc., 1967, p. 12.

Bellman, Richard. *Dynamic Programming*. Princeton: Princeton University Press, 1957, p. vii.

Blau, Peter, and R. Scott. *Formal Organizations*. San Francisco: Chandler Publishing Co., 1962, p. 140.

Brown, Fred, ed. *Management: Concepts and Practices*. Washington: Industrial College of the Armed Forces, 1967, p. 3.

Bush, Loren S., and J. McLaughlin. *Introduction to Fire Science*. Beverly Hills: Glencoe Press, 1970, p. 28.

Chapin, Ned. *An Introduction to Automatic Computers*. Princeton: D. Van Nostrand Co., Inc., 1957, p. 4.

Churchman, C. West, Russel L. Ackoff, and E. Leonard Arnoff. *Introduction to Operation's Research*. New York: John Wiley and Sons, Inc., 1957, p. 519.

Etzioni, Amitai. *Modern Organization*. Englewood Cliffs, New Jersey: Prentice-Hall, Inc., 1964, p. 72.

Ferguson, Robert O., and Lauren F. Sargent. *Linear Programming*. New York: McGraw-Hill Book Company, 1958, p. 3.

Fluntsberger, David. *Elements of Statistical Inference*. 2nd Ed., Boston: Allyn and Bacon, 1968, p. 1.

Gerth, H. H., and C. Mills. From Max Weber: *Essays in Sociology*. New York: Oxford University Press, 1946, p. 214.

Holzman, R. *Romance of Firefighting*. New York: Bonanza Books, 1965, p. 3.

Hooper, Frederic. *Management Survey*. Baltimore: Penguin Books, Inc., 1960, p. 11.

International City Managers' Association. *Municipal Fire Administration*. Chicago: International City Managers' Association, 1969.

————. *Planning and Budgeting in Municipal Government*. Chicago: International City Managers' Association, 1969, pp. 22–23.

James, Charles L. *Police and Fire Integration in the Small City*. Chicago Public Administration Service, 1955.

Johnson, Richard A., Fremont E. Kast and James E. Rosenzweig. *The Theory and Management of Systems*. New York: McGraw-Hill Book Co., Inc., 1963, p. 199.

Kaplin, Abraham. *The Conduct of Inquiry*. San Francisco: Chandler Publishing Co., 1964, pp. 295–296.

Kimball, Warren. *Fire Attack 1* and *Fire Attack 2*. Boston: National Fire Protection Association, 1966, 1968.

Layman, Lloyd. *Attacking and Extinguishing Interior Fires*. Boston: National Fire Protection Association, 1952.

Likert, Renis. *New Patterns of Management*. New York: McGraw-Hill Book Company, 1961.

Malcolm, Donald, Alan Rowe and Loumer McConnel. *Management Control Systems*. John Wiley and Sons, Inc., 1960, pp. 187–280.

Manne, Alan S. *Economic Analysis of Business Decisions*. New York: McGraw-Hill Book Company, 1961, pp. 19-20.

March, James, and H. Simon. *Organizations*. New York: John Wiley and Sons, Inc., 1958, p. 4.

More, Harry. *The New Era of Public Safety*. Springfield: Charles C. Thomas, 1970, p. vii.

NFBU, *Standard Schedule for Grading Cities and Towns of the U.S. with Reference to their Fire Defenses and Physical Conditions*. New York: National Board of Fire Underwriters.

National Fire Protection Association. *Handbook of Fire Protection*. Boston: National Fire Protection Association, 1969.

Novick, David, ed. *Program Budgeting*. Program Analysis and the Federal Budget. Cambridge: Harvard University Press, 1965, p. 311.

Pfiffner, J., and F. Sherwood. *Administrative Organization*. Englewood Cliffs: Prentice-Hall, Inc., 1960, p. 30.

Pfiffner, John and R. Presthus. *Public Administration*. New York: The Ronald Press, 1967, p. 7.

Riegel, R., and J. Miller. *Insurance Principles and Practices*. 4th Ed. Englewood Cliffs, New Jersey: Prentice-Hall, Inc., pp. 59–89.

Simon, Herbert S. *Fire Losses and Fire Risks*. Berkeley: Bureau of Public Administration, University of California, 1943.

————. *The New Science of Management Division*. New York: Harper and Row, Inc., 1960, p. 41.

Webster's New Collegiate Dictionary. Springfield: G. and C. Merriam Co., Publishers, 1961, p. 262.

Wilson, E. Bright, Jr. *An Introduction to Scientific Research*. New York: McGraw-Hill Book Company, 1952, p. 57.

Publications of the Government, Learned Societies, and Other Organizations

A Proposed National Fire Research Program. Washington: NA S 1969.

Ambrose, John F. *The Use of Models for the Investigation of Fire Spread*, prepared for Department of Defense. San Antonio: Southwest Research Institute, 1963.

Appley, Laurence. *Management and the American Future*. General Management Series 169. American Management Association, Inc., 1954, p. 11.

Bakke, E. W. Concept of the Social Organization. Psychology and the Study of Business: Joint Behavioral Sciences in Social Science Research on Business: Product and Potential. New York: Columbia University Press, 1959, pp. 35–36.

Baldwin, R. *Spread of Fire in Buildings Affect of the Source of Ignition*. London: Fire Research Station Post 1966.

Blum, Edward H. *Urban Fire Protection: Studies of the Operations of the New York City Fire Department*. New York: The New York City Rand Institute (R-681), January 1971.

Bureau of the Budget. *Automatic Data Processing Glossary*. Washington: U.S. Government Printing Office (1962), p.53.

Butler, C. P. *Camp Parks, Massachusetts Fires*. Office of Civil Defense Contract No. DAHC 20-67-C0149. San Francisco: U.S. N. Rad. Laboratory 1969.

————. *Measurement of the Dynamics of Structural Fires*. Office of Civil Defense Contract No. DAHC 20-70 C-0219. Menlo Park, California: Stanford Research Institute, 1970.

Committee for Economic Development. *Reshaping Government in Metropolitan Areas*, New York: Committee for Economic Development, 1970, p. 7.

Corliss, William. *Computers*. Washington: Division of Technical Information, U. S. Atomic Energy Commission, 20545, 1967, p. 13.

Danielson, W. F. *Should Policemen and Firemen Get the Same Salary?* Public Personnel Association Personnel Report No. 641. Chicago Public Personnel Association, 1964.

Dutchess County Department of Planning. *Fire Safety Service in Dutchess County.* Department of Planning, 1969.
Economic Justice. The Needs of Fire Fighters. A Study of Economic Perspectives for the Fire Services. Washington: Skullenberg Association, 1970.
Eggleston, Lester. *Fire Defense Systems Analysis Application of Concepts to the San Jose Metropolitan Area.* Office of Civil Defense DAH C20-70-c-0210. San Antonio: Southwest Research Institute, 1970.
Farrell, Milton. *Fire Department Consolidation in Los Angeles County.* Los Angeles: School of Public Administration, University of Southern California, 1956.
Fire Fighters Fight Fires Not People. A Report by a Special Commission on the Role of Fire Fighters in Times of Civil Disturbances. Washington: International Association of Fire Fighters, 1969.
Garvey, John, Jr. The Fire Protection Engineer and Tomorrow's Municipality. MP 65-17. Boston: National Fire Protection Association, 1965.
Greenville County Planning Commission. *Public Safety Study.* Fire Protection, Greenville, South Carolina. Greenville County Planning Commission, 1969.
Hanna, W., et al. *Evaluation of Police Fire Partial-Combination Program in the City of Peoria.* Vol. 1, Final Report and Recommendations. Santa Barbara Public Safety Systems, Inc., 1970.
Hickey, Harry E. *The Perceived Involvement of Fire Department Officers: Operational and Management Functions.* Albany: The International Fire Administration Institute, 1970.
Hogg, Jane W. *A Model of Fire Spread.* F. R. Report No. 2-71. London Home Office, Scientific Advisory Branch, Boreham Wood, England.
International Association of Fire Fighters (AFL–CIO) Apprenticeship Training Standards. Washington: U.S. Department of Labor, 1972.
Labes, Willis G. Fire Department Operations Analysis. Office of Civil Defense Contract No. N22 (62479) 69031, Chicago, Illinois: Illinois Institute of Technology Research Institute, 1966.
Lawton Metropolitan Area Planning Commission. *Fire Protection Plan.* Lawton, Oklahoma: Lawton Metropolitan Area Planning Commission, 1967.
League of California Cities. *Fire Protection Grading Process as Related to Economics of Fire Protection.* Berkeley: League of California Cities, 1961.
Levenson, G., and A. Tenzer. *The Service Facilities of the Bureau of Fire Commission. A Cost Analysis of a Proposed Consolidation Prepared for New York City.* Memorandum RM 5726, New York City, Santa Monica, California, 1968.
Minton, David. *Cost Effectiveness in Fire Protection.* 355, 8030, 3558031. Columbus: Battelle Memorial Institute, 1969.
National League of Cities. *The Grading of Municipal Fire Protection Facilities.* Washington: National League of Cities, 1967, p. 13.
National Fire Protection Association. *Management of a Fire Department.* 1968. National Fire Protection Association No. 4B. Boston: National Fire Protection Association, 1968.
———. *Organization of a Fire Department.* 1969 (4A), Boston: National Fire Protection Association, 1969, p. 4.
Osmanski, Col. Frank A. *Military Command and Business Management.* Washington: Industrial College of the Armed Forces, 1958 (M58–94) p. 147.
Price, Harold E. *A Survey of Human Factors Engineering Problems in Fire Fighting Equipment.* Office of Civil Defense Contract No. P664-3, Sherman Oaks, California. Serendipity Associates, 1964.

Prichard, Sherman A. *An Organizational and Procedural Study of the Durham Fire Department. Special Report #22.* Raleigh, North Carolina: League of Municipalities, 1969.
Recommended Standards for Fire Fighters with Minimum Requirements for Recruitment Training and Education. Washington: International Association of Fire Fighters, 1970.
Rome, Floyd. *Planning Commission F. S. P. Study,* Rome, Georgia, Coosa Valley Area Planning and Development Commission, 1969.
Salzberg, F., et al. *An Approach to Trans-Attack Fire Suppression in Urban Areas.* Office of Civil Defense Contract No. OS62-210. Chicago, Illinois: Illinois Technical Research Institute, 1964.
Salzberg, Fred. Fire Department Operations Analysis. Office of Civil Defense Contract DAH C20-70C0208. Chicago, Illinois: Institute of Technology, 1970.
Santone, L., and G. Berlin. *A Computer Model for the Evaluation of the F. S. Location.* National Bureau of Standards, U. S. Department of Commerce, R, 10093, Washington: National Bureau of Standards, 1969.
Senate. Fire Research and Safety Act of 1967. *Congressional Record.* Vol. 113, No. 31, February 28, 1967.
Williamsburg 70. Boston: National Fire Protection Association, 1970, p. 7.
Wingspread Conference on Fire Service Administration, Education and Research. Statements of National Significance to the Fire Problems in the U.S. Racine: The Johnson Foundation, 1966.

Periodicals

Ahern, John. "The National Fire Profile," *Fire Journal,* March 1972, p. 7.
Auchinleck, Robert. "A Look at the Future of Fire Department Communications," *Fire Chief Magazine,* January 1969, pp. 29–31.
Bahme, Charles. "The Watts Fires and Their Lessons," *Fire Journal,* March 1966, pp. 10–14.
Bland, Richard. "The Evaluation Program of the National Commission on Fire Prevention and Control," *Fire Journal,* July 1972, p. 18.
Blower, Bruce. "Volunteers Face Population Explosion," *Fire Engineering,* April 1967, pp. 50–51.
Boulding, Kenneth. "General Systems Theory The Skeleton of Science," *Management Science,* April 1956, p. 197.
Briffett, John, and Kardell, Dennis. "Information and Reporting Systems," *Firemen,* May 1970, pp. 21–23.
Briffett, John and Mitchel William. "Soyammis: Its Meaning to the City's Fire Science," *Fire Journal,* November 1966, pp. 57–59.
Briffett, John. "Systems Analysis: An Aid to the Fire Department," *Fire Journal,* January 1971, pp. 13–16.
Bryan, John L. "Leadership — Its Functions and Qualities," *Fire Command!,* March 1971, pp. 19–22.
Bullard, Assistant Chief. "Let a Computer Do It," *Fire Engineering,* September 1967, p. 129.
Bullard, Assistant Chief A. B. "Readout in Winston-Salem," *Firemen,* January 1967, pp. 42–43.
Burns, Robert. "Philadelphia Gets New Communications System," *Fire Engineering,* November 1968, pp. 49–50.
Canick, Paul. "What the Fire Chief of the 1970's Should Know About PPBS," *Fire Chief Magazine,* January 1970, pp. 35–37.
Casey, James. "Science Symposium Explores Needs of the Fire Service," *Fire Engineering,* January 1969, pp. 42–44.

Clark, Malcolm S. "Personnel Relations — Some New Concepts for the 70's," *Fire Chief Magazine*, January 1970, pp. 31–34.

Clark, William E. "Advantages of a County Fire Service," *Fire Engineering*, December 1968, p. 38.

———. "Fire Company Management. Part 2: Grievances and Discipline," *Fire Engineering*, May 1970, pp. 50–51.

———. "Fire Company Management. Part 3: Work Organization," *Fire Engineering*, June 1970, pp. 45–46.

———. "Fire Company Management. Part 4: Public Relations," July 1970, *Fire Engineering*, July 1970, pp. 92–93.

———. "Fire Company Management. Part 5: Safety," *Fire Engineering*, August 1970, pp. 41–42.

———. "Fire Company Management. Part 6: Care of Apparatus and Equipment," *Fire Engineering*, September 1970, pp. 43–44.

Cox, Emmett. "The IAFF Looks at the 70's," *Fire Command!*, August 1970, pp. 26–27.

Cruce, B. H. "What Should the City Manager Expect from the Fire Chief and the Fire Department," *Fire Journal*, May 1970, pp. 63–65.

Culleton, J. "Age of Synthesis," *Harvard Business Review*, September-October 1962, p. 358.

Danielson, William. "Fire Duty Schedules and Staffing," *Management Information Service*, March 1969, Vol. 1, No. L-3.

Deutsch, Karl. "On Communication Models in the Social Sciences," *Public Opinion Quarterly*, 1952, p. 356.

Doe, Chief Everett. "Effective Command at Large Fire Operations," *Firemen*, July 1968, pp. 30–32.

Earle, Robert. "Personal Implications of Police-Fire Integration," *Public Personnel Review*, July 1958, p. 192.

Editorial. "Conflagrations," *Fire Command!*, September 1970, p. 11.

Editorial. "Educational Requirements," *Firemen*, May 1970, p. 13.

Ellison, Assistant Chief R. H. "What Makes a Fire Chief an Executive," *Firemen*, February 1967, pp. 39–41.

Emmons, Howard. "What We Can Have by 1980 If," *Fire Engineering*, September 1967, pp. 126–128.

Enthoven, Alain. "Systems Analysis in Decision Making," *Military Review*, January 1953, p. 15.

Estepp, Capt. M. H. "Changing the Fire Service Image," *Fire Command!*, May 1971, p. 6.

Euband, John. "The Insurance Rating Bureau. What It Is, What It Does," *Fire Journal*, March 1971, pp. 25–28.

Everard, William. "FPE Offers Broader Viewpoint to Fire Services as Staff Aide," August 1970, pp. 37–38.

Favreau, Prof. Donald. "Crises in Higher Education," *Fire Engineering*, April 1968, pp. 57–58.

Fetters, G. I. "Command Posts," *Fire Chief Magazine*, September 1969, pp. 34–36.

Frenze, Robert. "How to Design a Fire Department Safety System," *Fire Chief Magazine*, March 1970, pp. 27–30.

Fried, Emanuel. "The High Cost of Fire Protection," *Fire Chief Magazine*, January 1969, pp. 36–37.

Fristrom, R. *Fire Research Abstracts and Reviews*, Vol. 13, 1971, No. 1, p. iii.

Gaade, R. P. R. "A Computerized Fire Service," *Firemen*, May 1969, pp. 28–33.

Getis, Robert L. "How Computers Can Be Useful to Fire Departments," *Fire Engineering*, December 1971, p. 24.

Golembiewski, Robert. "Authority as a Problem in Overlays: A Concept for Action and Analysis," *Administrative Science Quarterly*, June 1964, p. 23.

Granito, John A. "A Role of Fire Commissioners," *Fire Engineering*, February 1971, pp. 37–38.

———. "Variables in Effective Leadership," *Fire Engineering*, June 1968, pp. 48–49.

Grant, Robert. "Planning — the Basis for Future Control," *Firemen*, July 1967, pp. 28–31.

———. "The NFPA's Role in Systems Development," *Fire Journal*, January 1972, p. 10.

Gratz, Chief David B. "Spring's Maintenance," *Firemen*, March 1969, pp. 19–22.

———. "The U.S. Fire Service Problems Today and Tomorrow," *Fire Chief Magazine*, January 1970, p. 26.

———. "Understanding the Budget. Part 1," *Fire Command!*, January 1971, pp. 12–14.

Hall, R. "The Concept of Bureaucracy an Empirical Assessment," *American Journal of Sociology*, July 1963, p. 33.

Hanna, Chief W. E. "Tempe Uses a Computer," *Firemen*, May 1969, p. 21.

Holmgren, R. Bruce. "Collective Bargaining: Your Key to Strike Free Relations, Part II," *Fire Chief Magazine*, June 1969, pp. 19–23.

Jensen, Rolf P. E. "Fire Protection Revolution Facing Our Cities," *Fire Engineering*, October 1969, pp. 183–187.

———. "Fire Protection Revolution in Our Cities," *Actual Specifying Engineer*, March 1969, pp. 84–85.

———. "Fire Protection Systems: Emphasis on Engineering," *Actual Specifying Engineer*, June 1967, pp. 79–85.

Joint Fire Research Organization. "Fire Protection Services in USSR," *Fire Journal*, May 1965, pp. 33–42.

Kahrmann, Robert. "Can the Volunteers Survive the 70's," *Fire Command!*, July 1970, pp. 28–30.

Keller, Joseph E. "Scientists See U.S. Need to Expand Fire Research," *Fire Engineering*, January 1971, p. 40.

Kimball, Warren Y. "Changing Fire Fighting Problems," *Fire Command!*, October 1971, pp. 16–17.

———. "Fire Departments, Volunteer and Part Paid," *Firemen*, January 1968, p. 23.

———. "Fire Service Critics," *Firemen*, May 1970, p. 26.

———. "Fire Departments in a Receding Economy," *Firemen*, March 1967, pp. 36–37.

———. "How to Analyze Your Fire Department Operations System," *Firemen*, April 1969, pp. 29–31.

———. "On Duty Manning of United States Fire Departments," *Fire Journal*, July 1970, pp. 60–62.

———. "The British Look Ahead," *Firemen*, July 1969, pp. 29–30.

———. "Which Way for the Fire Service?" *Firemen*, May 1967, pp. 13–14.

Kirk, Joseph L. "Fire Department Organization — Its Relation to Leadership," *Fire Chief Magazine*, September 1968, pp. 52–54.

Landsberger, Henry. "The Horizontal Dimension in Bureaucracy," *Administrative Science Quarterly*, December 1961, p. 300.

Marks, Dr. Leonard. "Voluntary National Professional Certification Examination," *Fire Command!*, July 1971, p. 24.

Maguire, Hugh. "Computer for the Fire Service — A New Look," *Fire Chief*, January 1971, pp. 33–34.

Mello, Alfred J. "Coming Changes in Communications," *Fire Command!*, June 1971, pp. 19–21.

Mitchell, Captain Mike. "Task Force 9 — Can Handle," *Firemen*, August 1969, pp. 30–33.

Mitchell, Philip S. "Efficient Allocation of Fire Department Resources, Part I," *Fire Technology*, August 1971, p. 237.

Monasah, Walter. "One City Planner's View: The Challenge of New Cities," *Fire Journal*, November 1970, pp. 5–6.

Morris, V. B. "The Systems Approach Applied to Fire Department Operations," *Fire Chief Magazine*, July 1969 pp. 26–29.

Nailen, R. L. "A Look at Radio. Its Use and Abuses," *Fire Engineering*, December 1970, pp. 42–44.

Nielsen, H. G., and G. G. Ryland. "Computer Command — Control," *Firemen*, May 1968, pp. 38–41.

O'Brien, Donald M. "Current Problems of the Fire Service," *Firemen*, August 1967, pp. 14–15.

O'Hagan, John T. "A New Era in the FDNY Tactical Control Force," WNYF, 1st Issue, 1970, p. 45.

O'Hagan, Chief John T. "Operations Research in the Fire Service," *Firemen*, September 1967, pp. 32–33.

Parsons, Falcott. "Suggestions for a Sociological Approach to the Theory of Organizations," *Administrative Science Quarterly*, September 1956, p. 238.

Pelletier, G. E. "A Program to Reduce Losses," *Fire Engineering*, September 1970, pp. 35–36.

Peterson, Carl. "Fire Incident Reporting. What Does It Mean to the Changing Fire Service," *Fire Command!*, October 1971, p. 23.

Polker, John H. "The Image of the Firefighter. Is It Changing," *Fire Command!*, October 1970, pp. 16–18.

Randleman, Bill. "Learn by Simulation," *Fire Chief Magazine*, June 1970, p. 23.

Rieder, Robert J. "Status Displays for Fire Management," *Fire Journal*, July 1970, pp. 43–45.

Riepe, William. "Fire Services Challenges," *Fire Engineering*, June 1971, pp. 51–52.

Riopelle, Chief James H. "Challenges for the Fire Service," *Fire Command!*, August 1970, pp. 19–21.

Rockett, John A. "Planned Operation of the National Bureau of Standards Fire Research and Safety Office," *Fire Journal*, November 1969, pp. 41–42.

Royer, Keith. "Systems Analysis A Method for Information and Data Collection," *Fire Chief Magazine*, January 1971, pp. 25–29.

Salzberg, F., and F. J. Vodvarka. "Minimum Water Requirements for Suppression of Room Fires," *Fire Technology*, February 1970, p. 22.

Scott, W. "Organizational Theory. An Overview and an Appraisal," *Journal of the Academy of Management*, April 1961, pp. 7–26.

Shea, Edward J. "Two Tier System," *Fire Command!*, October 1970, pp. 7–11.

Shepard, H. "Superiors and Subordinates in Research," *Journal of Business*, October 1956, p. 261.

Staff. "Anticipating the Unexpected," *Firemen*, July 1969, p. 25.

———. "Budgets Show Where You're Going," *Fire Engineering*, October 1969, pp. 114–115.

———. "Certification Urged for the Fire Service," *Fire Engineering*, October 1971, p. 54.

———. "Changes in NYC," *Fire Command!*, February 1971, pp. 12–15.

———. "Fire Chiefs Look at the 70's," *Fire Chief Magazine*, January 1970, pp. 23–25.

———. "Fire Inquiry Bill Signed by Johnson," *Fire Engineering*, April 1969, pp. 60–61.

———. "Fire Record of Cities, 1970," *Fire Journal*, National Fire Protection Association, July 1971, p. 79.

———. "How Population Shifts Affect Fire Departments," *Fire Command!*, September 1970, pp. 25–27.

———. "Injuries to Fire Department Personnel," *Fire Journal*, March 1969, p. 23.

———. "National Research Council Symposium on Training and Education," *Fire Chief Magazine*, June 1970, pp. 38–39.

———. "Peoria, Illinois Drops Use of Policemen in Fire Companies," *Fire Engineering*, July 1971, pp. 54–55.

———. "Professional Standards for Fire Fighters," *Firemen*, May 1970, pp. 8–9.

———. "Seminars at IAFC Conference Cover Many Fire Problems," *Fire Engineering*, April 1967, p. 58.

———. "The Fire Chief and Galloping Socialism," *Firemen*, October 1968, pp. 44–46.

———. "The Seventy-third NFPA Annual Meeting," *Fire Journal*, September 1969, pp. 29–52.

———. "The Status of Safety in Fire Service," *Fire Chief Magazine*, October 1970, pp. 31–34.

———. "The Wingspread Conference," *Fire Engineering*, January 1967, pp. 38–40.

———. "The 1970's, the Challenging Years for the Fire Service," *Fire Engineering*, September 1967, pp. 106–120.

———. "Voice of the Fire Service," *Fire Command!*, August 1970, p. 6.

Statement from the Presidential Commission on Fire Safety. "A Fire Science National Academy," *Fire Command!*, April 1972, p. 6.

Sylvia, Dick. "British Look at Fire Service and See Problems Like Ours," *Fire Engineering*, October 1970, p. 40.

Volkamer, C. W. "What Lies Ahead for the Fire Service," *Fire Command!*, July 1970, p 81.

Unpublished Materials

Bryan, John and Richard Thornberry. "Development and Evaluation of a Systematic Analysis Procedure for the Selection of Fire Station Sites in Prince Georges County, Maryland," University of Maryland, 1970.

Canick, Paul M. "A Progress Report on Studies in New York City," National Academy of Sciences — Paper read, Washington, October 30, 1968.

Hickey, Harry E. "Protection Audit and Survey System," Washington, General Services Administration, 1969 (Mimeographed).

———. "Urban Fire Safety Systems in the Next Decade," paper presented to the 1970 Annual Meeting of the National Fire Protection Association, Toronto, Canada, May 22, 1970.

Pollak, W. "Pricing Fire Department Services," Mimeographed Working Paper 705–71, Washington, D.C., Urban Institute, 1970.

Six Months Fire Report, Chautauqua County, New York, January-June 1970.

Stehle, William. "A Simulation Model Study for Determining the Optimal Distance for Locating a Fire Department Building Site from a Shopping Center," unpublished, American University, Washington, D.C., 1968.

APPENDIX

A Selected Bibliography and Key Word List Related to Urban Fire Safety

Prepared by
HARRY E. HICKEY
December 1, 1971

Periodicals

Item Listing	Key Words Subject Area
Auchinleck, Robert J. "A Look At The Future of Fire Department Communications", *Fire Chief*, January 1969, 29–31.	Communications Computers
Bahme, Charles W. "The Watts Fires and Their Lessons", *Fire Journal*, 10–14.	Civil Disturbance Fire Defense Analysis Fire Suppression
Blower, Bruce G. "Volunteers Face Population Explosion", *Fire Engineering*, April 1967, 50–51.	Volunteer Fire Departments Fire Protection Problems Public Services
Briffett, John R. "Systems Analysis: An Aid To The Fire Department", *Fire Journal*, January 1971, 13–16.	Fire Defense Analysis Management Information System
Briffett, John R. and Dennis Kardell. "Information and Reporting Systems", *Firemen*, May 1970, 21–23.	Management Information Systems Related Municipal Functions Fire Defense Analysis
Briffett, John R. and William H. Mitchel. "SOGAMMIS: Its Meaning to the City's Fire Service", *Fire Journal*, November 1966, 57–59.	Management Information System Fire Defense Criteria
Bryan, Dr. John L. "Leadership — Its Functions and Qualities", *Fire Command!*, March 1971, 19–22.	Organization Administration Leadership
Bullard, Assistant Chief A. B. "Let A Computer Do It", *Fire Engineering*, September 1967, 129.	Management Information System Computer Application
Bullard, Assistant Chief A. B. "Readout in Winston-Salem", *Firemen*, January 1967, 42–43.	Computers Management Information System Training — Education
Burns, Robert T. "Philadelphia Gets New Communications System", *Fire Engineering*, 49–50.	Communications Command—Control Computers

Item Listing	Key Words Subject Area
Canick, Paul M. "What the Fire Chief of the 1970's Should Know About PPBS", *Fire Chief Magazine*, January 1970, 35–37.	Finance Fire Defense Analysis
Carter, Chief Walter H. "Communications Join Computer Era", *Fire Engineering*, February 1970, 57–58.	Computers Communications
Casey, James F. "Science Symposium Explores Needs of the Fire Service", *Fire Engineering*, January 1969, 42–44.	Fire Protection Problems Computers Fire Research
Clark, Malcolm S. "Personnel Relations — Some New Concepts for the 70's", *Fire Chief Magazine*, January 1970, 31–34.	Personnel Organization
Clark, William E. "Advantages of a County Fire Service", *Fire Engineering*, ——— 38.	Organization County Fire Service Fire Protection Efficiency
Clark, William E. "Fire Company Management", *Fire Engineering*, May 1970, 50–51. (Part 2: Grievances and Discipline)	Personnel
Clark, William E. "Fire Company Management", (Part 3: Work Organization), *Fire Engineering*, June 1970, 45–46.	Organization Fire Suppression Management Information System
Clark, William E. "Fire Company Management", (Part 4: Public Relations), July 1970, 92–93.	Public Relations
Clark, William E. "Fire Company Management", (Part 5: Safety), August 1970, 41–42.	Safety Training—Education
Clark, William E. "Fire Company Management", (Part 6: Care of Apparatus and Equipment), September 1970, 43–44.	Equipment Resource Allocation

Item Listing	Key Words Subject Area	Item Listing	Key Words Subject Area
Cox, Emmett T. "The IAFF Looks At The 70's", *Fire Command!*, August 1970, 26–27.	Organization Personnel Education—Training	Fried, Emanuel. "The High Cost of Fire Protection", *Fire Chief*, January 1969, 36–37.	Fire Problems Financing Fire Protection Costs
Cruce, B. H. "What Should The City Manager Expect From The Fire Chief and The Fire Department", *Fire Journal*, May 1970, 63–65.	Fire Risk Analysis Fire Problem Analysis Organization Fire Insurance Grading	Gaade, R. P. R. "A Computerized Fire Service", *Firemen*, May 1969, 28–33.	Computers Organizations Command—Control Data Processing
Danielson, William F. "Fire Duty Schedules and Staffing", *Management Information Service*, (March 1969) Vol. 1, No. L-3.	Urban Fire Safety: Fire Duty Schedules Fire Duty Staffing Personnel Legislation Fire Suppression	Granito, John A. "Role of Fire Commissioners", *Fire Engineering*, February 1971, 37–38.	Administration Organization Planning Policy Development
Doe, Chief Everett S. "Effective Command at Large Fire Operations", *Firemen*, July 1968, 30-32.	Organization Command—Control	Granito, John A. "Variables in Effective Leadership", *Fire Engineering*, June 1968, 48–49.	Administration Leadership Organization
Editorial. "Conflagrations", *Fire Command!*, September 1970, page 11.	Conflagrations	Grant, Robert W. "Planning — The Basis for Future Control," *Firemen*, July 1967, 28–31.	Planning Administration Leadership Volunteers
Editorial. "Educational Requirements", *Firemen*, May 1970, page 13.	Education—Training	Gratz, Chief David B. "Spring's Maintenance", *Firemen*, March 1969, 19–22.	Maintenance Repair and Improvement
Ellison, Assistant Chief R. H. "What Makes A Fire Chief an Executive", *Firemen*, February 1967, 39–41.	Administration Leadership Planning	Gratz, David B. "The U.S. Fire Service — Problems Today and Tomorrow", *Fire Chief Magazine*, January 1970, 26–30.	Fire Defense Analysis Fire Insurance Rating Organization Efficiency
Emmons, Dr. Howard. "What We Can Have By 1980 — IF", *Fire Engineering*, September 1967, 126–128.	Planning Computers Research	Gratz, Chief David B. "Understanding the Budget", (Part I), *Fire Command!*, January 1971, 12–14.	Finance Planning
Estepp, Capt. M. H. "Changing the Fire Service Image", *Fire Command!*, May 1971, p. 6.	Organization	Gratz, Chief David B. "Understanding the Budget", (Part II), *Fire Command!*, February 1971, 18–20.	Budgets Finance
Euband, John O. "The Insurance Rating Bureau: What It Is, What It Does", *Fire Journal*, March 1971, 25–28.	Organization Insurance Grading	Hanna, Chief W. E. "Tempe Uses a Computer", *Firemen*, May 1969, 21.	Computers Management Information System
Everard, William. "FPE Offers Broader Viewpoint To Fire Services As Staff Aide", August 1970, 37–38.	Organization Fire Protection Engineering	Holmgren, R. Bruce. "Collective Bargaining: Your Key to Strike Free Relations", Part II, *Fire Chief Magazine*, 19–23.	Collective Bargaining Personnel
Favreau, Professor Donald F. "Crisis in Higher Education", *Fire Engineering*, April 1968, 57–58.	Education—Training Personnel Problem Identification	Jensen, Rolf P. E. "Fire Protection Revolution Facing Our Cities", *Fire Engineering*, October 1969, 183–187.	Fire Defense Criteria Fire Problems Education Fire Protection Engineering
Favreau, Professor Don. "To Get On The Ball, Pick Your Goals", *Fire Engineering*, 54–55.	Fire Protection Objectives Organization Planning	Jensen, Rolf P. E. "Fire Protection Revolution in Our Cities", *Actual Specifying Engineer*, March 1969, 84–85.	Fire Protection Engineering Fire Problem Identification
Fetters, J. I. "Command Posts", *Fire Chief*, September 1969, 34–36.	Command—Control Fire Suppression	Jensen, Rolf. "Fire Protection Systems: Emphasis on Engineering", *Actual Specifying Engineer*, June 1967, 79–85.	Fire Protection Systems Fire Problem Identification
Firenze, Robert J. "How to Design a Fire Department Safety System", *Fire Chief Magazine*, March 1970, 27–30.	Safety Systems Organization	Joint Fire Research Organization. "Fire Protection Services in the U.S.S.R.", *Fire Journal*, May 1965, 33–42.	Organization Training Fire Research Fire Prevention

Item Listing	Key Words Subject Area	Item Listing	Key Words Subject Area
Keller, Joseph E. "Scientists See U.S. Need To Expand Fire Research", *Fire Engineering*, January 1971, 40.	Research Areas Urban Problems	Monasch, Walter J. "One City Planner's View: The Challenge of New Cities", *Fire Journal*, November 1970, 5–6.	Planning Fire Defense Analysis
Kimball, Warren Y. "Fire Departments in a Receding Economy", *Firemen*, March 1967, 36–37.	Financing Personnel Fire Problem Identification	Morris, V. B. Jr. "The Systems Approach Applied to Fire Department Operations", *Fire Chief*, July 1969, 26–29.	Computers Organization
Kimball, Warren Y. "Fire Departments — Volunteer and Part-Paid", *Firemen*, January 1968, p. 23.	Organization Volunteer Fire Departments	Nailen, R. L. "A Look at Radio . . . Its Use and Abuse", *Fire Engineering*, 42–44.	Communications Command and Control
Kimball, Warren Y. "Fire Service Critics", *Firemen*, May 1970, 26–27.	Fire Service Critics Fire Protection Engineers Insurance Ratings	Nielsen, D.J., and H. G. Ryland. "Computer Command-Control". *Fire Journal*, May 1968, 43–48.	Command—Control Communications Computers Organization Data Processing Fire Department Operations
Kimball, Warren Y. "How to Analyze Your Fire Department Operations Systems," April 1969, 29–31.	Fire Risk Analysis Fire Suppression	Nielsen, H. G. and H.G.Ryland. "Computer Command — Control", *Firemen*, May 1968, 38–41.	Computers Command—Control Communications
Kimball, Warren Y. "On Duty Manning of United States Fire Departments", *Fire Journal*, July 1970, 60–62.	Personnel Organization Fire Defense Analysis	O'Brien, Donald M. "Current Problems of the Fire Service", *Firemen*, August 1967, 14–15.	Fire Problems Organization
Kimball, Warren Y. "The British Look Ahead", *Firemen*, July 1969, 29–30.	Comparative Government Management Information Systems	O'Hagan, John T. "A New Era in the FDNY . . . Tactical Control Force", *WNYF* 1st Issue, 1970, 4–5.	Fire Suppression
Kimball, Warren Y. "Which Way — For the Fire Service", *Firemen*, May 1967, 13–14.	Organization Finances	O'Hagan, Chief John T. "Operations Research in the Fire Service", *Firemen*, September 1967, 32–33.	Problem Identification Organization
Kirk, Joseph L. "Fire Department Organization — Its Relation To Leadership", *Fire Chief*, September 1968, 52–54.	Organization Administration Leadership	Pelletier, G. E., "A Program To Reduce Losses", *Fire Engineering*, September 1970, 35–36.	Organization Fire Prevention Management Information Systems Fire Protection Objectives
Maguire, Hugh M. "Computer for the Fire Service — A New Look", *Fire Chief*, January 1968, 33–34.	Computers Management Information Systems		
Marks, Dr. Leonard G. "Voluntary National Professional Certification Examinations", *Fire Command!*, July 1971, 24.	Education—Training Personnel	Peterson, Carl. "Fire Incident Reporting: What does it mean to the Changing Fire Service", *Fire Command!*, October 1971, 23.	UFRIS Fire Data Collection Fire Data Analysis Fire Department Analysis
Mello, Alfred J. "Coming Changes in Communications", *Fire Command!*, June 1971, 19–21.	Communications Computers	Polker, John H. "The Image of the Firefighter — Is It Changing?", *Fire Command!*, October 1970, 16–18.	Civil Disturbance Personnel Organization Professionalism
Mitchell, Captain Mike. "Task Force 9 — Can Handle", *Firemen*, August 1969, 30–33.	Fire Suppression Organization	Randleman, Bill. "Learn by Simulation", *Fire Chief Magazine*, June 1970, 23.	Education—Training
Mitchell, Philip S. "Efficient Allocation of Fire Department Resources — Part I", *Fire Technology*, August 1971, 237.	Fire Department Analysis Fire Department Operations	Rieder, Robert J. "Status Displays For Fire Management", *Fire Journal*, July 1970, 43–45.	Management Information Systems Communications Fire Defense Analysis
Mobile Printer — *Fire Command!*, July 1971, 33.	Communications	Riepe, William. "Fire Service's 3 Challenges", *Fire Engineering*, June 1971, 51–52.	Fire Problems Fire Defense Analysis Administration

Item Listing	Key Words Subject Area	Item Listing	Key Words Subject Area
Riopelle, Chief James H. "Challenges for the Fire Service", *Fire Command!*, August 1970, 19–21.	Problems Organization Administration Computers	Staff. "The 1970's — The Challenging Years for the Fire Service", *Fire Engineering*, September 1967, 106–120.	Personnel Education—Training Volunteers Computers Management Information Public Relations
Rockett, John A. "Planned Operation of the National Bureau of Standards Fire Research and Safety Office", *Fire Journal*, November 1969, 41–42.	Fire Research Problem Analysis	Staff. "The Fire Chief and Galloping Socialism", *Firemen*, October 1968, 44–46.	Fire Protection Criteria Organization Problems Federal Government
Royer, Keith. "Systems Analysis . . . A Method for Information and Data Collection", *Fire Chief Magazine*, January 1971, 25–29.	Management Information System Organization	Staff. "The Seventy-third NFPA Annual Meeting", *Fire Journal*, September 1969, 29 52.	
Salzberg, F., and F. J. Vodvarka. "Minimum Water Requirements for Suppression of Room Fires", *Fire Technology*, February 1970, 22.	Fire Department Operations Water Requirements Structural Fires	Staff. "The Status of Safety in the Fire Service", *Fire Chief Magazine*, October 1970, 31–34.	Safety Organization
Shea, Edward J. " 'Two-Tier' System", *Fire Command!*, October 1970, 7–11.	Organization Personnel	Staff. "The Wingspread Conference", *Fire Engineering*, January 1967, 38–40.	Problem Identification Organization Professionalism Insurance Grading Mobility Labor-Management Relations
Staff. "Budgets Show Where You're Going", *Fire Engineering*, October 1969, 114–115.	Budgets Management Information System Planning		
Staff. "Changes in New York City", *Fire Command!*, February 1971, 12–15.	Organization Suppression Communications	Staff. "Seminars at IAFC Conference Cover Many Fire Problems", *Fire Engineering*, April 1967, 58–59.	Planning Fire Suppression Organization
Staff. "Fire Chiefs Look at the 70's", *Fire Chief Magazine*, January 1970, 23–25.	Fire Defense Analysis Education and Training Fire Prevention	Staff. "Voice of the Fire Service", *Fire Command!*, August 1970, 6.	Fire Service Critics Professionalism
Staff. "Fire Inquiry Bill Signed by Johnson", *Fire Engineering*, April 1968, 60–61.	Fire Research Fire Problems	Sylvia, Dick. "British Look at Fire Service and See Problems Like Ours", *Fire Engineering*, October 1970, 39–41.	Comparative Administration Volunteers Education—Training Fire Research
Staff. "How Population Shifts Affect Fire Departments", *Fire Command!*, September 1970, page 25.	Urban Fire Problems	Ulrich, Richard L. "Changing The Fire Service Image", *Fire Command!*, March, 1971,	Organization Problem Identification Personnel
Staff. "Injuries to Fire Department Personnel", *Fire Journal*, March 1969, 23—.	Safety Systems	Ulrich, Richard L. "Reflections on Better Manpower Utilization", *Fire Command!*, July 1970, 44–45.	Personnel Fire Suppression Volunteers
Staff. "National Research Council Symposium on Training and Education", *Fire Chief Magazine*, June 1970, 38–39.	Education —Training Fire Problems Personnel Fire Research	Ulrich, Richard L. "The Human Factor in Fire Department Management", *Fire Command!*, November 1970, 12–15.	Personnel Administration
Staff. "Peoria, Ill., Drops Use of Policemen in Fire Companies", *Fire Engineering*, July 1971, 55—.	Fire-Police Integration Organization	Vickery, Chief Gordon F. "What a Chief Should Know About Fire", *Fire Engineering*, March 1970, 47–48.	Management Information System Fire Suppression
Staff. "Philadelphia Gets More Out of Water", *Fire Engineering*, April 1967, 52–53.	Water Supply	Volkamer, Chief Fire Marshal Curtis W. "What Lies Ahead For The Fire Service?", *Fire Command!*, July 1970, 38–40.	Administration Civil Disturbances Budgets Training—Education Mobility Volunteers
Staff. "Professional Standards for Fire Fighters", *Firemen*, May 1970, 8–9.	Personnel Professional Standards		

Item Listing	Key Words Subject Area	Item Listing	Key Words Subject Area
Waterman, T. F. "Room Flashover — Scaling of Fire Conditions", *Fire Technology*, February 1969, p. 52.	Burn Histories Model Studies	James, Charles S. *Police and Fire Integration in the Small City.* Chicago: Public Administration Service, 1955.	Urban Fire Safety: Fire and Police Ingration Personnel Fire-Police Salaries Planning Consolidation Organization Records Financing
Waterman, T. F. "Room Flashover — Criteria and Synthesis", *Fire Technology*, February 1968, 25.	Burn History Fire Analysis Flashover Full Scale Burns		
Weitz, Harold. "A Model for the Simulation of the Fire Services of an Urban Community", *Fire Journal*, January 1969, 48–55.	Fire Defense Analysis Fire Suppression Fire Station Location	*Municipal Fire Administration.* 7th Edition. Washington: International City Managers' Association, 1967.	(Note:) All Key Words Except: Fire Brands Nuclear Blast Effect
Witzeman, Lou. "The Challenges Facing the Fire Service", *Fire Journal*, May 1970, 11–15.	Organization-Privately Owned Fire Departments Fire Risk Analysis	Pickard, Sherman A. *An Organizational and Procedural Study of of the Durham Fire Department.* (Special Report #22). Raleigh: North Carolina League of Municipalities, 1969.	Urban Fire Safety: Personnel Fire Suppression Planning Consolidation Fire Insurance Ratings Organization Station Location Records Fire Prevention
Yeager, Colonel Paul M. "Applying Systems Management Techniques To Fire Protection Operations", *Fire Journal*, January 1970, 55–58.	Fire Defense Criteria Management Information Systems		
Yeager, Colonel Paul M. "The Application of Systems Management Techniques to Fire Protection Operations", *Fire Chief Magazine*, August 1970, 30–31.	Management Information Systems Organization Planning	*Recommended Standards For Fire Fighters With Minimum Requirements For Recruitment, Training, and Education.* Washington: International Association of Fire Fighters, 1970.	Urban Fire Safety: Legislation Personnel Education Training
		Simon, Herbert A. *Fire Losses and Fire Risks.* Berkeley: Bureau of Public Administration, University of California, 1943.	Fire Loss Data Fire Risk Analysis

Books

Item Listing	Key Words Subject Area
Farrell, Milton R. *Fire Department Consolidation in Los Angeles County:* Los Angeles: School of Public Administration, University of Southern California, 1956.	Urban Fire Safety: Personnel Legislation Fire Suppression Planning Consolidation Fire Insurance Ratings Organization Station Location Financing Training Building Codes
Hickey, Harry E. *The Perceived Involvement of Fire Department Officers: Operational and Management Functions.* Albany (NY): International Fire Administration Institute, 1969.	Urban Fire Safety: Fire Duty Staffing Personnel Fire Suppression Planning Organization Records Fire Alarm Fire Prevention

Item Listing	Key Words Subject Area
Standard Schedule for Grading Cities and Towns of the United States With Reference To Their Fire Defenses and Physical Conditions. 1956 Edition. New York: National Board of Fire Underwriters, 1956.	(Note): All Key Words Except: Mass Fires Fire Brands Burn Histories Nuclear Blast Effect Toxic Products of Fire Experimental Building Fires Fire-Police Salaries

Publications of the Government, Learned Societies, and Other Organizations

Item Listing	Key Words Subject Area
A Proposed National Fire Research Program. Washington: National Academy of Sciences, 1969.	Fire Defense Criteria Fire Prevention Burn Histories Fire Suppression Life Hazards Structural Fire Spread

Item Listing	Key Words Subject Area	Item Listing	Key Words Subject Area
Ambrose, John E., and others. *The Use of Models for the Investigation of Fire Spread.* Prepared for: Department of Defense. San Antonio: Southwest Research Institute, 1963.	Mass Fires Structural Fire Spread Experimental Building Fires	*Fire Fighters Fight Fires — Not People.* A Report by a Special Committee on the Role of the Fire Fighter in Times of Civil Disturbance. Washington: International Association of Fire Fighters, 1969.	Urban Fire Safety: Civil Disturbance Planning Personnel Fire Suppression Legislation
Baldwin, R., and P. H. Thomas. *Spread of Fire in Buildings — Effect of the Source of Ignition.* London: Fire Research Station. (No Date) Post 1966.	Structural Fire Spread	Garvey, John Jr. *The Fire Protection Engineer and Tomorrow's Municipality.* (MP 65–17). Boston: National Fire Protection Association, 1965.	Fire Protection Engineers Planning Personnel
Butler, C. P. *Camp Parks Mass Fires.* Office of Civil Defense Contract Number DAHC20–67–C–0149. San Francisco: U.S. Naval Radiological Defense Laboratory, 1969.	Life Hazards Structural Fire Spread Toxic Products of Fire Experimental Building Fires	Greenville County Planning Commission. *Public Safety Study: Fire Protection.* Greenville (SC): The Greenville County Planning Commission, 1969.	Planning Consolidation Fire Insurance Ratings Organization
Butler, C. P. *Measurement of the Dynamics of Structural Fires.* Office of Civil Defense Contract Number DAHC20–70–C–0219. Menlo Park (Calif.): Stanford Research Institute, 1970	Urban Fire Safety: Structural Fire Spread Experimental Building Fires Life Hazards Toxic Products of Fire	Hanna, W., and others. "Evaluation of Police-Fire Partial-Combination Program in the City of Peoria: Volume 1, Final Report and Recommendations". Santa Barbara: Public Safety Systems Incorporated, 1970.	Fire-Police Salaries Pay Parity Planning Fire-Police Integration Records Fire Alarm
Chandler, Craig C. *A Study of Mass Fires and Conflagrations.* U.S. Forest Service Research Note — PSW–N22. Berkeley: U.S. Department of Agriculture Experiment Station.	Mass Fires Fire Defense Criteria Structural Fire Spread	Hanna, W., and others. "Evaluation of Police-Fire Partial-Combination Program in the City of Peoria: Volume 2, Appendixes". Santa Barbara: Public Safety Systems Incorporated, 1970.	Urban Fire Safety: Fire-Police Integration
Danielson, William F. *Should Policemen and Firemen Get the Same Salary?* Public Personnel Association, Personnel Report No. 641. Chicago: Public Personnel Association, 1964.	Personnel Pay Parity Fire-Police Salaries	Hogg, Jane M. *A Model of Fire Spread.* Fire Research Report No. 2/71. London: Home Office — Scientific Advisory Branch, 1971.	Structural Fire Spread Self-Protection Fire Defense Criteria Life Hazards Fire Suppression
Dutchess County Department of Planning. *Fire Safety Service in Dutchess County.* Poughkeepsie (NY): Dutchess County Department of Planning, 1969.	Urban Fire Safety: Legislation Station Locations Planning Organization Fire Suppression	Kimball, Warren Y. *Manning for Fire Attack.* (FSD–6). Boston: National Fire Protection Association, 1969.	Urban Fire Safety: Fire Duty Staffing Personnel Fire Suppression Organization Training Water Supply
Economic Justice: The Needs of Fire Fighters. A Study of Economic Perspectives for the Fire Services. Washington: Stanley H. Ruttenberg & Associates, Inc., 1970.	Urban Fire Safety: Financing Personnel Pay Parity Planning	Kimball, Warren Y. *Operation of Small Community Fire Departments.* (FDS–5). Boston: National Fire Protection Association, 1968.	Urban Fire Safety: Organization Planning Fire Suppression Personnel Training
Eggleston, Lester. *FIRE DEFENSE SYSTEMS ANALYSIS — Application of Concepts To The San Jose Metropolitan Area.* Office of Civil Defense Contract Number DAHC20–70–C–0210. San Antonio: Southwest Research Institute, 1970.	Fire Defense Criteria Peace Time Defense Elements Nuclear Blast Effect Water Supply Fire Suppression	Labes, Willis G. *Fire Department Operations Analysis.* Office of Civil Defense Contract Number N22(62479) 69031. Chicago: Illinois Institute of Technology Research Institute, 1966.	Fire Suppression Personnel Fire Duty Staffing Water Supply

Item Listing	Key Words Subject Area	Item Listing	Key Words Subject Area
Lawton Metropolitan Area Planning Commission. *Fire Protection Plan.* Lawton (Okla.): Lawton Metropolitan Area Planning Commission, 1967.	Urban Fire Safety: Fire Insurance Ratings Planning Organization Station Location Fire Suppression Financing		Fire Alarm Fire Prevention Building Codes
		Price, Harold E. and others. *A Survey of Human Factors Engineering Problems in Fire-fighting Equipment.* Office of Civil Defense Contract Number PS–64–3. Sherman Oaks (Calif.): Serendipity Associates, 1964.	Personnel Fire Equipment
League of California Cities. *The Fire Protection Grading Process as Related to the Economics of Fire Protection.* Berkeley: League of California Cities, 1961.	Fire Duty Staffing Personnel Fire Suppression Fire Insurance Rating Organization Station Location Records Training Water Supply Fire Alarm Fire Prevention Building Codes	Pryor, A. J. *Full-Scale Evaluation of the Fire Hazard of Interior Wall Finishes.* Prepared for the Hardwood Plywood Manufacturers Association. San Antonio: Southwest Research Institute, 1968.	Building Codes Structural Fire Spread Experimental Building Fires Toxic Products of Fire Life Hazards
Levenson, G. S., and A. J. Tenzer. *The Service Facilities of the Bureau of Fire Communications: A Cost Analysis of a Proposed Consolidation.* Prepared for: City of New York — Memorandum RM–5726–NYC. Santa Monica: California, 1968.	Fire Alarm Personnel Finance Operations Fire Defense Criteria	Rome-Floyd County Planning Commission. *Fire Service Protection Study.* Rome (Ga.): Coosa Valley Area Planning and Development Commission, 1969.	Urban Fire Safety: Records Station Location Organization Insurance Ratings Consolidation Planning Personnel Financing
Minton, David C. Cost-Effectiveness in Fire Protection. Project Number 355–8030, 355–8031. Columbus: Batelle Memorial Institute, 1969.	Fire Suppression Organization Fire Station Location Financing Structural Fire Spread Fire Defense Criteria Fire Duty Staffing	Santone, Louis C., and Geoffrey N. Berlin. *A Computer Model for the Evaluation of Fire Station Location.* National Bureau of Standards, United States Department of Commerce, Report 10,093. Washington: National Bureau of Standards, 1969.	Fire Suppression Planning Fire Station Location Fire Defense Criteria
National Fire Protection Association, *Management of a Fire Department 1968* (NFPA No. 4B) Boston: National Fire Protection Association, 1968.	Urban Fire Safety: Personnel Legislation Fire Suppression Planning Organization Records Financing Training Fire Prevention	Salzberg, Frederick. *Fire Department Operations Analysis.* Office of Civil Defense Contract DAHC20–70–C–0208. Chicago: Illinois Institute of Technology, 1970.	Personnel Fire Suppression Water Supply Structural Fire Spread Fire Defense Criteria Self-Protection Burn Histories
National Fire Protection Association. *Organization of a Fire Department — 1969.* No. 4A. Boston: National Fire Protection Association, 1969.	Legislation Fire Duty Schedules Fire Duty Staffing Organization Water Supply Fire Defense Criteria	Salzberg, F., and others. *An Approach to Trans-Attack Fire Suppression in Urban Areas.* Office of Civil Defense Contract Number OS–62–210. Chicago: Illinois Institute of Technology Research Institute, 1964.	Urban Fire Safety: Fire Suppression Structural Fire Spread Experimental Building Fires Water Supply Inter-Community Assistance Fire Defense Criteria Nuclear Blast Effect Self-Protection
National League of Cities. *The Grading of Municipal Fire Protection Facilities: Its Relationship to Fire Insurance and to the Municipality's Fire Protection Policy.* Washington: National League of Cities, 1967.	Urban Fire Safety: Fire Duty Staffing Personnel Fire Suppression Fire Insurance Rating Organization Station Location Records Training Water Supply	Takata, Arthur N., and Frederick Salzberg. *Development and Application of a Complete Fire Spread Model.* Office of Civil Defense Contract Number N0022867C1498.	Urban Fire Safety: Mass Fires Structural Fire Spread Firebrands

Item Listing	Key Words Subject Area	Item Listing	Key Words Subject Area
Takata, Arthur N. *Mathematical Modeling of Fire Defenses.* Office of Civil Defense Contract Number N0022867C2081. Chicago: Illinois Institute of Technology Research Institute, 1969.	Urban Fire Safety: Fire Defense Criteria Self-Protection Fire Suppression Structural Fire Spread Mass Fires	Zukoski, Edward E., and others. *Large Building Fires — Experiment and Analysis.* U.S. Department of Commerce — National Bureau of Standards Contract Number CST–902–5–69. Pasadena: California Institute of Technology, 1970.	Structural Fire Spread Building Codes Experimental Building Fires Fire Suppression

Item Listing	Key Words Subject Area
Takata, A. N. *Mathematical Modeling of Fire Defenses. Part II.* Office of Civil Defense Contract Number DAHC–20–70–C–0209. Chicago: Illinois Institute of Technology Research Institute, 1970.	Urban Fire Safety: Fire Suppression Structural Fire Spread Nuclear Blast Effect Fire Defense Criteria Self-Protection
Vodvarka, Frank J. *Full-Scale Burns in Urban Areas — Part I — Fire Spread Between Structures.* Office of Civil Defense Contract Number N00228–68–C–2368. Chicago: Illinois Institute of Technology Research Institute, 1969.	Urban Fire Safety: Structural Fire Spread Toxic Products Nuclear Blast Effect Firebrands Experimental Building Fires
Vodvarka, F. J., and T. E. Waterman. *Fire Behavior, Ignition to Flashover.* Office of Civil Defense Contract Number PS–64–50. Chicago: Illinois Institute of Technology Research Institute, 1965.	Urban Fire Safety: Fire Suppression Self-Protection Structural Fire Spread Experimental Building Fires Life Hazards
Vodvarka, Frank J. *Urban Burns — Full-Scale Field Studies.* Office of Civil Defense Contract Number DAHC 20–70–C–0213. Chicago: Illinois Institute of Technology, 1970.	Urban Fire Safety: Firebrands Structural Fire Spread Experimental Building Fires
Wingspread Conference on Fire Service Administration, Education and Research. Statements of National Significance to the Fire Problem in the United States. Racine: The Johnson Foundation, 1966.	Fire Defense Criteria Life Hazards Fire Prevention Training Education Organization Fire Insurance Ratings Fire Suppression

Unpublished Materials

Item Listing	Key Words Subject Area
John L. Bryan and Richard P. Thornberry. "The Development and Evaluation of a Systematic Analysis Procedure for the Selection of Fire Station Sites in Prince George County, Maryland". Unpublished Study at the University of Maryland, College Park, Maryland, July 1, 1970.	Fire Suppression Planning Fire Station Location Fire Defense Criteria
Hon. Paul M. Canick. "A Progress Report on Studies in New York City". Paper Read at the National Academy of Sciences, Washington, D. C., October 30, 1968.	Finance Fire Alarm Fire Defense Analysis Organization
William Pollak. "Pricing Fire Protection Services", Mimeographed Working Paper #705–71. Washington, D.C.: The Urban Institute, 1970.	Fire Suppression Planning Financing Structural Fire Spread Fire Defense Criteria
William N. Stehle, Sr. "A Simulation Model Study for Determining the Optimal Distance for Locating a Fire Department Building Site from a Shopping Center". Unpublished Term Paper. The American University, Washington, D. C., 1968.	Fire Suppression Station Location Water Supply Structural Fire Spread Fire Defense Criteria